DYSLEXIA

This book is dedicated to all those dyslexic children and adults whom I have met over the years and to the many concerned parents who were willing to talk to me about their children's problems.

DYSLEXIA

The Pattern of Difficulties

T. R. MILES

Professor of Psychology
University College of North Wales, Bangor

COLLINS
8 Grafton Street, London W1

Collins Professional and Technical Books
William Collins Sons & Co. Ltd
8 Grafton Street, London W1X 3LA

First published in Great Britain by Granada Publishing 1983
(ISBN 0-246-11345-6)
Reprinted by Collins Professional and Technical Books 1986

Copyright © T. R. Miles, 1983

British Library Cataloguing in Publication Data
Miles T. R.
Dyslexia.
1. Dyslexia
I. Title
616.85'53   RC394.W6

ISBN 0-00-383357-7

Printed and bound in Great Britain by Mackays of Chatham, Kent

Contents

Preface

Since this book has been written for interested laymen as well as for specialists I have tried to keep technicalities to a minimum. The notation used in the Summary Chart in Chapter 6 will, I hope, be intelligible without too much effort on the reader's part, and I have made use of end-of-chapter notes in order to refer to specialist information which would have been something of an encumbrance in the main text. Statistical tables are relatively infrequent. This is partly because such tables tend to be somewhat indigestible when they appear *en masse* and partly because my concern in this book has been primarily to 'set the stage' for further quantification rather than make use of every opportunity for quantification which occurred.

I have made no attempt to write impersonally. It seemed preferable to include in the book an indication of the ways in which my ideas developed – how I reacted to the earlier literature, for instance, and how the dyslexia test (on which many of my conclusions are based) evolved into its present form. In an important sense, too, each assessment was an interaction between (usually) the child, the parents, and myself, and there would have been some absurdity if I had tried to give the impression that I was merely a detached observer. My hope is that it has been possible to write in a personal way without thereby losing scientific objectivity.

It remains for me to thank the many people with whom I have been able to share ideas. These include Professor Oliver Zangwill, Dr Macdonald Critchley, Dr A. White Franklin, Mrs Sandhya Naidoo, and Miss Gill Cotterell, all of whom were involved in the work of the Word Blind Centre in London in the 1960s; they also include Mrs Helen Arkell, Mrs Joy Pollock, and Mrs Jill Playford, of the Helen Arkell Centre, Mrs Bevé Hornsby, formerly of the Dyslexia Clinic at St. Bartholomew's Hospital, Dr Harry Chasty, Mrs Wendy Fisher, and Mr Guy Gray of the Dyslexia Institute, Mrs Marion Welchman, Mrs Beryl Wattles, and other members of the British Dyslexia Association at both national and local level, and among my university colleagues Dr George Pavlidis of the University of Manchester and Dr Margaret Newton and Dr Michael Thomson of the

University of Aston. Coming nearer home, I should like to thank all those friends and colleagues who have worked with me in the dyslexia field at the University College of North Wales. I have learned from my wife, Mrs Elaine Miles, not only some of the basic principles needed in teaching dyslexic children but also much about the essential rationality (despite appearances) of the English spelling system. I have also had the chance over many years to discuss assessment procedures with Mr Alun Waddon, and some of the central theoretical ideas in this book owe their origin to Dr Nick Ellis (see especially Chapter 1 and Chapter 24). Among former postgraduate students I should like to mention in particular the contributions of Dr Tim Wheeler, Dr Ann Williams, and Dr Caroline Dobson, and, more recently, those of Mr John Done, Mr Ian Pollard, and, not least, Mr John Griffiths whose wide experience as a teacher of mathematics has made him a particularly valuable member of the research team. Elaine Miles, Alun Waddon and Nick Ellis have all been kind enough to read an earlier draft of this book and have made many useful comments. I have also received some helpful suggestions from Dr A. D. Baddeley, Professor G. A. V. Morgan, and Dr A. C. Wales. Finally I am grateful to Mrs Llio Ellis Williams for her patience in typing – and retyping – untidy pages of manuscript until the book reached its final form, and to my namesake, Mr Richard Miles, of Granada Publishing, for many points of help and advice.

Finally, I should like to thank those to whom the book is dedicated, the dyslexic persons of all ages who have been willing over the years to talk to me about their problems. A special word of tribute is also due to the parents, since in many cases they had not only to contend with their child's difficulties but also to convince a sceptical world that these difficulties needed to be taken seriously. If I had not believed them to be in the right, this book would not have been written.

T. R. Miles

CHAPTER ONE

Background

During the past twenty years I have had the opportunity of meeting large numbers of dyslexic children and their parents and a smaller number of dyslexic adults. This book is first and foremost a record of what took place.

Unrelated facts, however, cannot from the nature of the case be of any special scientific significance; and my policy has been to select those aspects of my subjects'[1] behaviour which seemed to me to be important. My task, as I have envisaged it, was not to function like a camera or tape-recorder which records everything that happened *as it happened*; nor have I tried to be like the student of unkind legend who is said to have conscientiously written down every word uttered by his lecturer including 'um' and 'good morning'. The role which I have taken on is perhaps more like that of a portrait painter who purposely highlights certain features of what is before him in order to convey a particular message. Whether this message is important is for others to decide, and I do not believe that the issue can be resolved by any single knock-down argument. One can present evidence – and I shall do so – which indicates that those classified as 'dyslexic' behave differently in certain situations from otherwise comparable people not so classified, and one can specify the procedures for determining if a person is dyslexic, thereby showing that the word can be given a relatively precise meaning.[2] In the last resort, however, acceptance of the concept of dyslexia calls for a change of orientation; and this is something which can come only when a large body of evidence is recognised as being coherent and meaningful. My policy in what follows will in effect be to take the concept for granted and then show some of the things which can be done with it. If these things are thought to be interesting and exciting then nothing more by way of justification is either necessary or possible. Conversely, if the concept generates only trivial observations then it will fall into oblivion and deservedly so.

I have sometimes been asked whether it would not be better to abandon the word 'dyslexia' and use a word that is less controversial. Now certainly if two words, 'a' and 'b', are exactly synonymous then it is a trivial matter – a 'purely verbal' point, as some would say – whether one adopts the word 'a' or the word 'b'; and if an expression such as 'specific learning difficulty' is regarded as having precisely the same implications as the word 'dyslexia' obviously I would have no objection to using it. Equally, however, I would be conceding nothing to a hypothetical opponent in so doing; for both sides the matter would be no more than one of marginal preference ('dyslexia – or specific learning difficulty if you would rather call it that'). To change to a word which is not synonymous with 'dyslexia', on the other hand, would be to make a change of substance, and I can find no good arguments for doing so. In particular, this is not a book about 'poor readers': there are many poor readers who are not dyslexic, and – as will be made clear – some of those described in this book were, at the time of testing, relatively adequate readers. Nor have I any special enthusiasm for the term 'specific reading retardation'[3]. It admittedly has the merit of emphasising that there may be special problems where reading performance is seriously out of line with intelligence level, but it appears to be stressing the need to train up reading without calling adequate attention to other aspects of the dyslexic picture, for example difficulties with spelling, with learning tables, and with remembering digits; and to that extent it involves faulty classification.

My starting-point, then, was that a person should be called 'dyslexic' if a particular pattern of difficulties was present. The nature of this pattern and the variations which occur within it will be described in later chapters. Dyslexic-type difficulties are not isolated phenomena, and one can make sense of a particular difficulty by showing that it is part of a regularly recurring pattern. The medical term 'syndrome' is helpful here. It means a cluster of symptoms which regularly go together, without necessarily implying that there is always one and the same unitary cause; and it seems to me entirely correct to describe dyslexia as a syndrome. With regard to the causation of dyslexia I have always advocated caution. That the difficulties are constitutional in origin I have no doubt, but it may be decades before an adequate physiological theory is forthcoming. Meanwhile one needs to take into account the following points: (i) the same pattern of difficulties occurs in children of widely different backgrounds; (ii) it often runs in families; (iii) it is more common in boys than in girls; (iv) there are obvious analogies between dyslexic-type difficulties and some of the language difficulties displayed by adults as a result of acquired injury.[4] It by no means follows, however, that one and the same cause regularly produces these patterns of difficulty, and the debate as to whether or not dyslexia is a 'unitary condition' seems to me unprofitable since it is not clear what is at stake.

When I came to study the relevant literature I found many reports of children's difficulties which were remarkably similar to those which I myself was meeting. For example, Dr Pringle Morgan, writing in 1896, describes a 14-year-old boy called Percy who wrote his name as 'Precy' and 'did not notice his mistake until his attention was called to it more than once'[5]. Similarly Dr Hinshelwood gives some fascinating examples of intelligent children who were able to cover up their reading difficulties by learning the lesson by heart[6]. Both writers emphasise the analogies between word-blindness (as they called it) which is acquired and word-blindness which is congenital, and Hinshelwood cites evidence to show that the condition was more frequent in boys than in girls and that it ran in families[7].

It seems, however, that in educational circles these ideas were largely ignored; and it was again a medical man, Dr Orton, who in the 1920s and 1930s called attention to this group of difficulties [8]. I think it can fairly be claimed that Orton did more than any other early pioneer to put dyslexia 'on the map', and the society in the U.S.A. which is named after him is now recognised and respected internationally.

A further important influence on my thinking was a booklet by MacMeeken[9] published in 1939. This reported a survey of 383 children in Scotland in which the author made a special study of those children whose reading performance lagged behind their intelligence level. She gives some interesting examples of what would now be regarded as typically 'dyslexic' mistakes, and she concludes that 'there can be no doubt whatever that we are here in touch with a pattern of difficulty *aphasic* in type'[10]. When I first read her work the analogies with acquired aphasia seemed to be altogether convincing, and I have never had occasion to revise this view.

For the next two decades, however (that is, in the 1940s and 1950s), it appears that large-scale educational measurements were in fashion rather than the detailed study of individual cases. Surveys which gave figures for 'reading age', 'spelling age', and 'IQ' were plentiful, and in some cases the figures were subjected to elaborate statistical treatment. It may be my personal prejudice, but I have serious doubts as to whether such surveys provide data of any lasting scientific value, and I certainly wish that the researchers had spent more time looking at individual children.

Alongside the emphasis on educational measurement was a quite different approach to children with problems, viz. an approach which emphasised the importance of family dynamics. According to this view an effective way of helping children often involves the ability to understand and bring into the open those subtle forces which are necessarily present in every family even if they are not consciously recognised for what they are – feelings of inadequacy, resentment, and jealousy, for instance, which sometimes hamper the growth of warm relationships. Such an approach can sometimes lead to the view that if a child is failing at reading and spelling this must be because of fears or perverseness (or both) on his part or inappropriate pressures on the part of his parents; and it follows that if child and parent, each with the aid of a suitably skilled therapist, are able to 'work through' their aggressive feelings the child will learn to master reading and spelling as a matter of course. I am in no way disputing the value of what can be done by sensitive therapists with suitably selected families, but such a climate of opinion was not one in which the concept of dyslexia – a specific, constitutionally-caused handicap – gained ready acceptance, and, as will be seen in Chapter 22, there is evidence, in the case of dyslexic children, of a certain *lack* of sensitivity among those who claim to have a psychodynamic orientation. If, in addition, one is told, without any detailed supporting evidence, that when a particular child reverses letters he is trying to attack his mother by 'turn(ing) the English taught at school into Hebrew by writing it backwards'[11], one's lack of confidence in such an approach – at least as far as the dyslexic child is concerned – becomes even greater. In my experience the situation since the 1950s has changed considerably, but I suspect that misuse of psychodynamic notions is still not wholly dead.

The first occasion on which I was consciously aware that I was meeting someone with a dyslexic-type handicap was in the autumn of 1949. This was the girl, Brenda, whose difficulties I later described in a published paper[12]. She was aged 10 when I first met her, and her headmistress's description is one that has since become extremely familiar; 'Appears very bright and is keen to answer in oral work, but . . . she is very slow at any written work – possibly she is a little afraid of making mistakes. Her entire inability to spell is her great weakness'. There was the opportunity to give teaching to Brenda on an individual basis, and some years later I gave similar teaching to Michael, a bright boy who was seriously handicapped at spelling. At the time I did not use the word 'dyslexia', but, following the lead of MacMeeken (see above) I spoke of 'developmental aphasia'. As I have indicated, any word which carries the correct theoretical implications is acceptable (and for this reason I would still not object to speaking of 'developmental aphasia'), but there are advantages in having a uniform terminology; and, as things are, 'dyslexia' seems to me not only a theoretically correct term, since by derivation it implies a difficulty with 'lexis', language, but also one which has established usage behind it[13]. There is no merit in neologisms.

Until the 1960s my work in the dyslexia field had been on a very limited scale. An important landmark was the year 1962 when, on the strength of my article about Brenda and Michael, I was invited to a conference on dyslexia in London organised by Dr A. White Franklin of the Invalid Children's Aid Association. This conference tended to be acrimonious at times: one speaker, for example, said that in using the word 'dyslexic' one was 'tying a ball and chain' round the children. (I believe that he was under the quite false impression that if a child was said to be dyslexic there was nothing one could do about it.) The outcome, however, was the setting up of the Word Blind Centre in London, and I was lucky enough during the next seven or eight years to be able to attend its committee meetings and discuss problems of dyslexia with the members. It was at this time that I first met Dr Macdonald Critchley whose writings on dyslexia have been influential on a world-wide scale[14], while shortly afterwards I met Mrs Naidoo whose book, published in 1972, contains a wealth of valuable comparisons between dyslexic and control subjects[15].

Since the early 1970s interest in dyslexia grew rapidly. Even the partially negative comments of the Tizard Report published in 1972[16], whose members did not draw the distinction between dyslexia and 'poor reading', and the sparse and inconsistent comments of the Bullock Report[17], published in 1975 did little to stem the tide. More constructively, the Warnock Report[18], published in 1978, has paved the way for official recognition of dyslexia by its emphasis on the concept of 'special educational needs'. During this period a number of individuals who were already in the public eye have admitted to being dyslexic and thereby demonstrated that the handicap does not necessarily prevent a happy and successful life[19]. Another interesting occurrence was the emergence of a number of local 'Dyslexia Associations', whose aim was to increase public awareness of the problem and give help to dyslexic children and their parents in whatever ways they could. In 1972 a parent body, the British Dyslexia Association, was formed, and there are now branches in almost every part of the U.K. I have been impressed not only by the dedication of workers in this field but by the remarkable unanimity with which they have pursued their common objective; had 'dyslexia' been the poorly defined concept which some of its critics supposed, it is hard to see how this unanimity would have been possible.

As a result of my experiences in the 1960s I was encouraged to write a short book, primarily on teaching methods, which I thought might be of help to parents and others[20]. This was followed by a later book of the same kind, much of which was contributed by my wife[21]. Partly as a result of 'grape-vine' information and partly because of the increasing references to dyslexia in the press, the number of children coming to me for assessment was rapidly increasing; and as a result I was able to try out a variety of methods for pinpointing specifically dyslexic weaknesses. These eventually led to the development of the dyslexia test as described in Chapter 3. By 1972 my assessment procedure had more or less stabilised; and when in 1978 I came to examine the files which had accumulated since that date I found that it was possible to provide data on over 250 dyslexic subjects who had been tested in standard conditions. I therefore decided to look at the files of all those who came for assessment within certain specified dates, viz. the 6-year period between April 1972 and March 1978. From these I selected a 'dyslexic population' as described in Chapter 4, and their behaviour forms the subject matter of the present book.

During the early stages of the research my intention was primarily to get to know dyslexic children and their parents, to give myself the clinical 'feel' of what dyslexia was like, and to find out from experience what difficulties to expect. Although my training had been as an experimental psychologist it did not seem sensible to attempt systematic experiments in highly controlled conditions until I had a clear idea of what was worth investigating[22]. During the early 1970s, however, I became more and more convinced that dyslexia was basically a memory problem. The evidence suggested to me that the memory of a dyslexic person easily became overloaded, and in a somewhat speculative paper I and my former pupil, Tim Wheeler, put forward the view that what was involved was 'a failure to retain complex information over time'[23]. The difficulties over reading, over spelling, and over direction, as well as many of the other difficulties which I had regularly observed, could in that case be regarded as particular examples of a more general limitation in the area of 'information processing'. It was at this point that I decided to make use of the tachistoscope, a device for exposing visual material for controlled periods of time, and to investigate how much time was needed to respond correctly to strings of, say, 5, 6, or 7 digits. I therefore began to present digits to dyslexic persons of all ages and found that regularly they performed less effectively than suitably matched controls[24]. As a result, it became increasingly clear that interesting links would be found with the work of those psychologists who for the last decade and more had been systematically investigating the phenomena of memory. Their approach (which is known as 'cognitive psychology') treats the human nervous system as a device for 'processing information', that is, for registering, transforming, coding, and storing energy-changes in the environment in such a way that the person can make suitable responses from the many different muscular movements available to him[25]. The next step was therefore to use the techniques of cognitive psychology with dyslexic children as subjects. The theory which has emerged as a result of this research is largely the brain-child of my colleague, Dr Nick Ellis. I shall not discuss it in detail in this book, since we have done so elsewhere[26], but to conclude this chapter I should like to indicate some of its more important features, so as to provide a framework for the data which follow in the rest of the book.

We took as our starting-point the commonly accepted view that a human being, provided he has mastered the requisite language skills, is equipped with an internal lexicon (or dictionary), as a result of which he is able to produce a verbal response, whether spoken or written, which is 'correct' or 'appropriate' for his particular circumstances[27]. The lexicon is regarded as a kind of 'standard' in the brain against which in-coming stimuli can be checked, and if the stimulus is of a particular kind, a particular entry in the lexicon is activated. For example, the marks on this page, DOG or dog, or the same letters in Gothic script or in handwriting (provided it is reasonably legible), can be expected to activate the same lexical entry in any person who can read English. Our theory can in fact be stated quite simply: it is that the lexicon of a dyslexic person does not function so efficiently as that of a non-dyslexic person. This, of course, does not mean that it does not function at all, but only that its growth is stunted. For various reasons we argued that the lexicon contained entries corresponding not only to whole words but to parts of words (for example prefixes and suffixes), to single letters, and to various other symbols in common use (for example ' = ', '%', '&', and arithmetical operators such as ' + '). All these symbols can be mastered by the dyslexic person, though the theory predicts that he is likely to need a relatively wider experience of them than does the non-dyslexic person. Moreover, even when appropriate entries in the lexicon have been formed, it seems that they are less readily available for use. For example we know that when colours are presented to a dyslexic person he needs a longer time than the non-dyslexic person to come up with the correct colour-names[28].

At one stage I was content to say that the memory of the dyslexic person easily becomes overloaded. I still believe this to be true, but from a theoretical point of view this formulation accounts only for some of the facts, not for all of them. Thus although it makes sense of the dyslexic person's weakness at recall of digits, it does not explain the commonly observed confusions between left and right, between east and west, and between 'b' and 'd', since none of these distinctions involves a particularly heavy 'load'. Nor is it entirely correct to say that dyslexia is a weakness of immediate memory, since although success at digits requires instant recall of what has been presented, distinguishing between left and right and between 'b' and 'd' is not a matter of immediate recall but rather of correct identification. Nick Ellis and I have suggested somewhat speculatively that certain pairs of terms cannot easily be 'tagged' on to the world as we experience it, since, for instance, the same mountain which is on the left (or to the east) as we face one way may be on the right (or to the west) if we face the other way. Similarly 'b' and 'd' are confusable both visually and auditorily, and it is this dual confusability which puts at risk those whose lexicons are immature or inefficient. According to this theory the word 'dyslexia' is correctly used of a variety of deficiencies in the internal 'lexicon'; these include both deficiencies in immediate memory for symbolic material and a tendency to confuse any pair of terms (e.g. left/right, east/west, and b/d) which cannot easily be 'tagged' on to permanent features of the environment. (Pairs such as son/daughter and black/white can much more easily be 'tagged', and even the word 'I', though it 'tags' on to different people depending on who is using it, always 'tags' on to the same person when one uses it oneself.) Despite his weak 'lexicon', a dyslexic person may still be able to understand complex ideas and manifest intelligence in a variety of ways (compare Chapter 2). In general, therefore, we need a word (whether 'dyslexia' or some synonym) to describe those situations where adequate intelligence in other respects is accompanied by stunted growth of the lexicon.

I shall return to this theoretical formulation in Chapter 24. Meanwhile the reader may like to bear it in mind as an attempt to 'tie together' the phenomena which will be described. Our suggestion is that, if one postulates a faulty system of information processing which affects the functioning of the lexicon, then all or most of the difficulties experienced by dyslexic subjects can be brought under the same explanatory principle.

CHAPTER TWO

Assessment Procedure

At the start of the assessment the parents and child were invited in for a talk which lasted about 15 minutes. Next, I saw the child on his own for, say, an hour and a quarter to an hour and a half. Finally, after about a 20-minute break for scoring and interpreting the test results and studying the child's exercise books, I again saw the child and his parents together, explaining my findings and discussing with them the decisions which needed to be taken. This sometimes took a further hour or more, and the total time for most assessments was about three hours. Often, though not invariably, both parents accompanied the child, and I did not object if brothers, sisters, or even friends of the family were present at the final discussion; this was a matter which depended on the parents' wishes and on the individual circumstances of each case. On a few occasions the child was brought by a teacher from his school and not by the parents, and in these cases the final discussion comprised a joint conversation between the teacher, the child, and myself. All the children and adults (264) whose numbers appear in the Summary Chart were seen by me personally. In many cases no one else participated in the testing, though on some occasions I was helped by trainee post-graduate students, particularly with the administration of reading and spelling tests. I was involved in every case in both the evaluation of the evidence and the final interview. Occasionally results in the Summary Chart are given in brackets; this means that a particular test had already been given (usually within the last two months) and that I therefore thought it unnecessary to give it again. Asterisks in the Summary Chart indicate that the information is incomplete. This sometimes happened as a result of shortage of time and a deliberate decision to omit a particular item, though occasionally there was 'human error' in the sense that either I or a trainee unwittingly failed to follow the standardised procedure in exact detail. Data in respect of 34 children or adults whose records are incomplete are given at the end of the Summary Chart. These data do not regularly figure in the statistical calculations, but since the diagnosis was unaffected by minor gaps in the record I have referred to these cases, when it seemed appropriate, in some of the discussions. One of my first tasks at the initial interview was to try to put the subject at his ease, particularly in the case of younger children. Most of them were carrying a long history of failure, and some were reported by their parents as having been anxious or apprehensive as to what I might do to them. Indeed, since their poor performance at reading and spelling had often been a source of rebuke in the past, they may well have expected that their weaknesses would be exposed yet further by me. In the case of younger children in particular I therefore made clear that I had seen plenty of people who had difficulties over reading and spelling and that they were not to worry if they could not do some of the things which I asked them to do. I then explained that it was of special help to me to know what they could *not* do since we could then set about putting things right. Early in our talk the parents often described their struggles in getting anyone to recognise that there was a specific problem. Many reported that they had been told, in connection with the child's reading and spelling, 'Don't worry; it will come', but had found that this was not the case. These points were noted down, and will be discussed in Chapter 22. I also asked if there were any specific areas where advice might be helpful, e.g. over whether to make a change of school or over choice of courses, and I indicated that this would help me in carrying out the assessment[1].

When the parents went out I had a brief talk with the child, after which I gave him a reading test, a spelling test, the dyslexia test, and an intelligence test, usually in that order. To determine his standard of reading I decided to use the Schonell R_1 word-recognition test[2]. The great advantage of this test is that words are presented out of context and there is therefore no opportunity for clever guessing. There is the further advantage that the test is suitable for persons of all ages from five upwards, and as a result it was possible both to compare my subjects with each other and to determine the position of any particular subject in relation to the norm for his age. The figure under the heading 'R_1' in the Summary Chart indicates, for each subject, the number of words read correctly, out of a maximum of 100, and against each age-level will be found the expected score in accordance with the original norms provided[3]; for example, subjects between the ages of 10 and 11 are expected, according to these norms, to read between 50 and 60 words correctly. If any of my subjects were within 80% of the norm a line has been placed under their score. This is a reminder that, as far as untimed word-recognition is concerned – and with intelligence level not taken into account – the subject is not grossly different from the average for his age. This does not, of course, exclude a diagnosis of dyslexia; there may still have been a history of earlier difficulty in learning to read (compare Chapter 8) and in any case it is necessary to look at the total picture, not at the result of a single test taken in isolation. To obtain an indication of the subject's spelling level the Schonell S_1 spelling test[4] was used. Like the R_1 word-recognition test it is suitable for all ages from 5 upwards, and under the heading 'S_1' in the Summary Chart I have again indicated the number of words spelled correctly by each subject. As in the case of the R_1 test the maximum possible score is 100, and the same norms are applicable; thus 50 words spelled correctly on the S_1 test represents a 'spelling age' of 10, just as 50 words read correctly on the R_1 test represents a 'reading age' of 10. Scores within 80% of the norm were again underlined. It will be seen from the Summary Chart that for 40 out of the 223 subjects there was underlining in the case of both reading and spelling scores. This may seem surprising, since even if it is agreed that a person whose reading is somewhere near the norm for his age can still be dyslexic in the sense of having other signs of dyslexia, is there not some absurdity in classifying a subject as dyslexic if neither his reading nor his spelling presents him with any major problem? This was my view at the start of the research. When, however, I examined the records of the 40 subjects in question the evidence left me in no doubt that they *were* dyslexic, even though they had learned to read and spell not too badly. The situation as I see it is that reading and spelling are important as social skills, whereas other signs of dyslexia, for example, the inability to repeat strings of digits correctly, are less crippling. This, however, is not justification for giving any particular test a privileged position as a diagnostic indicator; it is consistent absence of 'positive' indicators over a *variety* of tests which justifies a negative diagnosis.

In the case of the R_1 test accurate pronunciation was required if the word was to count as having been read correctly (for example if the subject said 'cánary' as opposed to 'canáry' this was scored as wrong); in the case of the S_1 test words in which 'b' was substituted for 'd' and vice versa were scored as incorrect[5], though no account was taken of whether the subject used capital or lower-case letters. Many of us are aware of the feeling that it is more 'charitable' to score a response as correct than to score it as incorrect, but there is, of course, nothing charitable in purveying incorrect information about a subject's performance[6].

The problems which arise in assessing the intelligence of a dyslexic subject are very complex, and I shall not attempt to discuss the issue exhaustively. Briefly, however, one of the central difficulties was this. Almost all intelligence test items involve a variety of component skills, and some of these skills – at times seemingly irrelevant ones – may be lacking in a dyslexic subject. For example, there is a series of items in the Terman Merrill intelligence test[7] which involve awareness of direction, for example, 'If you are going *west* and then turn *right*, in what direction are you going now?' Now I have met subjects who have marked out the points of the compass on a piece of paper and have clearly grasped what is needed but, as they say the word 'right', have turned their pencil to the left and hence incorrectly given the answer as 'south'. (For further details see Chapter 11.) Similarly there may be failure at the Terman Merrill 'ingenuity' items, which involve complex problems of filling and emptying cans of water with the correct number of pints, and this failure may arise not because they do not understand what is needed but because they do not know that $9 + 4 = 13$. (For further details see Chapter 15.) If, therefore, a subject has grasped the necessary reasoning but makes an error over calculation one has either to score the response as wrong – and hence underestimate his reasoning power – or depart from the standardised instructions by allowing pencil and paper or suggesting that he should check his calculations[8].

There are similar difficulties with the Wechsler Intelligence Scale for Children[9]. It is now well established that dyslexic subjects have difficulty with some of the sub-tests of this scale and not others[10]. In particular they regularly obtain low scores on the Digit Span sub-test (where the tester reads out strings of numbers of increasing length and the subject has to repeat them either as they were said or in reverse order), the Information sub-test (which is a series of items on general knowledge), the Arithmetic sub-test (which involves a number of arithmetical items and in the later stages calls for a knowledge of tables), and the Coding sub-test (which is a timed test involving the reading of numerals and the writing of the appropriate 'code-mark' against each numeral). According to the manual the overall I.Q. figure is in effect obtained by averaging out the different sub-test scores. For the dyslexic subject, however, such an average may be a composite of widely differing sub-test scores and may therefore in no way represent his 'typical' or 'standard' performance. The alternative, however, is to ignore those sub-test scores which represent the weakest part of the subject's performance and base an I.Q. figure on the remainder; and this, too, seems a highly questionable procedure. Unfortunately, once one departs from standardised procedures at all, one is on the first stages of a slippery slope. At the upper parts of this slope one is not too unhappy. As has been pointed out already there appears to be no particular difficulty in asking what is a person's reasoning power independently of his ability to read instructions. Nor does there seem any absurdity in trying to assess the reasoning power of a person who sometimes muddles up left and right. Ability to remember strings of digits, however, has traditionally been regarded as a component of 'intelligence', and it is starting to become uncomfortable if one asks what a person's intelligence level would have been had he been able to remember digits better. It is even more uncomfortable to ask what his intelligence level would have been had he been able to carry out the operations of adding, subtracting, multiplying, and dividing; and in particular one should surely be unhappy about the question, What would his intelligence level have been if he had not been dyslexic? This seems almost like asking, What sort of a person would he have been if he had been different? I do not myself believe that one need be committed to this degree of absurdity. Whatever else an I.Q. figure represents – if indeed anything else at all – it can be taken to be a reasonably good predictor of academic success in children of similar backgrounds provided other things are equal in terms of environment, opportunity, etc. Now for a dyslexic child other things are not equal; in particular, unless he acquires the necessary standards of literacy his prospects of academic success are appreciably less. It makes perfectly good sense, however to make a prediction as to what his success is likely to be if these standards are attained. Such predictions may be difficult in practice in the case of the dyslexic person, and it is important to make clear to parents and teachers the extent of the uncertainty; but at least the results of an intelligence test reduce the uncertainty to some extent. Often, indeed, they serve as confirmation of views reached by parents and teachers on independent grounds, viz. that in some respects the child is extremely bright. In this context, too, of course, they can be used as a source of encouragement which is recognised by all those concerned as being realistic. In contrast, if one gives a conventional I.Q. figure based on the results of a battery of tests which includes items where dyslexic subjects are known to perform badly, one is making an under-estimate; and this is no way to handle a person who has in all probability seriously under-estimated himself already.

The practical problems arising from these difficulties were not, on the whole, all that difficult to solve. When I cited I.Q. figures to parents I was as careful as possible to add the necessary reservations and qualifications, and I emphasised that at best the figure was a rough guide. In some cases I called the subject's attention, and that of his parents, to a particularly diffi-cult test item – one which we could all see to be difficult – where he had been successful. Sometimes, after showing some of the details on the test-form, I would simply say, 'It looks from the evidence as though you shouldn't set your sights too low'. With these and similar remarks it was possible to be encouraging without committing myself to giving an exact I.Q. figure[11].

A more difficult problem was that of devising a notation which would indicate the subject's intelligence level in the Summary Chart but would not at the same time invite inappropriate statistical procedures. An I.Q. figure, though having the merit of brevity, was clearly unsatisfactory in this respect, since it would have represented an average of sub-test scores in a context where taking an average was inappropriate, and it would have been misleading to present a figure as though it were an I.Q. if it was based on selected items or on items where the procedure in the manual had not been fully adhered to. At quite an early stage of the research I decided to exclude the Digit Span test from the items designed to measure intelligence and instead to use it diagnostically as part of the dyslexia test. I also decided that if one specified particular test-items in advance and had good reason, in the context of assessing for dyslexia, for picking on these particular items it was legitimate to think in terms of a 'selected I.Q.', i.e. a figure based on selected test items, which could then be contrasted with a 'composite I.Q.', i.e. one which represented a composite of the results on all the test items specified in the manual. The selected I.Q. could then be based on items which were not 'dyslexia-laden', that is, did not present distinctive difficulty to the dyslexic person; and such a procedure would not be misleading provided (i) that one made clear what one was doing, and (ii) that one specified the items in advance of giving the test. On this basis I decided to use the Similarities, Vocabularly, and Comprehension from the so-called 'verbal' scale of the Wechsler test, and the Picture Completion, Block Design, and Object Assembly sub-tests from the 'performance' scale[12]. In the case of the Terman Merrill test, I selected the Vocabulary, Ingenuity, Direction, Similarities, Abstract Words, Enclosed Boxes, Proverbs, and the 'tree' item. I departed from the strict rules of the manual in permitting the use of pencil and paper if the subject found this helpful, and if there was an obvious slip over 'left' and 'right' in the Direction items or a blatant error of calculation in the 'tree' item I sometimes allowed myself a comment such as 'Are you sure?'. My usual policy was to give the Terman Merrill test to older subjects (from about age 11 upwards) and the WISC to younger ones. There is, of course, more variety in the WISC; but I found it somewhat incongruous to give 'jig-saw' items (particularly the Object Assembly sub-test) to bright 13-year-olds, the more so as it was a central part of my policy to talk to my subjects as their intelligence merited and avoid any suggestion of asking them to carry out tasks which might seem childish. In addition I have always found many of the later Terman Merrill items particularly interesting and challenging; and it is an important principle that testers should use tests which suit their personal style. In a small number of cases I gave the Advanced Progressive Matrices[13], since experience showed that this was a test on which older dyslexic subjects sometimes obtained strikingly high scores. On the basis of the subjects' performance on the Wechsler or Terman Merrill tests it was possible to calculate a 'selected' I.Q. for each of them. Since a precise figure, however, would have implied an accuracy level which was spurious, I decided to limit myself to six categories rather than the far larger number which the traditional concept of I.Q. makes available. The letters used, Z to U[14], represent a rank order in accordance with the following conversion table:

Selected I.Q.	Grade
140 or above	Z
130–139	Y
120–129	X
110–119	W
100–109	V
90–99	U

Subjects with a selected I.Q. of below 90 were assigned to yet another group, viz. Group III (see Chapter 4).

As a very rough approximation one can say that a selected I.Q. comes out about 10–15 points higher than a composite I.Q.[15]. In the Summary Chart I have used the above grade labels rather than figures for selected I.Q. This was in part a 'safety device' designed to prevent myself – or an unwary reader – from confusing selected I.Q. with composite I.Q. and in part a way of emphasising the approximate nature of the gradings. I have also converted the scores on the Advanced Matrices test into letter grades which, once again, are comparable only within broad limits[16]. The following are the conversion figures:

Score on advanced matrices	Grade
26 or above	Z
22–25	Y
17–21	X

This procedure, though rough and ready, ensures that the grades U to Z represent a rank-order of intelligence level and that anyone who achieves grade U is within the average range. It also makes possible the matching of intelligence grades between dyslexic and control subjects (see Chapter 7) and establishes that the difficulties shown by many of my subjects on the dyslexia test items could not have been simply the result of low intelligence. A further important consideration is this. If one is looking for evidence of the kind of reasoning powers that are necessary for academic success, the fact that the subject passed *any items at all* at the difficult end of the scale must surely be relevant. An important device, therefore, which I decided to use was to present two figures for each subject indicating what he did at the 'top' end of the scale. In the case of the Terman Merrill test I have recorded the level of 'mental age' where the subject obtained his two highest passes[17] while in the case of the Wechsler test I have recorded the highest two sub-test scores. Suitable levels are sufficient on their own to exclude any possibility of dullness and can be made the basis for discussion since one has confirmed that there are some difficult reasoning items which the subject *can* do.

To sum up, nearly all the subjects in this study were given either (a) selected items from the Terman Merrill test (with use of pencil and paper sometimes permitted even where the instructions indicate the contrary) or (b) selected items from the Wechsler Intelligence Scale for Children, or (c) the Advanced Raven Matrices. In a few cases, where the Wechsler test had already been administered, an I.Q. figure is given in brackets in the Summary Chart and the grade letter is adjusted so as to be one grade higher than that given in the conversion table.

Central to my argument is the claim that the difficulties of the dyslexic person are incongruous; in other words they are at variance with what one might expect in view of his age and the other skills which he possesses. The results of testing showed that my subjects *did* possess other skills, and the items in the Summary Chart marked 'int.' (intelligence) and 'limits' can be used in conjunction as an approximate indication of their intelligence level.

CHAPTER THREE

The Dyslexia Test

Details of the dyslexia test are given in Appendix I. In this chapter I shall say something about the way in which it evolved and how the decisions on scoring it were reached. In the early stages of the research it was necessary to try out particular items without knowing in advance whether they would present any special difficulty to a dyslexic subject. By reading the literature, however, by talking to other workers in the field, and above all by letting my subjects talk to me I was able to choose items which seemed *prima facie* as though they might be useful. The procedure was neither based on firm evidence on the one hand nor totally random on the other, but something in between. Thus I knew – or thought I knew – that dyslexic subjects had unusual problems over 'left' and 'right', and it was clearly useful to ask the subject in the first place if he could show me his right hand. I came to realise that slight hesitations and pauses might be relevant, and it was in any case useful to add the supplementary question, 'Did you have any difficulty when you were younger?' and give the subject a chance, if he so wished, to tell me about earlier problems or the use of compensatory strategies. I wondered if the 'double' command, 'Touch your right ear with your left hand' would present any extra difficulty compared with the single one, and I felt confident that the 'inverted' command by which the subject had to say which was *my* right hand would be more difficult still. At a later stage I noticed that some subjects turned in their seats in order to answer this question. I do not even now know for sure whether this response is more common in dyslexic subjects than in controls, but at least it seemed significant enough to be taken seriously and to be noted for purposes of scoring. To increase the difficulty I combined a 'double' command with an 'inverted' command, for example, 'Touch my right hand with your left hand'; and finally, since a correct response to a single item does not guarantee that the subject will consistently give the right answers, I drew up a series of variant items involving the subject's left and right hands and my own right and left hands, eyes, and ears.

It was also obvious at a fairly early stage that my subjects tended to be weak at digit span items when these occurred in the Terman Merrill and Wechsler intelligence tests. I therefore discontinued using the 'digit span' items as possible measures of intelligence (compare Chapter 2) and included them in the dyslexia test as diagnostic indicators. On one occasion I was told that a boy who was to come to me for tuition in reading and spelling had also showed considerable difficulty in learning his tables. Without attaching any special significance to the matter, I decided that I might as well try to help with the tables as well as with the reading and spelling. It immediately became apparent that this boy's difficulty with his tables was no accident; on the contrary, it was obviously part of the overall dyslexic picture. From that moment onwards I asked all my subjects to recite their tables, with results that never cease to amaze me (compare Chapter 16). After I had administered the Schonell R₁ word-recognition test on a number of occasions to older subjects it occurred to me that many of them were stumbling over the word 'preliminary', and discussion with friends and colleagues at the Word Blind Centre in London confirmed that dyslexic children were quite frequently liable to become 'tied up' in saying words, e.g. 'par cark' for 'car park'. I therefore included a series of such items. 'Anemone' seemed a good word because of possible complications over the 'm' and 'n' and 'statistical' contains a complicated arrangement of s's and t's. 'Contemporaneous' was included because of its length, though I suspect that length of word on its own is not a decisive factor. Finally, the mother of three dyslexic boys who were coming for tuition told me that their father was also dyslexic and that when he tried to say that he wanted to be philosophical about the matter he had become 'tied up' over the word 'philosophical'! Into the list, therefore, went the word 'philosophical'. The original dyslexia test also included the word 'competition', but this word was omitted when it became plain that neither dyslexic nor control subjects were having the least difficulty with it. I also came on some children – and in at least one case a highly intelligent dyslexic adult – who needed to use their fingers for simple addition and subtraction. I therefore included some subtraction tests of graded difficulty. I suspected that taking away small numbers (less than about 5) might be relatively easy and I thought it might be interesting to compare '9 − 2' and '24 − 2' because the latter was at a higher point in the number scale. I also thought that if a larger number had to be subtracted and/or if it was necessary in calculation to pass a 'ten barrier' (e.g. '44 − 7') there would be more difficulty. Why I included '6 − 3' I do not remember! Nor do I remember exactly how I came on the idea that dyslexic subjects might have difficulty in saying the months of the year, but presumably some intelligent subject whom I believed to be dyslexic surprised me by the difficulty which he showed: and certainly when a B.B.C. camera team came to film the behaviour of a dyslexic boy and a control the dyslexic boy named only a few of the months – and even these were in the wrong order – whereas the control, who had been less successful on two intelligence test items, gave all twelve in the correct order with no difficulty. At one stage I included tests for finger agnosia. For example the subject would be told to shut his eyes and I would touch, say, two or three of his fingers and ask, 'How many fingers am I touching?' or 'How many fingers are there in between?' I was not sufficiently sure, however, that this was a useful test to feel justified in continuing with it. Even now I do not know if dyslexic subjects would find it distinctively difficult. A small number of children were also failing at the 'rhymes' item in the Terman Merrill test. This is set at age 9 and the subject is asked to give 'a number that rhymes with "tree"', 'a flower that rhymes with "nose"', etc. At one stage, therefore, I gave this item routinely, and I have collected a small quantity of data (see Chapter 18), though I have not used the results in the Summary Chart. I have also collected some data on 'memory for sentences' using three items of graded difficulty from the Terman Merrill test (again see Chapter 18).

Originally I found myself trying out items in a somewhat unsystematic way, without necessarily giving each subject the same item. I soon decided, however, that it would be helpful to use prepared and standardised material; and when a number of copies were run off on a stencil this in effect marked the birth of the dyslexia test. It has been modified over the years but the basic items in it have remained the same.

After having given the test on a number of occasions I became increasingly convinced that the idea of dyslexia from which I had started was basically correct. A recognisable pattern of difficulties was clearly emerging: in particular the spelling of many subjects seemed bizarre; many of them continued to confuse 'b' and 'd' at a relatively advanced age, and they were regularly showing some or all of the difficulties mentioned above – problems over left-right, over repeating polysyllables, over subtraction and tables, and over repeating the months of the year and strings of digits. I was also confronted with clear evidence that the condition sometimes runs in families. Confirmation of these ideas came not only from discussions with colleagues and a study of the relevant literature but from the fact that what I said was clearly making sense both to the children and their parents.

Provisionally, therefore, I decided to classify a person as dyslexic if his performance at reading and/or spelling was discrepant with his intelligence level and if enough of the above signs were present. I had at this stage to leave in abeyance the question of what exactly constituted 'enough'; there was clearly a difference between a dyslexic and a non-dyslexic person in straightforward cases, and I was not unduly troubled by the fact that from time to time I came on doubtful or marginal cases. I also came to realise that no *one* of the criteria listed above was a necessary or sufficient condition for a diagnosis of dyslexia. Even in the case of reading and spelling a *history* of early difficulty seemed more important than the subject's score at the time of testing (compare Chapter 8). I did not doubt that people could be found who were distinctively weak at reading and spelling for other reasons, including lack of opportunity or unhappy personal circumstances; but in these cases I believed that there would be no reason to expect the distinctively dyslexic pattern of difficulties[1]. I also realised that there would be subjects for whom the items in the dyslexia test were too difficult, viz. those aged under about 8 and those older subjects who were of limited ability. In general, however, it seemed to me that I could usefully pick out a relatively homogeneous population of children, who coincided fairly well with those whom others had designated as 'dyslexic', by looking for past or present problems over reading and spelling of a kind that were incongruous with the subject's intelligence level, in a context where there were a number of distinctive difficulties over items in the dyslexia test.

It has sometimes been said that the grounds for a diagnosis of dyslexia are negative, or, in other words, that one diagnoses dyslexia when one cannot find any other explanation for the literacy problems. This has never been my view. For all I know, there may be children whose reading and spelling is poor relative to their intelligence level for no obvious reason, but unless they responded in characteristic fashion to some or all of the items in the dyslexia test I would not wish to class them as dyslexic. This is quite different from saying that they are dyslexic because no other cause of their difficulties can be found.

Now I was fairly confident, after a small amount of investigation, that it was possible to diagnose someone as dyslexic on 'clinical' grounds, that is, by the 'feel' of the case even in the absence of convincing statistical evidence. When people claim to be making a clinical judgement, however, I suspect that they are in effect making use of a large number of 'cues' or signs of which they are not always explicitly aware. I myself have sometimes been tempted to say that it does (or does not) *feel* like a case of dyslexia. To carry conviction, however, it is clearly necessary for the investigator who claims to be relying on the 'feel' of a case to specify the signs or cues on which he is basing his conclusion. In the case of the dyslexia test I found that I could draw inferences from the fact that my subjects used unusual strategies, for instance, or showed unusual hesitations even though they ended up with the correct answer. I therefore decided to try to devise a scoring system which took such things into account.

Some years ago I delivered a paper on this topic which I entitled, 'How do I score the ''crikey''?' The situation which I envisaged was one in which a bright 11-year-old is asked to recite the months of the year and in reply says, 'Oh, crikey!', in a tone of voice suggesting that it is a difficult task, yet after something of a struggle gives the correct answer. If one fails to score the 'crikey' at all one is throwing away potentially useful data (since the fact that the task is difficult is clearly important), yet if one says 'I took the ''crikey'' into account clinically but I did not score it' one is losing objectivity. I suggested as a solution that factors other than correctness of response could be taken into account – for example exclamations or pauses – provided these were specified with enough precision to be identifiable. By this procedure one could take into account the clinical 'feel' of the case without sacrificing objectivity.

At about the same time I had become convinced that dyslexia involved some kind of limitation of immediate memory[2]; and this led to the thought that dyslexic subjects might need more 'props' for memory than did controls. Now one such 'prop' is to ask for the question to be repeated, and a further prop is to say the instruction over to oneself while one is thinking out the answer. Thirdly there was the response-characteristic for which I took over the grammarians' term *epanalepsis*, that is, the taking up of something which has been said just before; for example if a child is in difficulty over 'seven eights' he may re-orientate himself by going back to 'five eights are forty', and by giving himself a fresh start may then come up with the right answer. Successful memorising often seems to depend on becoming 'cued in'[3]. I therefore devised the following symbols for recording on the subject's response sheet:

RR = the subject asked for the question to be repeated
EQ = the subject echoed the question, i.e. said it to himself as a 'prompt'
EP = the subject 'cued' himself in by returning to what he had said before

These symbols, along with the symbol 'hes' to indicate that the subject hesitated, are included in the instructions for scoring the dyslexia test given in Appendix II. Basically what was needed was a notation which summarised relevant aspects of the situation in such a way that it indicated whether or not the subject was producing responses typical of the dyslexic person. It seemed, therefore, that the most helpful procedure would be to specify certain kinds of responses as 'dyslexia-positive' and other kinds as 'dyslexia-negative'. A single 'dyslexia-positive' response, or indeed a single 'dyslexia-negative' response, would be of little significance on its own, but if, in the appropriate context as regards age, opportunity, and intelligence level, a cluster of 'dyslexia-positive' responses were found, then in combination they would be evidence that further dyslexic-type responses were likely. In practice I also found it convenient to have an intermediate classification for those responses which were neither unambiguously dyslexia-positive nor unambiguously dyslexia-negative.

Correct responses, if given without hesitation and without any compensatory strategy, would be scored as dyslexia-negative. Incorrect responses, however, and responses which, though correct, were made only after hesitation or as a result of compensatory strategies would be scored as dyslexia-positive.

The obvious notation in this context was to label as ' + ' a dyslexia-positive response, to label as ' − ' a dyslexia-negative response, and to label intermediate responses as '0'. In what follows, therefore, I shall speak of dyslexia-positive responses as 'pluses', dyslexia-negative responses as 'minuses', and intermediate responses as 'zeros'.

Full details of what responses should be scored as 'plus', 'zero', and 'minus' are given in Appendix II; and in the present chapter I shall limit myself to giving some brief indications as to how particular decisions were reached.

This is an area where further investigation and further statistical treatment of the data are likely to lead to greater accuracy. How to score the items so that they would best differentiate dyslexic subjects from controls was to some extent a matter of guesswork. In a sense I had to begin by begging the question: I had some idea of the ways in which the subjects whom I called 'dyslexic' would behave differently from most other children of the same age, experience, and intellectual level, and by suitably modifying my criteria I hoped to define the two groups with greater precision. I was helped at this stage of my enquiry by having available the data which had been collected in ordinary schools in the Manchester area by my friend and former pupil, Ian Pollard. These data had not at this time been scored, but they helped me to determine what might be expected of a typical non-dyslexic child in the age range 9-12 and they influenced my choice of what exactly should count as 'plus', 'zero', and 'minus'. For example, a single error on the subtraction tasks was scored as 'minus'; this was necessary because at this item very few of the controls were error-free and one clearly cannot use as an indicator of dyslexia a criterion which is satisfied by dyslexic and control subjects alike[4].

The following further comments on the scoring of individual items are perhaps worth recording. For convenience I have set these out in the order in which they appear in the Summary Chart.

Digits forwards and digits reversed
In view of the inconsistent performance of dyslexic subjects I thought it would be helpful to record the lowest number of digits at which there was a failure as well as the highest number at which there was a success; hence for each name in the Summary Chart there are two entries for 'digits forwards' and two entries for 'digits reversed'. It will also be noted that a 'double inversion', where the first entry is greater by 2 than the second (for example if there is a pass at '7 digits forwards' but a failure at '5 digits forwards'), is scored as 'plus', since this appears to reflect unevenness of performance. (The only exception is if a weaker performance, for instance 65 in the above example, would count as 'minus'). Moreover, for the 9-year-olds and upwards, any failure at 'three digits reversed' was striking enough to merit a 'plus'.

Left – right (body parts)
I was not convinced that the *number* of errors in this test was a valid measure, but it seemed reasonable to say that a person was having some degree of difficulty if he made a single error (this was scored as 'zero') and was having appreciable difficulty if he made two or more errors (this was scored as 'plus'). Some intelligent dyslexic children consistently gave me the

mirror-image of the correct answer, and some of them turned in their seats (or made slight movements of pretending to turn) in order to work out which were the right and left sides of the tester's body. All such responses were scored as 'plus'. Reports of earlier difficulty over left and right seemed to me less convincing than the evidence of my own eyes; and in general I tended to score reported difficulties (including difficulties over 'b' and 'd' and hearsay evidence of dyslexia in other members of the family) as 'zero' in contrast with actually observed difficulties which were scored as 'plus'. Where the subject had worked out compensatory strategies his response was scored as 'zero' (though it did not count as two separate 'zeros' if he both reported earlier difficulty and had worked out a compensatory strategy). Hesitations, corrections, requests for the question to be repeated, and echoing the question were all scored as 'zero', and if more than one condition for a 'zero' was satisfied the two 'zeros' counted in conjunction as a 'plus' (This was also true in the case of subtraction, tables, months forwards, and months reversed).

I have not so far defined what exactly counts as a hesitation, and there is therefore still some degree of inexactitude on this point. It would be helpful in the future if the subjects' responses could be timed by means of apparatus having suitable precision and, if possible, apparatus which recorded slight movements in the muscles of the *wrong* hand even when the correct hand was used.

Repeating polysyllabic words
A sympathetic headmaster tried out, in my presence, some of the members of his 8-year-old class on the word 'preliminary'. Only a relatively small number could say it, and in a pilot study by one of my undergraduate students[5] a 'nil' success rate with this particular word was reported.

I therefore decided that the responses of children under 9 should not be scored as 'plus' unless there were 4 or 5 errors. At the other end of the age-range it seemed to me that even a single error in anyone aged 15 or over was worth a 'zero' and that two errors were worth a 'plus'. Some approximate interpolations then gave me the rest of the table.

Subtraction
The scoring here is mostly self-explanatory. Use of fingers or marks on paper was an automatic 'plus'. Also I had the suspicion that it was no accident when a subject suspected on other grounds of being dyslexic used unusual strategies, for example, in the case of $44 - 7$, breaking the 7 into 4 and 3 and counting backwards from 40; and any strategy which seemed to me 'unusual' (in an admittedly ill-defined sense) was scored as 'zero'.

Inspection of Pollard's data indicated that a large number of the control subjects made at least one error, and I therefore set the standard for a 'plus' as three errors and the standard for a 'zero' as two errors.

Tables

All kinds of interesting responses occurred in this test. Any response of the form 'Where have I got to?' was scored as 'plus', and I was interested in the fact that some of my subjects had learned to avoid this kind of difficulty by omitting the 'preamble' (e.g. 'One six is . . .', 'Two sixes are . . .', etc.) I thought it likely that slower children would make the simple response that they 'couldn't do it' whereas dyslexic children might try to apply the rules which they had grasped even after going wrong; for this reason I scored as 'plus' the 'consistent error' – for example, if, having said that six threes were twenty, the subject – with full consistency – said that seven threes were twenty three. In addition, breaking into the 'wrong' table (e.g. 'Six sevens are forty-two, seven sevens are forty nine, eight eights are sixty four') seemed to be another example of 'losing the place' and was therefore scored as 'plus'.

Any attempt by the subject to 'cue' himself in by repeating an earlier product ('epanalepsis') was scored as zero, and on the basis of not wholly arbitrary guesses, 3 pauses, 2 'slips', whether corrected or not (e.g. 'eight eighties, I mean eight eights') and one 'skip' (e.g. from six eights to eight eights) were all scored as 'zero'. All such responses seemed to me to be possible – though not fully certain – indicators of memory overload and therefore, in the right context, possibly confirmatory of a diagnosis of dyslexia.

Months forwards

Occasional errors were made by the control subjects, and I therefore decided that more than two omissions or inversions were necessary for a 'plus'. Uncertainty over where to start was scored as 'plus', and the fact that an intelligent subject within that age range *even asked the question* as to whether the order mattered also seemed to me to give good grounds for assigning a plus.

In accordance with policy in other parts of the test evidence of earlier difficulty was scored as zero.

Months reversed

Here, too, two omissions or inversions were needed for a 'plus', a single omission or inversion counting as 'zero'. Both in this item and 'months forwards' a single correction was scored as 'minus' on the grounds that single corrected errors are sufficiently common to be regarded as insignificant.

b-d confusion

First-hand evidence was scored as 'plus', for example if the subject, in reading, said 'done' for *bun* or if his exercise books or his spelling test contained 'b's for 'd's or vice versa. Second-hand evidence, i.e. reports of such confusion, were scored as zero.

Familial incidence

If I had myself assessed two or more members of the same family and found them to be dyslexic or if a diagnosis had been made by one of my colleagues using similar criteria, I scored this item as 'plus'. The difficult point for decision was to determine how weak the evidence had to be before one scored it as 'minus'. The statement 'Uncle Jack was a poor speller', on its own, is by no means decisively significant! Approximate guide-lines are given in Appendix II.

Finally, administration of the tests for handedness and eyedness, as given in Appendix I, is self-explanatory. If the subject consistently used his right hand for writing, cleaning his teeth and throwing a ball he was scored as R (= right) in the first column, representing handedness; and if he consistently brought the paper to his right eye when asked to 'spy' a pencil through the hole he was scored as R (= right) in the second column, representing eyedness. Consistent use of the left hand was similarly scored as L in the first column and consistent use of the left eye as L in the second column. Any inconsistency in the 'handedness' items was scored as M (= 'mixed') in the first column and any inconsistency in the eyedness items was scored as M (= 'mixed') in the second column. This gives the nine possibilities RR, LR, RL, LL, MR, ML, MM, RM, and LM. Administration of the 'memory for sentences' and 'rhymes' tests is also self-explanatory.

The procedure for scoring the responses to the ten items used in the Summary Chart is given in Appendix II. It is thus possible to determine the 'index-figure' for each subject, that is, the number of 'dyslexia-positive' responses out of a possible 10. My intention was to use this 'index-figure' not so much as a measure of the severity of the subject's dyslexia – as though there were some kind of 'dyslexia continuum', which is perhaps a doubtful notion – but rather as a guide to clinical diagnosis. I have never claimed, and do not wish to claim, that a subject with, say, 7 'pluses' is in some way 'more dyslexic' than a subject with, say, 5 'pluses'; still less do I want to stipulate that a person should be defined as (or 'deemed') dyslexic if he scores over a certain number of 'pluses'[6]. The position seems to me rather that the subject's score can legitimately be taken into account in deciding whether the total picture is one of specific handicap. A high score, in the right context, can increase one's confidence that such a handicap is present; and since there is little possibility at present of adequate confirmation from direct neurological evidence, a diagnosis of dyslexia is in a sense a 'bet' that other behavioural manifestations of dyslexia will be present[7]. This is a point to which I shall return at the end of Chapter 4.

CHAPTER FOUR

Selection of Subjects

When I came to take stock of the data which I had collected, I decided to make my first task an examination of the files of all those whom I had assessed during a given period of time. The period chosen was between April 1972 and March 1978 and the number of usable files turned out to be 291[1]. Now clearly in any educational survey one can expect to find a large number of children who show no particular difficulties of either reading or spelling. For obvious reasons few such children could be expected to be referred to me for assessment, though in fact there were 3 subjects among the 291 who seemed to me to have very little the matter with them from an educational point of view. From an initial inspection of the files it seemed that it would be helpful to distinguish those who were undoubtedly dyslexic from those who were either very slightly dyslexic or about whose dyslexia there was any appreciable doubt. Dr Critchley and his wife have indicated that there can be 'formes frustes' – variants of dyslexia where some of the signs are present but only to a limited degree [2], and in the years before 1972 I myself had come on a few boys, known to have dyslexic relatives, who were not grossly weak spellers and whose performance on the dyslexia test was not fully typical of the dyslexic person but who showed slight or occasional dyslexic signs. I decided therefore to implement this distinction by assigning to Group I those who were clearly and unambiguously dyslexic and to Group II those who were marginally or slightly dyslexic. I also decided to have a third category, Group III, which I provisionally called 'contaminated cases', i.e. cases where there were other major contaminating factors. Even, therefore, if they scored 'pluses' on some of the dyslexia-test items the subjects in this group could not be classified as pure or typical cases of dyslexia. These three groups, along with Group IV, those with no appreciable educational problems, were so defined that one or other of them would fit every child who might be studied in any large-scale survey. Clearly those in Group III would comprise a wide variety of children who for other purposes might need some more accurate classification; but for present purposes the important point was that, because of contaminating factors, none of them be classified as a 'pure' or standard case of dyslexia.

I adjudged 24 subjects to come in Group III. Their details have not been included in the Summary Chart, but it may illuminate the concept of dyslexia if I indicate the kinds of reason which led to their exclusion.

From the point of view of research it seemed desirable to assume that low I.Q., even on its own, was a contaminating factor; and for this reason I excluded from Groups I and II anyone with a 'selected' I.Q. of below 90. This is not, of course, because I believe that those with a 'selected' I.Q. of below 90 can never be dyslexic; on the contrary it seems to me likely from the nature of the dyslexic handicap that it can fall on anyone, regardless of ability. With slower children, however, it is hard to be sure that one is seeing a pure or typical case, since many of the items in the dyslexia test may be too difficult for them independently of any dyslexic handicap. The decision was purely one of convenience in view of the purpose of this book: if I had included in my dyslexic population those of lower ability there would have been risk of contaminating the data by an unknown amount and no compensating gain. This accounted for 9 cases out of the 24.

It was not my intention to exclude anyone from Group I simply because he was known to have had psychiatric problems. In 3 cases, however, the psychiatric problems were too severe to enable adequate testing to be carried out[3]. In 10 further cases there was a history of autism, non-communication, suspected brain damage or the like; and although the justification for any of these expressions is to some extent controversial, it was at least clear that these were not true or typical cases of dyslexia. In the remaining 2 cases I was somewhat unsure of the diagnosis; one appeared to have a visual problem and one a hearing problem but neither showed unambiguous dyslexic signs. For present purposes the significance of those in Group III is not that they were in any way a homogeneous group but simply that none of them was straightforwardly dyslexic[4].

It is also worth recording that of the 24 subjects in Group III 12 were male and 12 were female. Since there is clear evidence of a male to female ratio in dyslexia of about 3:1[5] this supports the view that the members of Group III did not constitute a typical dyslexic population. In contrast, of the 223 Group I cases 182 were male and 41 were female, which gives a ratio of 4:1. As a matter of interest, cases 224-257 may also be compared. These were all subjects whom I had diagnosed as dyslexic but for whom the data were not fully complete; here there were 26 males to 8 females, a ratio of over 3:1, which again suggests a genuinely dyslexic population.

The Summary Chart shows that 7 cases were eventually assigned to Group II, i.e. those who were marginally or slightly dyslexic. In my earlier attempts at classification I had supposed it wise to 'play safe' by including in this group anyone about whom there could be any serious degree of doubt. When I came to re-examine about 20 such cases, however, I became increasingly convinced that in all of them there was a genuine dyslexic problem. This accounts for the fact that in the Summary Chart subjects are to be found in Group I having 3 'pluses' or less on the dyslexia test. In these cases there was enough independent evidence of dyslexia despite the relatively small number of 'pluses'. If one regards a diagnosis of dyslexia as a kind of 'bet' that other dyslexic manifestations will be found (see Chapter 3), there is nothing inconsistent in making such a bet about a bright subject with 3 pluses and being unwilling to make it about a less bright subject with 4 pluses since there may be independent confirmatory evidence in the one case and not in the other[6].

In a few cases the entry in the Summary Chart has been marked by an asterisk. This has been done where the information is incomplete but where the total number of 'pluses' is not affected. Where there was a definite 'gap' in the information the subjects were assigned to a separate place in the Summary Chart (nos. 224-257). I shall refer to some of these cases in later chapters but most of my statistical calculations relate only to subjects 1 to 223.

The final figures can therefore be summarised as follows:

Group I	223
Group II	7
Group III	24
Group IV	3
Incomplete records	34
TOTAL	291

As a result of the above classification I believed myself to have a 'pool' of 223 subjects who could be regarded as pure or typical cases of dyslexia.[7] These are the subjects whose behaviour will be described in the chapters which follow.

CHAPTER FIVE

Sample Case Histories

In this chapter I present four case histories. My purpose in so doing is threefold: first to give the reader an indication of my sources of evidence; secondly to illustrate the scoring of responses as 'plus', 'zero', and 'minus' on the Summary Chart, and thirdly – and perhaps most important – to call attention to the fact that those whose responses are recorded in this way were real people, each with his or her own distinctive life-style. Without such descriptions there is a risk that awareness of the individual *as an individual* may be overlooked; and although the material in the Summary Chart is of course central to the arguments in this book (since adequate generalisations would be impossible without it), it should never be forgotten that the impersonal symbol ' + ' represents a human being struggling against a handicap. He may, for instance, have endured years of anguish in trying to learn his tables and still be relatively unsuccessful. Before making any generalisations, therefore, I decided that it would be helpful to introduce the reader to some of the people about whose behaviour the generalisations were made.

The four cases which I have selected were taken more or less at random, though with the constraint that they should belong to different age levels. Any other selection would, I am sure, have illustrated similar basic difficulties. All names have been changed.

S7. John

A letter from John's mother ran as follows:

> 'We are anxiously seeking advice and diagnosis as it would seem that John could be dyslexic to some degree. John will be eight years old next birthday. A brief resumé of his achievements and difficulties so far might be of help. I hope you don't find them too tedious and beg forgiveness in advance'.

Further extracts from her letter are given in Chapter 8. The gist was that from the age of five John had encountered severe difficulties in reading and writing and had become withdrawn; ITA (initial teaching alphabet) had been of no help to him, and although teachers had, in the main, been sympathetic, he none the less had a real sense of failure. At the age of seven he had been given the WISC.

> 'John is very bright indeed and much above average. Remedial reading work suggested with the Remedial Reading teacher attached to the Child Guidance Clinic. A colleague of mine took John daily for reading; he enjoyed the sessions with a one-to-one relationship. . . quickly progressed through the Schonell Happy Venture series. . . showed difficulty in remembering any phonetic combinations but got along fast by reading content. . . Discharged (age 7¾). . . quite able to read the meaning by going for the content of the reading matter. . .
>
> Dyslexia occurred to me in the early months of John's school difficulties three years ago, but as his traumas got worse we increasingly cast around for reasons within the context of our family life and John's emotional experiences. . . his father's unavoidable adsence (sic) from home on business; having a clever elder sister, and of course, ITA. . . I now realise we need proper diagnostic help. . . There is so much more we need to know before we can help John. I wonder if there are degrees of dyslexic disability, how badly or otherwise John is affected, if at all. Whether he is by I.Q. ability managing to overcome dyslexia; whether he is now likely to achieve his potential without specialised help? Where this help should come from and what form it should take. Whether we should try and persuade a local prep. school with small classes to take him on, or whether I should do remedial work with him and how I could be trained in order to do this?
>
> Yours very sincerely. . .'

John was in fact 7 years 11 months when I first met him. He read 32 words on the Schonell R_1 word recognition test correctly, which according to the original norms give him a 'reading age' of 8.2 years (slightly above his chronological age) but he spelled only 5 words correctly on the Schonell S_1 spelling test which gives him a spelling age of 5½. I had managed to obtain the results of his intelligence test: with all items taken into account (apart from Picture Arrangement, for which no score was given) his overall I.Q. figure has been found to be 128; on the basis of the 'selected' items only (see Chapter 3) the figure came out as 142, which gives a Z on my notation.

A piece of spontaneous writing was shown to me as follows:

> Im going to 8angr to morow, becoes a man is inerasitb in me I am gowing bie car   I am going to sta if scool and Elesebth is going to scool And rapre is loking aftr the boq colb tesr

(Elisabeth was his sister, and the last sentence, so I was told, was an attempt to write, 'Grandpa is looking after the dog called Tessa'). When I asked him to show me his right hand he did so correctly, but when I asked him which was *my* right hand he pointed to my left hand, and in all subsequent items, e.g. 'Touch my left hand with your right hand' he got *his own* side right but *my* side systematically wrong. On the method of scoring given in Appendix II this counts as 'plus'.

He could not repeat the words 'preliminary' and 'statistical' but managed the other words. At the age of seven this is insufficient evidence to be scored as 'plus' or 'zero' and therefore counts as 'minus'.

He failed one of the two trials when asked to repeat five digits, and when the series-length was increased to six he failed both trials. This counts as a 'plus'. In the case of 'digits reversed' the results were:

Stimulus	His response
927	279
25	52
574	759
259	592

This also counts as 'plus'.

When asked '9 take away 2' he paused and then said 'six'. Asked to explain, he said, 'I just go nine, eight, seven, six'. '6 take away 3' was answered correctly, as was '24 take away 2'; but '19 take away 7' was given as 'fourteen': 'I started to think nineteen, eighteen, seventeen, sixteen counting in my head how many numbers I took away'. This result is also a 'plus'.

Asked to say the months of the year he said, 'November, December, October, November, December, March, April, May, June, July, November, December'. This, and 'months reversed', were both scored as 'plus'.

Asked to say his 2 × table he replied, 'Once two is two; two twos are four;. . . three' (as if about to say 'three twos'). . . 'two twos are four' (reorientating himself); 'three twos are six; seven. . . four twos are eight; five twos are ten; six twos are twelve; seven twos are fourteen; eight twos are sixteen; nine twos are twenty; ten twos are thirty'.

When I started him off on the 3 × by saying 'Once three is three', he said 'Once three is three; two threes are six; four threes are nine; three twos. . . four twos are. . . five threes are (long pause) fifteen'. He explained that he went 'one-two-three; four-five-six; seven-eight-nine; ten-eleven-twelve; thirteen-fourteen-fifteen'. His performance on 'tables' was clearly 'plus'. John was right-handed and right-eyed by the tests described in Chapter 3.

John's father said that he himself was a very poor speller, and his mother said that she herself still used her fingers for arithmetical calculation. My suspicion is that both parents are dyslexic. The 'plus', under 'familial', in the Summary Chart, however, arises not from discussion with John's parents (since such evidence would at most be scored as 'zero') but from the fact that they afterwards asked me to assess John's sister, S 74, whose dyslexia – as they afterwards realised – had been masked by high intelligence and adequate reading skill. Father said that many of the family had been architects, and I suspect – though I have not the figures– that this is often a suitable occupation for those with high ability who are handicapped by dyslexic tendencies.

In my report I wrote as follows:

> 'I confirm the earlier finding that he is an extremely bright boy with a special learning problem – one which affects reading, spelling, number work, and various other memory-tasks involving orientation and sequencing.
>
> This group of difficulties (often referred to as "dyslexia") appears to be constitutional in origin; and it is therefore incorrect to attribute John's failure to any of the traditional educational "scapegoats" (poor teaching, the i.t.a., parental pressure, etc.). It seems right, instead, to think of a specific *handicap*, which is affecting John in a few special areas.
>
> It therefore seems important that all his teachers should *know of* his handicap and adjust their standards accordingly; dyslexic children often give the appearance of being "careless" or "lazy" when in fact their pathetic attempts to get things down on paper are the result of an enormous effort.'

This is not a book about the practical handling of dyslexic children, and in general I shall not be citing from the reports which I wrote. The present report, however, is reasonably typical: the problem both in John's case and many others was not so much in making the diagnosis as in ensuring that, once it was made, appropriate help was forthcoming. In some cases it is helpful if one or other parent learns the special teaching techniques that are needed, and this was the obvious answer in John's case.

Two months after the assessment John's mother wrote reporting progress and saying that 'the future seems much brighter'. Seven months after that I received a letter from an educational psychologist saying that he had met John during his training; and the following are extracts from his report:

> 'He read fluently, paid attention to punctuation marks and obviously enjoyed reading for me. . . His spelling has also improved though he has still some way to go in this area. His spelling age is 7.4 years on the Schonell Spelling Test and this compares with a spelling age of less than 6 years when he was seen by Professor Miles. Spelling is still a great struggle for him and on every word he had to think very hard before writing it down. . . John's number work is still behind. He take a long

time to work out very simple additions and subtractions and unless he used his fingers he frequently made errors when adding single digit numbers. . . his handwriting is fairly neat and legible. . . However, reversals are still common, particularly the letters d and b, and the number 5. He is starting to write in cursive script which will, I think, help him to orientate his letters. Mr ____ is relatively pleased with the way John is progressing in school'.

S 95. Brian

I received through the post a letter from Brian's mother which included the following:

'I have been planning to write to you for some time, to seek your advice about my eleven year old son, Brian.

As a result of hearing several discussions about dyslexia on the radio and television, I sent a description of my son's learning problems to the British Dyslexia Association. . . An educational psychologist. . . who said she was not an expert on dyslexia felt that Brian was probably not dyslexic. She felt that because Brain could read another explanation was more likely, in his case nervous tension.

However his remedial teacher after a year's work with my son believes that he reads almost entirely by remembering the shape of words. . . His handwriting is very poor for his age, slow, cramped and wobbly. . . his spelling, although showing some improvement as a result of his remedial work is still sub-standard. He does seem to have corrected the b-d confusion recently, but often leaves words out and transposes letters. He still shows occasional confusion between left and right but will work it out if given time. He finds arithmetical tables extremely difficult to learn and tends to lose his place when reciting them. He seems to have a reasonable concept of figures, however, for example when asked – How many minutes in two hours? – worked it out as follows:

$$
\begin{aligned}
1 \text{ hour} &= 60 \text{ mins} \\
60 &= 50 + 10 \\
2 \text{ hours} &= (50 \times 2) + (10 \times 2) \\
&= 100 + 20 \\
2 \text{ hours} &= 120 \text{ mins.}
\end{aligned}
$$

This is a typical approach to his arithmetical work, compensating for not knowing his tables.

On the other hand his maths teacher finds he has a fine analytical mind, able to accept, understand and implement new concepts, often before any other member of his class. He was a late speaker. When he was younger he was very clumsy.

. . .If you feel that because Brian can read, he cannot be dyslexic, then I will accept your advice and simply try to help my son over his difficulties as best I can.

Yours faithfully. . .'

Brian was aged 11.3 when he came to see me. He read 60 words correctly from the Schonell R_1 word recognition test, which by the old norms gave him a 'reading age' of 11.0, and he spelled 21 words correctly on the Schonell S_1 test which gave him a 'spelling age' of 7.1. He passed all four items in the Terman Merrill intelligence test at the xiii year level and all four items at the xiv year level. He placed 'east' and 'west' the wrong way round, however, and used 'concrete aids' (marks on paper) in order to solve the two more complicated 'cans-of-water' items. Asked how 'beginning' and 'end' were alike he immediately said 'Both are places'. I arrived at a 'selected I.Q.' figure of 130, which places him in category Y in the Summary Chart.

One of the interesting points which emerged, particularly when I gave him the dyslexia test, was his ability to be explicit about his compensatory strategies. Thus, when I said 'Touch my left hand with your right hand', he repeated the question to himself, gave the correct answer, and cryptically explained, 'You twist round – your right hand changes'.

The running commentary as he struggled with his $7 \times$ table is worth quoting in full. After going correctly to 'five sevens are thirty five' he said, 'I usually say five sevens are thirty six. What's next? That's five sixes. Six sevens are forty two; eight sevens. . . now, let's see. . . ah! it's fifty six. Five - six - seven - eight so seven eights are fifty six. Where am I? I've forgotten where I am; I was on seven. Five, six, seven, eight: seven nines are sixty three; seven sev-, no, seven tens are seventy; seven elevens are seventy seven and seventy twelves. . . seven twelves. . . no wonder I'm getting all confused. . . are. . . fourteen, eighty four using the same system' (I think this means that he knew $7 \times 10 = 70$, and that the reference to 'fourteen' was a way of arriving at 7×12 since twice seven needed to be added).

He repeated six digits forwards correctly but failed in two out of his three attempts at saying three digits in reverse order. With slight corrections he just about managed to say the months of the year, but used his fingers to check that he had not left any out. There was no evidence of any close relative being similarly affected, though his mother spoke of a first cousin who had 'educational problems'. (This evidence seemed to me insufficient for a 'zero' and was scored as 'nk', though one certainly could not claim that one had *excluded* dyslexia in other members of the family.)

Brian's tally of 'pluses' was in fact 7, which is, of course, well outside normal limits for a boy of his age and ability.

His comments on how he tried to read words by examining their shape are referred to in Chapter 8.

He said that he wanted to be a radio engineer, and I confirmed with his parents that this seemed to me a perfectly realistic ambition.

I have no detailed follow-up evidence, but a letter from an educational psychologist twenty seven months later reported 'considerable progress' despite his still having difficulties with handwriting and spelling, while an informal conversation with his sister also gave grounds for optimism.

I end by citing a typewritten effort written shortly before the assessment:

'Homewrke

Haw to do you,r ti

Fist put you'r ti under you'r Coler then mack the fat bit longer than the shot bit. Put the long bit (*crossings out*) The sort bit and go raond twice. Now btween you'r neck and wer the bit that go's rand yor'r Neck gone up you put the fat bit through the tip of upside daow r then you see one of the loppes that you made were you saw the tie gone up you put you'r (crossings out, with 'bit' added) under this lop and put until it looks allright (prcsuming you have git a mirror).'

S 142. Simon

A letter from Simon's mother said: 'Simon is 13 years of age and finds great difficulty with reading. I would be most grateful if you would arrange for tests to be carried out as I feel that dyslexia may be his problem'.

When I met her personally she said she wished that she had asked earlier. 'I kept thinking, I'll wait; I won't make a nuisance of myself. . . They said he was lazy and didn't try. . . You can tell him something and a minute later he'll say, "What did you say?" or will have forgotten a message'.

Simon read 28 words correctly from the Schonell R_1 test ('reading age' 7.8) and spelled 18 words correctly from the Schonell S_1 test ('spelling age' 6.8). Use of both Terman Merrill and Wechsler tests showed that he was not slow. Yet he made an error in repeating *four* digits (3147 for 3417) and failed both trials at five digits. Surprisingly his performance at 'digits reversed' was considerably better, with one success at *five* digits reversed. (I do not understand this anomalous result, to which the Summary Chart shows virtually no parallels).

Asked to repeat his 4 × table he said 'Two fours are eight; three fours are twelve; four fours are fifteen; five fours are nineteen; six fours. . . I can't remember, twenty seven. . . thirty one; eight fours are thirty one; nine fours are thirty five; ten fours. . . I've gone wrong'.

The following are some extracts from his school books.

Ju Des The Scarcat ptrad Jesus. . . necs Day The tumeston was roald a way and The gads was not a slep and Jesus went to The Foloas

His mother reported that he had regularly put 'b' and 'd' the wrong way round and that sometimes his '6' and '9' were 'back to front', though he did not now confuse 'p' and 'q' any more. (This evidence is scored as 'zero' on the Summary Chart since it is based on a report and is not first-hand). She also said that he could not tell the time until he was 10½ and that in giving the days of the week he would omit Monday even up to age 10. Her own father, so she told me, had been a very poor speller; and in fact I afterwards saw Simon's two brothers (S 16 and S 88) both of whom were undoubtedly dyslexic.

In my report I wrote as follows:

> Unlike most dyslexic children he was remarkably successful over 'digits reversed' and unlike some dyslexic children he did not need 'concrete aids' to help him with calculation. Despite these two 'counter'-indicators, however, there seems to me to be a whole group of positive signs – b-d reversals (normally outgrown by children of average ability when they are about 8), special difficulty with digits forwards, 'losing his place' both in reciting the 4 × table and months of the year (with reported similar difficulty over days of the week), difficulty over left and right, and in repeating polysyllables, and reported difficulty over telling the time. His spelling has the 'bizarre' character often associated with dyslexia, e.g. 'ptrad' for 'betrayed', 'Foloas' for 'followers', and, as with many dyslexic children, there is uncertainty over boundaries between words. Finally, it seems very likely that other members of the family are, or have been, affected, and this I regard as a particularly strong piece of evidence for a specific handicap.

It is worth recording that, unlike the two cases cited so far, Simon was of near-average ability rather than outstandingly bright. This no doubt meant that it was relatively more difficult for him to devise compensatory strategies. It was possible, however, to arrange for him to receive dyslexia-centred teaching, and two years later he was found to have a 'reading age' of 10.4 (gain 2½ years) and a 'spelling age' of 8.4 (gain 1½ years). A report from his teacher reads:

> 'He is keen to improve his reading and writing and has been encouraged by the comments of his teachers in school about his progress. He reads quite fluently and, where his interest is engaged, with pleasure. . . He can use a telephone directory and a dictionary. He has practised writing cheques and filling up forms. . . His written work has improved, though his handwriting is jerky. But he is using words more freely, asks questions more confidently and converses readily. He used to be very diffident but has become more willing to talk as time has passed. . . He has grown in confidence generally.'

S 208. Joanna

Joanna's mother wrote to me as follows:

> 'I have a daughter of 17 who wishes to enter a Teacher Training College

but she is having difficulty in being accepted, partly due to being dyslexic.

'Joanna is apparently (sic) typical of many dyslexics in that she was always a bright child, though at Junior School she now tells us that the teachers told her she was alternatively stupid or lazy. . . When (she) went on to a senior school she was put in the 'B' stream in a Secondary Modern School and her reports showed average and above average results. . . She has learned to live with her dyslexia and has overcome things like remembering which is left or right by wearing her watch and a ring on her left hand.

'So far (she) has sat for and obtained 6 C.S.E.'s including Mathematics, English, and Needlework at Grade 1. (At 'O' level she has Mathematics Grade 1, Domestic Science Grade 3 and English Grade 9.) At present she is studying Physics 'O' level and Mathematics and Needlework at 'A' level to be taken this summer.

'Joanna is quite determined to be a teacher, no matter how long it takes her to get into College. She is not only a hard worker but also a perfectionist and from first being told she has stupid apparently her attitude has been "I'll show them that I am not stupid".

'We feel we badly need advice from someone who not only understands studying, but who also has a real knowledge of dyslexia as well. My husband is particularly concerned as he is also dyslexic and therefore knows the problems Joanna is encountering. We wondered if it would be possible to have Joanna assessed. . .'

When she came for assessment Joanna read 79 words out of 100 correctly from the Schonell R_1 word-recognition test (the 'ceiling' is age 15 and this score gives a 'reading age' of nearly 13), and she spelled 57 words correctly from the Schonell S_1 spelling test which gave her a 'spelling age' of just over 10½. Her errors included 'liquicd' for *liquid*, 'assiced' for *assist*, 'amoc' (crossed out), then 'acomplished' for *accomplished*, and 'primalily' for *preliminary*. Her mother said that there was a large amount of 'mirror writing' in her school books and that Joanna had been told, 'It is stupid'. I copied the following from her geography book.

MAꟼ Oꟻ THE AꓤƎA
CROSꙄROAD
MATLOƆꓘ
CARBOИIꟻƎROUꙄ LIMEꙄTOИƎ

She obtained a score of 23 on the Advanced Matrices intelligence test (where average for a university student is set at 21) and she passed 3 items out of 4 at the second highest level of Superior Adult on the Terman Merrill test.

On the left-right test she pointed to her own right hand correctly, but she made mistakes over 'Touch my right hand with your right hand', 'Point to my left eye with your right hand', and 'Touch my right hand with your left hand', and responded correctly to 'Point to my left ear with your left hand' only after detecting an initial error. She said, 'I've got to turn myself round' (though in fact she did not do so overtly). These responses were a clear 'plus'.

She failed to say the word 'preliminary' correctly and her attempt at 'anemone' was 'moneneney'. At the age of 17 the presence of two errors also gives a 'plus'.

On the subtraction test she asked me to repeat 'nineteen take away seven' and commented, 'I thought you said "seven take away nine"'. She gave the answer '47' to '52 − 9' and said, 'I got the number in my head but had to think'. The error counts as a quarter of a plus and the request for repetition as a quarter; this item is therefore scored as 'zero'.

She reported considerable earlier difficulty over tables, and, after saying her 7 × correctly up to 'eight sevens are fifty six', she said 'Nine sevens' — pause — 'are sixty four, no, sixty three, nine' (corrected to 'ten') 'sevens are seventy; eleven sevens are seventy seven; twelve sevens are' — pause — 'eighty four. It didn't sound right when I said it'. The earlier difficulty counts as half a 'plus', and the two corrections count as a further half, so that there is a full 'plus' even when the two pauses are not taken into account. She made the further interesting comment: 'I can never get eight eights. I have to say "seven eights" or "nine eights" and take away but I can say what is eight squared'.

In the case of 'months forwards', she said, 'I've learned them recently', and she in fact went through them with nothing worse than a slight pause after June. By the scoring rules this response had to count as 'minus', though it still remains astonishing from the point of view of clinical assessment that a person of her ability should have learned the months of the year 'recently' at the age of 17.

In the case of 'months reversed' she said: 'January – no, that's the beginning; December, October – no, November, September, October, November – no'; and, starting again, she said 'December, November, October, September, June – August, June' – pause – 'July'. This was clearly a 'plus'.

On the digits test, when asked to say 8-4-2-3-9 she said '9-3-8; I've gone wrong' and when asked to say 5-2-1-8-6 she said '6-8-1-2-5' (which is correct in the reverse order). When asked to say '3-8-9-1-7-4' she said '3-8-9; 1-4-7' and when asked to say '7-9-6-4-8-3' she said '7-9-4-6-8-3'. This gives her 'highest success' as 4 and her 'lowest failure' as 5; a tally of 45 counts as 'plus'.

She passed both attempts (and the practice attempt) at 3-digits reversed but failed both attempts at 4-digits reversed. A tally of 34 also counts as 'plus'. It is perhaps worth recording that the 4-digits reversed item is given to nine-year-olds in the Terman Merrill test, while the 5-digits reversed item is given to twelve-year-olds. Yet on this test Joanna was passing items at the level of Superior Adult II.

There had been earlier reports of b-d confusion, and this item was therefore scored as 'zero'. The familial incidence item was clearly 'plus', since Joanna was the sister of S 177 and the cousin of S 172. Although I had no reason to doubt that her father was dyslexic (and the only written communication that I received from him was further confirmation), the score of 'plus' did not depend on this.

The writing of letters the wrong way round is certainly not typical of dyslexic subjects in general; but Joanna was said to have had problems with her eye muscles quite apart from her dyslexia, and it is possible that the two factors in conjunction made her sense of direction even weaker than it otherwise would have been. When her eye-movements were photographed by my colleague, George Pavlidis, they were found to be extremely irregular[1].

I was able to confirm that Joanna was very bright and to encourage her in her attempts to train as a teacher. She in fact settled for taking a Nursery Training course rather than a full-scale Teacher Training course, and her mother reported that she had no regrets. Two years later her perseverance received striking recognition in the form of a Duke of Edinburgh award.

I end with extracts from a press cutting sent to me by Joanna's mother:

'An invitation to Buckingham Palace arrived last week at the home of. . . – the great reward for years of effort to overcome adversity.

At the Palace (Joanna) will be presented with the gold award of the Duke of Edinburgh's scheme – an outstanding achievement for anyone, let alone one fighting the handicap of dyslexia with colour blindness and a further optical defect adding to the problems. . .

She is now starting nursery nursing at _____ College . . .to use her understanding of the problems to help others. . . In all modesty (Joanna) can claim that her success has been achieved largely through her own determination'.

CHAPTER SIX

The Summary Chart

The following pages contain a summary of the assessment results in respect of 264 subjects, of whom 257 seemed to me to be unambiguously dyslexic and 7 to be marginally so. The 257 cases are made up of 223 where there are complete records and 34 where the records are incomplete (see p.26).

The following abbreviations are used:

Int.	=	intelligence grade
R_1	=	number of words read correctly on Schonell R_1 test
S_1	=	number of words read correctly on Schonell S_1 test
DF	=	digits fowards
DR	=	digits reversed
L-R	=	left-right
Pol	=	polysyllables
Sub	=	subtraction
Tab	=	tables
MF	=	months forwards
MR	=	months reversed
b-d	=	presence of b-d confusion
Famil.	=	presence of dyslexic tendencies in other members of the family

For details of procedure see pp. 203-213. Where a line is placed under the score in the R_1, S_1, DF, and DR columns this indicates that the result is within normal limits for a non-dyslexic person. An asterisk indicates incomplete data; where a result is given in brackets this indicates that the testing had already been done at the time of the assessment. An (m) before the subject's number indicates that he was matched for age and intelligence with a member of the control group.

In the 'limits' column, Arabic numerals indicate the highest two sub-test scores on the WISC (or, in one case, on the WAIS); Arabic numerals preceded by the letters AM indicate the score on the Raven Advanced Matrices, and Roman numerals indicate the mental age level of the highest two passes on the Terman Merrill test (AA, SA I, SA II, and SA III are the conventional abbreviations for 'average adult' and the three grades of 'superior adult'). Where an I.Q. figure is

SUMMARY CHART

Case no.	Sex	Age	Hand	Eye	Int.	Limits	R₁	S₁	DF	DR	L-R	Pol	Sub	Tab	MF	MR	b-d	Famil. Index
1)	M	7.5	L	L	W	14,13	8	2	55	3*	+	+	+	+	+	+	0	7½
(m) 2)	M	7.5	R	R	X	18,16	27	26	44	33	+	+	+	+	+	+	+	9
3)	M	7.6	M	L	X	16,15	0	3	56	33	+	−	+	+	+	+	nk	5½
(m) 4)	M	7.7	R	R	Z	19,16	26	22	45	23	+	−	+	+	+	+	0	8½
5)	M	7.9	R	L	W	17,14	12	15	45	33	+	+	+	+	+	+	0	8½
(m) 6)	M	7.9	M	R	X	18,17	21	15	56	33	+	+	+	+	+	+	+	7½
(m) 7)	M	7.11	R	R	Z	(18,16)	32	5	55	22	+	−	+	+	+	+	+	8
(Expected scores on the R₁ and S₁ tests for 7-year-olds: 20 to 30)																		
(m) 8)	F	8.0	R	R	U	10,11	8	15	56	33	+	+	+	+	+	+	nk	7
(m) 9)	M	8.0	M	L	X	16,15	12	20	56	34	+	+	+	+	+	+	nk	7
(m) 10)	M	8.1	R	L	Z	20,17	31	24	65	33	0	−	+	+	+	+	nk	5½
(m) 11)	M	8.2	M	R	U	12,11	7	1	45	34	+	−	+	+	+	+	nk	6
(m) 12)	M	8.4	R	R	X	17,16	24	24	55	33	+	−	+	+	+	+	+	7
(m) 13)	M	8.4	R	R	X	xii,xi	22	18	67	43	0	−	+	+	+	+	nk	6
(m) 14)	M	8.5	R	R	Y	17,17	41	22	65	34	−	0	+	+	+	+	+	6½
(m) 15)	M	8.6	M	R	W	xi,xi	40	29	45	44	+	−	−	+	+	+	nk	5
(m) 16)	M	8.6	R	R	X	17,16	38	41	45	33	+	0	−	+	+	+	+	6
(m) 17)	M	8.6	R	R	X	17,15	24	16	75	34	0	−	0	+	+	+	+	5
(m) 18)	M	8.6	R	R	X	17,17	8	16	55	45	+	0	−	+	−	+	+	6½
(m) 19)	M	8.7	M	R	W	17,14	40	30	55	43	+	0	+	+	+	+	0	5
20)	M	8.7	R	R	X	xiv,xiv	26	18	45	33	+	−	+	+	+	+	0	7½
(m) 21)	F	8.7	M	R	X	xiii,xii	36	22	67	53	+	−	0	+	−	−	nk	2½
(m) 22)	M	8.8	R	R	W	xi,xi	29	23	65	44	+	−	+	+	+	+	+	6½
(m) 23)	M	8.9	L	L	Y	20,16	28	21	67	34	+	−	+	+	+	+	+	7

Case no.	Sex	Age	Hand	Eye	Int.	Limits	R_1	S_1	DF	DR	L-R	Pol	Sub	Tab	MF	MR	b-d	Famil. Index
(m) 24)	M	8.10	R	R	W	15,11	25	15	34	33	+	0	+	+	+	+	0	8
(m) 25)	M	8.10	R	R	X	17,16	17	14	45	33	0	+	+	+	+	+	+	8
26)	F	8.10	R	R	V	xii,x	12	12	67	23	+	+	+	+	+	+	nk	8
(Expected scores on the R_1 and S_1 tests for 8-year-olds: 30 to 40)																		
27)	M	9.0	R	R	X	16,16	50	24	67	33	-	-	-	+	+	+	nk	4½
(m) 28)	F	9.1	R	R	V	13,11	47	27	55	43	0	-	0	+	0	+	+	6½
29)	M	9.1	R	R	X	xiii,xiii	31	25	45	44	0	-	-	+	0	+	nk	5½
30)	M	9.1	R	R	Z	20,17	39	30	66	56	-	0	0	+	0	-	nk	3
(m) 31)	M	9.2	R	R	W	14,13	37	24	65	43	-	-	+	+	-	+	nk	4½
32)	F	9.2	R	L	V	xii,xi	37	39	56	33	+	0	-	+	-	+	nk	5½
(m) 33)	M	9.2	L	M	X	xiv,xiii	44	36	45	33	+	0	-	+	+	0	nk	5
34)	M	9.2	R	L	Z	SAII,SAI	43	25	88	34	-	+	-	+	+	0	+	5½
(m) 35)	M	9.4	R	M	X	15,15	19	22	66	34	-	-	+	+	+	+	nk	5
(m) 36)	M	9.4	R	R	W	14,14	15	17	56	33	+	-	0	+	+	+	0	7½
37)	M	9.5	R	R	W	(IQ 103)	31	21	67	34	+	-	+	+	+	+	nk	6
(m) 38)	F	9.5	L	L	V	15,11	13	22	45	23	+	0	+	+	+	+	0	8½
(m) 39)	M	9.5	R	R	W	(15,14)	16	17	56	33	+	-	-	+	+	+	+	7½
(m) 40)	M	9.6	M	L	W	17,13	35	28	34	23	+	+	0	+	+	+	0	9½
41)	M	9.7	R	R	Y	19,17	34	25	55	33	+	0	0	+	+	+	nk	6½
(m) 42)	F	9.7	R	L	V	15,13	26	22	55	33	-	-	+	+	+	+	0	4½
43)	M	9.7	R	L	Y	15,15	34	28	65	34	-	-	0	+	+	+	0	7
44)	M	9.7	R	L	Y	19,19	26	19	55	33	+	+	+	+	+	+	nk	6½
(m) 45)	M	9.8	R	L	W	xiii,xiii	54	23	9‑	23	+	-	+	+	+	-	0	6½
46)	M	9.8	R	R	X	18,14	31	25	87	34	+	-	+	+	-	+	0	6½

Case no.	Sex	Age	Hand	Eye	Int.	Limits	R_1	S_1	DF	DR	L-R	Pol	Sub	Tab	MF	MR	b-d	Famil.	Index
47)	M	9.8	R	R	Z	20,19	59	36	65	33	+	–	+	+	+	+	–	nk	6
48)	M	9.9	M	R	Z	SAII,SAI	39	25	45	33	+	–	+	+	–	0	+	nk	5½
(m) 49)	M	9.9	R	L	W	13,12	22	19	34	33	+	–	–	+	+	+	+	nk	8
(m) 50)	M	9.10	R	R	X	xiv,xiv	47	27	56	45	+	–	+	+	+	+	–	nk	4½
(m) 51)	M	9.10	L	R	Y	19,19	46	26	55	45	+	+	0	+	+	–	+	+	5
(m) 52)	M	9.11	M	L	X	18,17	30	25	54	33	+	+	+	+	+	+	–	nk	8
53)	M	9.11	R	R	X	16,16	45	34	56	33	+	0	–	+	+	+	0	nk	5½
54)	M	9.11	R	L	W	15,13	33	34	56	23	+	0	+	+	–	+	+	0	7
55)	M	9.11	R	R	U	12,12	30	18	45	23	0	–	+	+	+	+	–	+	7½

(Expected scores on the R_1 and S_1 tests for 9-year-olds: 40 to 50)

Case no.	Sex	Age	Hand	Eye	Int.	Limits	R_1	S_1	DF	DR	L-R	Pol	Sub	Tab	MF	MR	b-d	Famil.	Index
(m) 56)	M	10.0	R	R	X	xiii,xiii	39	34	45	34	0	+	–	+	+	+	–	0	7
(m) 57)	M	10.1	M	L	U	xi,xi	43	40	44	33	0	0	0	+	+	+	+	nk	7½
(m) 58)	M	10.1	R	R	V	16,12	10	16	45	23	+	+	+	+	+	–	–	nk	8
(m) 59)	M	10.1	R	M	Y	17,17	48	26	45	33	+	+	+	+	+	+	+	nk	9
(m) 60)	M	10.2	M	R	U	12,11	18	13	45	34	+	0	+	+	–	0	0	0	9
61)	M	10.3	R	R	Y	SAI,AA	70	56	67	34	+	–	+	–	+	–	0	+	5½
(m) 62)	M	10.3	R	R	W	xiv,xiii	54	42	56	34	+	0	+	+	+	+	0	nk	8½
(m) 63)	F	10.3	R	R	Z	SAI,AA	56	42	43	33	+	+	0	+	–	+	0	nk	6
(m) 64)	M	10.4	R	R	Y	19,17	26	19	67	43	+	+	0	+	+	+	+	nk	7½
(m) 65)	M	10.6	R	L	W	xii,xii	25	27	65	33	+	0	+	+	+	0	0	nk	8
(m) 66)	M	10.7	R	R	X	AA,xiv	39	33	67	34	+	+	0	–	–	0	0	nk	6
(m) 67)	M	10.7	R	R	Y	17,17	47	37	65	44	+	+	–	+	–	+	+	nk	6
(m) 68)	M	10.7	M	L	X	xiv,xiii	41	35	56	33	+	0	0	+	+	+	0	+	9
(m) 69)	M	10.7	M	L	W	15,13	40	31	65	33	+	–	–	0	–	+	+	0	6

Dyslexia

Case no.	Sex	Age	Hand	Eye	Int.	Limits	R₁	S₁	DF	DR	L-R	Pol	Sub	Tab	MF	MR	b-d	Famil.	Index
(m) 70)	M	10.7	R	R	X	14,14	30	10	67	54	+	+	0	+	+	+	−	0	6
(m) 71)	M	10.8	R	R	W	14,13	46	26	67	34	+	0	−	+	−	−	−	nk	3½
(m) 72)	M	10.8	R	R	X	AA,xiv	33	29	55	45	+	+	0	+	+	+	+	+	8½
(m) 73)	M	10.8	M	L	W	13,12	41	35	56	33	+	0	−	+	+	+	−	nk	6½
(m) 74)	F	10.9	R	R	Z	SAI,SAI	76	42	55	34	0	0	0	+	−	−	−	+	6½
(m) 75)	M	10.9	R	L	X	17,16	75	30	55	33	+	0	0	+	0	+	+	nk	7
(m) 76)	F	10.9	R	R	X	16,14	40	29	45	34	+	+	−	+	0	+	0	nk	7
(m) 77)	M	10.9	R	M	X	xiv,xiv	52	29	95	44	0	+	0	+	0	+	0	nk	6
(m) 78)	M	10.9	R	R	V	13,14	29	12	55	44*	+	+	+	+	+	+	0	nk	7½
(m) 79)	M	10.9	L	R	W	xiii,xiii	45	33	56	33	+	0	0	−	+	+	−	nk	6½
(m) 80)	M	10.10	R	R	Y	20,16	59	48	56	43	+	−	0	+	+	+	0	0	7½
(m) 81)	M	10.10	R	R	X	SAI,xiv	35	28	67	43	+	0	0	+	−	−	−	nk	4½
(m) 82)	F	10.11	R	L	W	14,13	30	26	55	54	+	−	+	+	−	+	+	+	7
(m) 83)	M	10.11	R	R	X	19,18	17	13	45	23	+	0	+	+	+	+	+	nk	8½
(m) 84)	M	10.11	M	L	Z	SAI,SAI	40	45	67	33	−	+	−	−	+	+	0	0	6

(Expected scores on the R₁ and S₁ tests for 10-year-olds: 50 to 60)

Case no.	Sex	Age	Hand	Eye	Int.	Limits	R₁	S₁	DF	DR	L-R	Pol	Sub	Tab	MF	MR	b-d	Famil.	Index
(m) 85)	F	11.0	R	L	V	14,13	41	41	55	34	+	0	0	+	−	−	0	nk	5½
(m) 86)	M	11.0	R	R	W	(IQ 104)	54	27	55	34	+	0	0	+	−	+	−	nk	6
(m) 87)	M	11.0	R	L	X	AA,xiv	41	27	45	33	0	0	+	+	−	+	0	nk	6½
(m) 88)	M	11.0	R	R	U	15,10	24	17	66	33	+	0	+	+	+	+	−	+	7½
(m) 89)	M	11.1	R	R	Z	20,18	78	55	65	43	+	0	−	−	−	0	0	nk	7
(m) 90)	M	11.2	M	R	Y	SAIII,SAII	76	54	56	34	+	0	0	+	+	0	+	0	7
(m) 91)	M	11.2	R	R	W	AA,xiv	33	29	45	33	+	+	+	+	+	+	0	nk	8½
(m) 92)	M	11.2	M	L	W	13,14	52	16	56	33	+	0	−	+	0	+	0	+	7½

Case No.	Sex	Age	Hand	Eye	Int.	Limits	R_1	S_1	DF	DR	L-R	Pol	Sub	Tab	MF	MR	b-d	Famil.	Index
(m) 93	M	11.2	M	L	V	xiii,xiii	30	26	45	33	+	+	0	+	0	-	+	nk	7
(m) 94	M	11.3	R	R	Y	SAI,SAI	37	28	45	53	-	0	+	+	-	+	0	0	6½
95	M	11.3	R	R	Y	AA,xiv	60	21	65	33	0	0	+	+	-	0	+	nk	7
(m) 96	M	11.3	M	L	X	16,16	32	22	55	34	0	0	+	+	-	+	+	0	7½
(m) 97	M	11.4	R	R	X	16,15	60	53	67	53	0	+	-	0	-	-	-	+	4
(m) 98	F	11.4	R	R	V	14,12	42	29	34	33	0	+	0	+	0	+	+	nk	7½
(m) 99	M	11.4	R	R	W	AA,xiv	67	42	67	44	-	+	+	+	+	+	0	nk	6½
100	M	11.4	R	R	X	(IQ 120)	67	45	56	33	+	0	+	+	0	+	0	nk	7½
(m)101	M	11.4	R	L	U	xiii,xii	50	35	45	33	+	0	0	+	-	-	0	nk	6
(m)102	M	11.5	R	R	X	SAI,AA	37	23	45	33	+	-	0	+	0	+	-	nk	6
(m)103	F	11.5	R	R	U	xiii,xiii	27	24	55	23	+	+	+	+	-	+	+	+	8½
(m)104	M	11.5	R	R	V	13,13	39	31	45	43	+	+	+	+	0	+	0	+	9½
(m)105	M	11.5	M	R	X	15,15	31	34	45	34	-	0	-	+	+	+	-	nk	6½
(m)106	M	11.5	R	R	X	15,14	60	44	55	34	0	0	0	+	+	+	0	+	7½
(m)107	M	11.6	R	R	W	18,15	37	25	55	33	-	0	-	+	+	+	0	nk	6½
(m)108	M	11.8	R	M	Y	SAII,SAI	42	21	65	33	+	0	0	+	-	-	+	+	8½
109	M	11.8	R	R	Z	SAII,SAII	75	63	67	55	+	-	-	+	-	0	-	nk	2½
(m)110	F	11.9	R	R	X	AM 17	45	32	66	33	+	+	-	+	-	0	0	+	6
(m)111	F	11.10	M	L	W	(IQs 97 & '110-120')	26	20	45	23	+	+	+	+	-	0	+	0	8
112	M	11.10	M	R	Z	SAIII,SAII	65	69	78	65	+	+	-	+	-	0	+	0	5
113	M	11.10	R	R	X	SAI,AA	65	28	56	33	+	+	0	+	+	+	+	0	9½
114	M	11.11	M	M	Y	SAIII,SAI	48	33	55	43	+	0	+	0	-	+	0	0	7
115	M	11.11	L	R	X	19,15	55	36	65	33	0	-	-	+	-	+	0	nk	5½
(m)116	F	11.11	R	L	V	xiv,xiii	72	34	45	33	+	-	-	+	+	0	+	+	7½
(m)117	F	11.11	R	R	V	(IQ 'bright normal')	55	41	45	45	-	-	+	+	+	+	0	+	6½

(Expected scores on the R_1 and S_1 tests for 11-year-olds: 60 to 70)

Case no.	Sex	Age	Hand	Eye	Int.	Limits	R_1	S_1	DF	DR	L-R	Pol	Sub	Tab	MF	MR	b-d	Famil.	Index
118)	M	12.0	R	R	Z	SAIII,SAI	76	38	66	33	−	+	0	+	+	0	0	nk	5½
119	M	12.0	R	R	Z	SAIII,SAI	74	48	78	34	+	0	−	−	−	−	0	0	3½
(m)120)	M	12.1	R	R	W	15,14	38	33	55	34	−	0	0	+	+	+	0	+	7½
(m)121)	M	12.1	R	L	X	SAI,SAI	56	42	55	44	−	+	0	+	+	+	+	nk	6½
(m)122)	M	12.2	R	L	W	AA,xiv	61	38	67	45	0	0	−	+	+	−	0	+	4½
123)	M	12.3	R	R	Z	SAII,SAII	78	59	78	33	−	−	−	+	+	−	0	0	3
(m)124)	M	12.5	R	R	V	(IQ 99)	10	12	67	34	+	0	0	+	+	+	0	nk	6½
(m)125)	M	12.5	R	L	X	SAII,SAI	60	54	56	55	+	+	−	0	+	−	−	nk	6
(m)126)	M	12.7	R	R	Z	SAIII,SAIII	82	52	77	44	0	−	−	0	−	+	+	nk	2
(m)127)	M	12.7	R	R	Z	SAIII,SAII	82	56	45	33	+	0	0	+	+	+	+	nk	7
(m)128)	M	12.7	R	R	X	20,17	26	18	67	53	+	+	−	−	−	0	0	0	6½
(m)129)	M	12.8	R	L	X	SAI,SAI	60	41	66	55	+	−	−	0	+	0	+	+	3½
(m)130)	M	12.10	L	L	X	(IQ122,117)	(36)	(26)	76	34	+	−	+	+	+	+	+	0	7
(m)131)	F	12.11	M	L	U	10,10	37	36	55	44	0	0	−	+	−	+	0	nk	4½
132)	M	12.11	R	L	X	SAII,SAI	56	29	67	43	+	0	0	+	+	+	+	nk	7
133)	M	12.11	R	R	Z	SAII,SAII	57	43	67	34	+	+	+	+	+	+	0	nk	8½

(Expected scores on the R_1 and S_1 tests for 12-year-olds: 70 to 80)

134)	M	13.0	R	R	V	16,13	50	46	56	33	+	+	−	+	−	−	−	nk	5
135)	M	13.0	M	R	Y	SAIII,SAIII	69	52	55	34	+	+	0	+	−	+	−	nk	6½
(m)136)	F	13.1	R	R	W	SAI,AA	35	33	56	53	0	+	0	+	−	0	−	nk	5½
137)	M	13.1	R	R	Z	SAIII,SAIII	89	71	56	34	+	0	+	+	−	+	−	nk	5½
138)	M	13.2	R	L	X	SAI,AA	62	61	78	64	−	−	+	+	−	0	+	0	5

Case no.	Sex	Age	Hand	Eye	Int.	Limits	R₁	S₁	DF	DR	L-R	Pol	Sub	Tab	MF	MR	b-d	Famil.	Index
139)	F	13.3	R	L	Y	SAIII,SAIII	83	57	56	43	0	−	−	−	−	−	+	nk	4½
(m)140)	M	13.4	R	R	W	SAI,SAI	24	21	65	33	−	+	+	+	+	+	−	+	8
141)	M	13.4	R	R	X	SAIII,SAI	54	28	76	33	+	0	0	+	+	+	0	0	7
(m)142)	M	13.5	R	R	U	xiii,xiii	28	18	44	55	+	0	0	+	+	+	0	+	6
143)	F	13.6	M	R	X	17,14	62	61	65	23	+	+	+	+	−	+	0	nk	7
144)	M	13.7	R	R	Z	SAIII,SAIII	70	66	56	43	−	+	0	+	−	−	+	nk	4½
(m)145)	F	13.8	R	M	W	SAI,AA	75	35	77	55	+	0	+	+	−	0	−	0	5½
(m)146)	M	13.9	R	L	V	SAI,AA	59	37	45	44	−	0	0	+	+	+	+	nk	7
(m)147)	M	13.9	R	R	V	SAI,AA	69	46	77	34	+	+	+	+	+	0	−	0	7½
148)	M	13.9	M	R	Z	SAIII,SAII	85	67	55	34	+	+	0	+	−	0	−	+	7
(m)149)	M	13.10	R	R	V	13,12	53	40	66	33	0	0	+	+	+	+	+	nk	6
(Expected scores on the R₁ and S₁ tests for 13-year-olds: 80 to 90)																			
(m)150)	F	14.0	R	L	W	15,13	62	41	55	34	0	0	+	+	+	+	+	nk	8
(m)151)	M	14.1	R	R	W	SAII,SAI	71	46	77	33	0	0	+	+	+	0	+	0	7
152)	M	14.1	R	R	V	SAI,AA	49	35	45	34	0	+	0	+	−	+	−	nk	6
153)	M	14.1	L	L	X	SAI,SAI	75	62	66	23	+	0	+	+	+	+	−	nk	6½
154)	M	14.2	R	R	X	AM 18	74	45	56	33	+	0	+	+	+	−	−	nk	7½
(m)155)	M	14.2	R	R	Z	SAIII,SAII	78	62	67	44	−	−	−	+	−	+	+	nk	4
(m)156)	F	14.3	R	R	U	AA,xiv	59	44	76	33	−	+	+	+	−	−	−	0	5½
(m)157)	M	14.3	R	L	V	15,13	54	23	67	43	+	0	+	+	−	+	+	0	7
158)	M	14.4	R	M	Z	SAIII,SAII	75	48	45	33	+	+	+	+	+	+	0	0	9
(m)159)	M	14.4	R	R	X	AM 19	75	58	56	33	0	+	+	−	−	+	0	0	7½
(m)160)	M	14.5	R	R	U	SAI,AA	61	45	55	43	+	0	+	+	+	+	0	nk	7
161)	M	14.5	M	R	Z	SAII,SAII	82	54	78	23	+	−	+	+	+	+	−	nk	6

Case no.	Sex	Age	Hand	Eye	Int.	Limits	R₁	S₁	DF	DR	L-R	Pol	Sub	Tab	MF	MR	b-d	Famil.	Index
(m)162)	M	14.8	M	R	X	SAIII,SAII	47	25	55	33	+	-	+	+	+	+	0	nk	7½
163)	M	14.9	R	R	U	xiv,xiv	46	39	45	33	+	+	-	+	+	+	0	nk	7½
164)	M	14.10	R	R	V	12,11	49	25	55	34	-	0	+	+	+	+	+	nk	7½

(Expected scores on the R₁ and S₁ tests for 14-year-olds: 90 to 100)

Case no.	Sex	Age	Hand	Eye	Int.	Limits	R₁	S₁	DF	DR	L-R	Pol	Sub	Tab	MF	MR	b-d	Famil.	Index
165)	F	15.0	R	R	V	AA,AA	53	40	55	43	+	+	0	+	+	+	0	0	8½
(m)166)	M	15.0	R	R	V	SAI,AA	63	37	78	33	+	-	0	+	+	+	-	nk	4½
167)	M	15.0	R	M	V	AA,AA	30	28	67	43	+	+	-	+	+	+	0	nk	7½
168)	M	15.1	R	R	Z	(IQ 132)	92	80	56	23	+	-	+	+	+	-	0	0	7
169)	M	15.1	M	L	Y	SAIII,SAIII	72	51	50	34	+	-	0	+	-	+	0	0	6½
170)	F	15.2	R	L	U	SAI,AA	43	24	55	34	+	+	-	+	-	+	+	nk	7
(m)171)	M	15.2	R	R	Y	SAIII,SAII	64	46	67	43	0	+	0	0	+	+	0	nk	7
172)	M	15.2	M	R	Y	SAIII,SAII	90	77	78	55	0	-	-	0	-	-	-	+	2
173)	M	15.3	M	R	Z	(IQ 141)	86	74	66	55	+	-	-	0	+	-	-	nk	4½
174)	M	15.3	R	R	Y	SAIII,SAIII	76	42	89	55	-	+	+	0	-	+	0	nk	4
(m)175)	F	15.3	R	L	W	SAI,AA	88	80	55	34	0	-	+	-	-	+	-	nk	5
(m)176)	M	15.3	R	L	W	SAII,SAII	53	33	67	34	0	+	0	+	-	+	-	nk	6
177)	M	15.4	R	R	Z	SAIII,SAII	55	47	65	44	+	-	+	+	-	-	+	+	7
178)	M	15.5	R	L	V	AA,AA	65	46	65	33	+	+	+	+	+	-	-	+	7
179)	M	15.7	L	R	V	SAII,SAI	75	30	78	53	+	+	+	+	+	+	-	0	7½
(m)180)	M	15.8	R	R	W	17,14	48	36	55	44	0	+	-	+	-	+	-	0	6
181)	F	15.8	R	L	Y	SAI,SAI	53	36	56	33	+	-	+	+	+	+	-	0	6½
(m)182)	M	15.8	R	R	X	AM 19	81	55	65	44	0	+	+	+	+	+	-	0	7½
(m)183)	M	15.8	R	R	X	SAIII,SAII	93	64	99	44	+	-	-	-	+	+	-	nk	5
(m)184)	M	15.9	R	R	X	SAIII,SAII	87	70	55	43	0	+	-	-	+	-	-	nk	4½

Case no.	Sex	Age	Hand	Eye	Int.	Limits	R₁	S₁	DF	DR	L-R	Pol	Sub	Tab	MF	MR	b-d	Famil.	Index
185)	M	15.9	R	R	Y	AM 28	85	62	77	53	−	+	+	+	−	+	+	0	6½
186)	M	15.11	R	L	Y	SAIII,SAII	90	54	76	64	−	+	0	+	−	−	−	nk	3½
187)	F	15.11	R	L	W	SAII,SAI	85	71	75	65	+	+	+	+	−	−	−	nk	5
188)	M	15.11	R	R	Y	SAIII,SAII	87	72	56	44	−	+	+	+	+	0	−	nk	5½
189)	M	15.11	M	R	Y	SAIII,SAII	79	44	55	33	−	−	−	+	−	+	−	+	5
190)	M	15.11	R	R	V	SAII,AA	(58)	(50)	67	55	−	+	0	+	+	+	−	nk	5½

(Expected scores on the R₁ and S₁ tests for 15-year-olds: over 90)

Case no.	Sex	Age	Hand	Eye	Int.	Limits	R₁	S₁	DF	DR	L-R	Pol	Sub	Tab	MF	MR	b-d	Famil.	Index
(m)191)	M	16.0	R	L	W	17,16 (WAIS)	73	58	77	45	0	+	0	0	+	−	+	−	nk	5
192)	M	16.0	L	L	W	(IQ 108)	64	59	67	33	+	+	0	0	−	0	0	0	5½
(m)193)	M	16.1	R	R	X	SAIII,SAII	58	33	67	33	+	0	+	+	−	−	−	0	6
(m)194)	F	16.1	R	R	Y	AM 23	95	85	56	34	+	+	−	+	−	+	−	nk	6
195)	M	16.2	M	R	Z	AM 31	75	57	56	64	+	+	−	0	−	−	+	nk	5½
196)	M	16.3	R	R	X	SAIII,SAII	86	54	67	43	0	+	0	+	−	−	−	nk	5
197)	F	16.5	R	R	Y	SAIII,SAII	75	75	56	43	+	+	+	+	−	−	0	nk	6½
198)	F	16.6	R	R	W	SAII,SAII	76	65	56	43	+	0	+	+	−	−	0	nk	6
199)	F	16.9	M	R	W	SAII,SAII	74	77	56	33	0	+	+	+	−	−	−	0	6
200)	M	16.9	R	R	Z	AM 31	79	60	78	33	+	+	−	+	+	+	−	nk	5
201)	M	16.11	R	R	Y	SAIII,SAIII	60	15	56	33	+	+	0	+	+	0	−	nk	7
202)	M	16.11	L	L	W	SAI,SAI	42	22	67	43	+	+	0	+	+	−	+	0	8

(Expected scores on the R₁ and S₁ tests for 16-year-olds: over 90)

Case no.	Sex	Age	Hand	Eye	Int.	Limits	R₁	S₁	DF	DR	L-R	Pol	Sub	Tab	MF	MR	b-d	Famil.	Index
203)	M	17.0	R	R	Y	AM 25	99	86	56	43	+	+	0	+	−	+	−	nk	6½
204)	M	17.2	R	R	W	SAII,SAII	80	53	45	44	+	+	+	+	−	+	−	+	8
205)	F	17.3	R	R	W	SAII,SAII	82	73	67	33	+	0	+	+	−	−	−	nk	5½

Case no.	Sex	Age	Hand	Eye	Int.	Limits	R₁	S₁	DF	DR	L-R	Pol	Sub	Tab	MF	MR	b-d	Famil.	Index
206)	M	17.4	R	R·	V	SAII,SAI	81	43	55	34	+	+	+	+	+	+	0	0	9
(m)207)	M	17.4	R	R	X	SAIII,SAII	78	58	56	43	−	+	0	+	−	+	0	0	6½
(m)208)	F	17.4	M	M	Y	AM 23	79	57	45	34	+	+	0	+	−	+	0	+	8
(m)209)	F	17.5	R	M	Z	SAIII,SAIII	89	76	55	34	+	+	+	+	−	−	−	nk	6
(m)210)	M	17.11	L	L	Z	AM 30	92	60	67	64	−	−	0	−	+	−	+	nk	4½

(Expected scores on the R₁ and S₁ tests for 17-year-olds: over 90)

Case no.	Sex	Age	Hand	Eye	Int.	Limits	R₁	S₁	DF	DR	L-R	Pol	Sub	Tab	MF	MR	b-d	Famil.	Index
(m)211)	M	18.0	R	R	Z	SAIII,SAIII	92	67	78	43	+	+	+	+	+	+	0	0	6
212)	F	18.1	R	R	Y	AM 25	94	87	75	34	+	−	−	−	−	−	−	nk	3
213)	F	18.2	R	R	Y	AM 24	96	80	55	43	+	0	0	+	−	+	+	0	7
214)	M	18.2	R	L	U	AA,AA	75	39	56	34	+	+	+	+	+	+	0	+	9½
215)	M	18.4	R	L	Y	SAIII,SAII	92	85	76	44	0	+	−	0	−	−	−	nk	4
216)	F	18.5	R	L	Z	AM 31	98	89	67	34	+	0	−	−	−	−	−	nk	3½
217)	M	18.6	R	R	Y	AM 22	94	86	65	55	−	+	−	+	−	−	−	nk	4
(m)218)	F	18.11	R	L	X	SAIII,SAII	90	88	78	55	0	+	0	−	+	−	−	0	4½
219)	M	19.0	R	R	X	AM 18	98	88	67	43	+	−	+	+	−	0	0	+	6½
220)	M	19.2	R	R	Z	SAIII,SAIII	93	75	55	44	+	0	−	+	−	−	−	0	5½
221)	M	20.1	R	M	Y	AM 22	99	93	67	45	0	−	−	0	−	−	−	+	4
222)	M	20.9	R	L	Z	AM 30	99	77	67	43	−	0	−	0	−	−	−	nk	3
223)	M	23.5	R	M	Y	AM 30	93	78	76	55	0	0	−	−	−	−	−	nk	3

(Expected scores on the R₁ and S₁ tests for 18-year-olds: over 90)

INCOMPLETE RECORDS

Case no.	Sex	Age	Hand	Eye	Int.	Limits	R₁	S₁	DF	DR	L-R	Pol	Sub	Tab	MF	MR	b-d	Famil.	Index
224)	F	8.5	R	R	V	xi,x	9	1	55	33	*	0	+	*	+	+	+	+	5½+
225)	M	8.6	R	R	W	xii,xi	10	13	67	33	+	+	+	+	*	*	+	nk	5+
226)	M	8.10	L	R	W	(14,13)	13	9	45	23	+	+	+	+	*	*	+	nk	7+
227)	M	9.1	M	R	U	11,10	25	23	45	43	+	0	+	+	0	*	+	nk	7+
228)	M	9.5	R	L	X	xiii,xii	*	*	65	33	+	0	+	+	+	+	0	nk	7
229)	M	9.5	R	*	U	15,14	12	13	67	34	-	+	+	*	+	+	+	+	7+
230)	M	9.10	R	L	W	xiii,xii	39	(34)	55	43	+	0	+	+	0	*	+	0	6½+
231)	F	9.11	R	R	V	xi,x	34	25	55	23	+	+	+	+	*	*	-	nk	5+
232)	M	9.11	R	R	X	18,14	37	34	78	33	+	-	+	+	+	*	0	nk	5½+
233)	M	10.0	R	L	W	xiii,xiii	34	(14)	55	33	-	+	+	*	*	*	+	0	5½+
234)	M	10.7	R	L	W	13,13	27	23	55	34	0	0	-	+	-	*	+	0	5½+
235)	M	10.8	M	M	U	15,13	24	22	45	*3	+	+	+	+	+	+	+	0	9½
236)	F	10.10	R	R	X	SAI,AA	42	29	56	34	-	+	-	+	-	*	-	0	3½+
237)	M	11.2	R	R	Y	20,20	69	*	65	33	+	+	+	+	+	0	+	0	8
238)	M	11.3	R	R	Y	SAI,AA	65	46	78	53	0	-	-	*	+	0	+	+	4+
239)	M	11.11	R	R	Y	SAII,SAI	57	*	88	43	-	+	-	+	-	+	+	0	6
240)	M	12.1	L	R	*	*	30	25	45	33	+	+	0	+	0	-	+	nk	6½
241)	M	12.2	R	R	Z	SAIII,SAII	64	41	55	33	+	+	0	+	*	*	+	0	7+
242)	F	12.9	R	L	X	SAIII,SAI	64	32	55	34	+	0	+	+	-	*	0	0	6½+
243)	M	13.4	R	R	X	SAII,SAI	67	58	65	43	0	+†	-	+	-	-	-	nk	3½+
244)	M	13.9	*	*	W	SAI,SAI	68	45	55	33	0	0	-	+	+	+	0	0	7
245)	M	13.9	*	*	U	AA,xiv	39	23	56	44	*	*	-	+	0	+	+	0	5+
246)	F	14.3	R	R	Z	AM 31	86	67	89	67	+	-	-	*	*	*	+	+	3+
247)	M	15.2	*	*	Z	SAIII,SAIII	79	62	78	74	+	-	-	0	+	+	0	nk	5
248)	F	15.2	M	M	X	AM 20	70	*	45	33	+	+	0	+	+	-	-	+	7½+

† This item was omitted because the subject had a severe stammer

Case no.	Sex	Age	Hand	Eye	Int.	Limits	R_1	S_1	DF	DR	L-R	Pol	Sub	Tab	MF	MR	b-d	Famil.	Index
249)	M	15.5	R	R	V	SAIII,SAII	79	63	67	34	+	+	+	+	*	*	–	0	6½+
250)	F	15.8	M	R	X	SAI,AA	61	51	78	43	0	0	+	+	*	*	–	nk	4+
251)	M	15.10	M	R	Y	AM 25	84	68	9–	65	–	0	0	+	–	–	–	0	1½
252)	F	16.9	L	L	Z	AM 26	93	93	76	43	+	–	0	*	–	–	0	0	4½+
253)	M	17.5	*	*	Y	SAIII,SAII	78	80	67	44	+	+	–	0	+	–	–	nk	4½
254)	M	18.0	M	R	C	SAIII,SAII	96	*	65	55	+	–	0	+	–	–	–	nk	5½
255)	M	19.2	R	R	A	AM 28	83	65	77	44	+	+	+	–	–	*	–	nk	4½+
256)	M	25	M	R	A	AM 31	*	*	77	73	–	0	*	+	–	–	–	nk	3+
257)	M	38.8	R	R	A	SAIII,SAIII	89	56	75	44	+	+	+	+	*	*	–	0	6½+
MARGINAL CASES																			
258)	F	8.1	R	L	Y	xii,xiii	32	24	67	55	+	–	+	+	–	0	–	0	4
259)	F	9.3	R	R	Z	20,20	60	42	67	23	+	–	–	*	–	0	–	+	3+
260)	M	9.6	R	L	Y	18,16	29	32	65	45	0	0	–	0	–	–	–	+	2½
261)	F	12.7	R	L	Y	SAI,SAII	91	74	77	45	0	0	–	0	–	–	0	nk	2
262)	M	13.9	R	R	U	xiii,xiv	68	68	65	34	–	*	*	+	–	–	–	0	4+
263)	F	15.6	M	R	W	SAI,SAII	84	80	78	43	+	0	0	+	–	–	–	–	3½
264)	M	18.0	R	R	V	SAI,SAI	85	66	86	54	–	–	–	+	–	–	–	0	3½

given in brackets this represents a 'composite I.Q.' (see p. 12) obtained elsewhere, the grade-letter for intelligence level being adjusted to one grade higher.

Chapters 8 – 23 will contain further information about the subjects whose particulars are given in the Summary Chart. My intention in these chapters is to examine in turn some of the different areas where dyslexic-type weaknesses show themselves and to indicate what are the typically dyslexic ways of responding. Not every subject behaves in exactly the same way, but time and time again the same 'picture' emerges: that of unexpected difficulty in a variety of tasks (unexpected, that is, in view of the intelligence and the opportunities that have been available to him), the resultant frustration, in some cases the compensatory strategies (with varying degrees of success), and the relief when the pattern of the handicap is explained.

The evidence contained in the Summary Chart is an integral part of my argument. If, for example, I had simply indicated that subject X mistook left for right on a particular occasion or that at the age of 11 subject Y made errors in reciting the months of the year, then, in the absence of further information, these would be descriptions of isolated occurrences which did not necessarily have any special significance. If, however, there is the additional information that the person who made a mistake in reciting the months of the year was a boy of above-average ability who had had every opportunity to learn them, there is perhaps something a little puzzling, even though an unsympathetic critic might still feel justified in saying, 'He hasn't learned them: so what?' But suppose, further, that the boy is a very poor speller, that he has had difficulty over his tables, that he has a father and first cousin who are also poor spellers and that he still sometimes puts 'b' and 'd' the wrong way round. Even here, these might simply be particular things which this particular child happens to find difficult, though if I were the critic I think that at this stage I should be starting to wriggle somewhat. If it is then shown that large numbers of other people, quite unlike this boy in respect of age, social background, type of schooling, etc. display many of the same difficulties, it becomes all but impossible to view such difficulties in isolation.

What I am saying, in effect, is that the phenomena discussed in the following chapters make sense only if considered in conjunction with the information given in the Summary Chart. It is not just *any* person who made a mistake, say, over left and right: it is case no. such-and-such who also displayed the other 'dyslexia-positive' indications which have been systematically recorded.

The central purpose of the Summary Chart is thus to supply a context in the light of which the responses described in Chapters 8 to 23 can be interpreted.

It has a secondary purpose, however, viz. that of serving as a source of data for statistical description and inference. Although quantification has not been my main aim in this book it by no means follows that all statistical calculation is irrelevant. There is in the first place plenty of scope in the Summary Chart for so-called 'descriptive' statistics, for example statements as to *how many* of my subjects were left-handed or had dyslexic relatives; and indeed the reader will be able to supply his own descriptive statistics from the data if he so wishes. In addition I decided to use a small number of somewhat more elaborate statistical techniques for purposes of comparison. In particular I wished to compare the performance on the dyslexia test of some of my dyslexic subjects with that of controls matched as far as possible for age and intelligence. My reasoning was that if the two groups behaved no differently then there was no justification for speaking of a 'dyslexia' test, since it was failing to pick out distinctively dyslexic subjects; in so naming it I could rightly have been accused of begging the question. The evidence presented in Chapter 7 shows that there were in fact considerable differences between the two groups, and the method of scoring the dyslexia test makes possible a provisional and preliminary attempt to submit these differences to quantification.

Much more, of course, remains to be done. Further comparison of dyslexic and control subjects could well lead to a more sensitive method of scoring. Suitable 'weighting' of the different items in the dyslexia test according to the extent that they differentiated the two groups would almost certainly lead to a more accurate 'index' of dyslexia, while factorial analysis or a related statistical technique could conceivably contribute towards a more accurate classification of the information-processing tasks required in the dyslexia test. Had these procedures been included, however, I would have been writing a different kind of book.

The only other major attempt at quantification occurs in Chapter 19, where I examine the issue of 'improvement over time'. For this purpose I have extracted from the Summary Chart data comparing the performance of older and younger subjects at the same task; and it has been possible to show in particular that in the 'digits forwards' and 'digits reversed' tasks my older subjects performed very little better than my younger ones. In contrast, in the case of the heavily practised skills, including reading in particular, the scores of the older subjects were appreciably higher.[1]

Despite the number of questions which remain unanswered, I think it can be claimed that the information in the Summary Chart 'sets the stage' for further quantification. The criteria for scoring responses as 'plus', 'zero', and 'minus' have been determined on the basis of what makes sense clinically, and the resultant symbols lend themselves easily to statistical treatment.

CHAPTER SEVEN

Control Data

As was pointed out in Chapter 3, the items in the dyslexia test were chosen because it seemed that dyslexic subjects were having unusual difficulty with them. For many years, however, I was, in a sense, working in the dark. I believed that the test was tapping something relevant and important, but I was in no position to convince the sceptical that this was so, and I was not without my own moments of doubt. For example, I knew that some dyslexic subjects had difficulty in saying the word 'preliminary', but it was possible that many other persons who were not dyslexic would also have had difficulty. Similarly, even though some of my older subjects could not say the months of the year in reverse order was it not still possible that many non-dyslexic persons would also have stumbled or hesitated? With some regularity, too, I seemed to be meeting people who were perfectly adequate spellers but who reported that they sometimes hesitated or made mistakes over 'right' and 'left'. Finally I could not help remembering press reports of literacy surveys in schools: x% of children could not do simple addition; y% could not give the date of Christmas day, etc. This led me to wonder whether even those tests about which I felt most confidence – for example, saying the months of the year – were more difficult for, say, the average 11-year-old than I had supposed.

Now it was clearly not the case that dyslexic subjects *always* made these mistakes while non-dyslexic subjects *never* made them. It was still possible, however, that dyslexic subjects were more vulnerable on such tasks – that there was a greater *risk* of their making mistakes. The obvious thing, therefore, was to give the dyslexia test to children of the same ages, if possible matched for intelligence, and check whether the adequate spellers performed any differently from the dyslexic subjects. If they did not, then the words 'dyslexia test' were a misnomer and the attempt to pick out children who had distinctively 'dyslexic'-type difficulties by means of it was a failure. In contrast, if there were more 'pluses' among the dyslexic subjects one could say, not indeed that the value of the concept of dyslexia was from that moment fully established, but at least that the classification into 'dyslexic' and 'non-dyslexic' had thus far resisted refutation[1].

It could still be objected that reading and spelling failure – however caused – engenders lack of confidence and that lack of confidence engenders uncertainty when a complete stranger fires questions about 'left' and 'right' or makes unexpected requests such as 'Can you say the months of the year?' If this were so, however, one would expect similar lack of confidence to affect the subject's responses to intelligence test items, and one would then have to explain why lack of confidence affected performance on some items and not on others. To meet this objection, therefore, it was necessary to compare the performance on the dyslexia test of the dyslexic subjects with that of a control group matched as far as possible for intelligence level. Full scale assessment of control subjects has not so far been possible for reasons of time; but although more remains to be done, a start has been made in that a brief intelligence test, a spelling test, and seven items from the dyslexia test, viz. digits reversed, left-right, polysyllables, subtraction, tables, months forwards and months reversed, have been given to pupils who were adequate spellers[2].

For convenience the control subjects have been divided into three age-groups, 7 to 8, 9 to 12, and 13 to 18. The 7- and 8-year-olds were given the Standard Progressive matrices[3], as were the 13- to 18-year-olds, while the 9- to 12-year-olds were given the Similarities and Picture Completion items from the WISC. I then devised a rough-and-ready procedure for converting their scores into the grade labels which I had used for my dyslexic subjects[4]. The result was the following table of equivalents:

| Grade | Raven Matrices Score | | | WISC Scaled Score |
	Age 7	Age 8	Ages 13–18	Ages 9–12
Z	31+	38+	57+	32+
Y	28–30	34–37	55–56	29–31
X	25–27	30–33	53–54	26–28
W	22–24	26–29	51–52	23–25
V	19–21	21–25	47–50	20–22
U	15–18	16–20	43–46	16–19

Any subject was excluded from the control group if his spelling age on the Schonell S₁ test was less than 80% of the bottom of the scale for his age-level (e.g. 7-year-olds with a score of 16, 8-year-olds with a score of 24, 9-year-olds with a score of 32, and so on.[5] Any subject whose first language was not English was also excluded.

This procedure gave a 'pool' of potential control subjects, of whom 132 were selected on the grounds that each could be 'paired' for intelligence grade with a dyslexic subject of the same age[6].

Appendix III gives the relevant particulars for each control subject, that is, sex, age, intelligence grade, S₁ score and performance on the seven items of the dyslexia test mentioned above. As a result it is possible to indicate the number of 'pluses' obtained both by the control subjects and by the dyslexic subjects on the same seven items.[7]

Table 7.1 gives further details:

Table 7.1 *Particulars of dyslexic and control subjects at 3 different age-levels*

		Dyslexic subjects	Control subjects
I. Ages 7 and 8			
No. of subjects		21	21
Mean age (years and months)		8.4	8.4
No. in each intelligence grade	Z	3	3
	Y	2	2
	X	10	10
	W	4	4
	V	0	0
	U	2	2
Mean score on S_1 spelling test		19.95	38.19
s.d.		8.29	10.74
II. Ages 9, 10, 11, and 12			
No. of subjects		80	80
Mean age (years and months)		10.10	10.10
No. in each intelligence grade	Z	3	3
	Y	9	9
	X	26	26
	W	22	22
	V	13	13
	U	7	7
Mean score on S_1 spelling test		29.3	61.3
s.d.		10.99	13.47
III. Ages 13, 14, 15, 16, 17, and 18			
No. of subjects		31	31
Mean age (years and months)		15.4	14.10
No. in each intelligence grade	Z	4	4
	Y	3	3
	X	8	8
	W	8	8
	V	3	3
	U	3	3
Mean score on S_1 spelling test		49.81	88.16
s.d.		18.39	6.71

Table 7.2 shows the mean (or 'average') number of 'pluses' for dyslexic and control subjects in each of the three age-groups.

Table 7.2 *Number of 'pluses' for dyslexic and control subjects in each of the different age-groups*

	Dyslexic subjects	Control subjects	Confidence level
Ages 7–8 ($n=21$)			
Mean no. of pluses	4.95	3.40	$p <0.001$
Standard deviation	1.00	1.46	
Ages 9–12 ($n=80$)			
Mean no. of pluses	5.14	2.24	$p <0.001$
Standard deviation	1.20	1.37	
Ages 13–18 ($n=31$)			
Mean no. of pluses	4.87	2.05	$p <0.001$
Standard deviation	0.95	1.21	

Table 7.3 shows the percentages of dyslexic and control subjects who scored 'pluses' on each of the 7 dyslexia test items. (For convenience 'zeros' have been assigned half to 'plus' and half to 'minus'[8]).

Table 7.3 *Percentages of dyslexic and control subjects who scored 'pluses' on each of the 7 dyslexia-test items. (For convenience 'zeros' have been assigned half to 'plus' and half to 'minus')*

	Dyslexic subjects	Control subjects
Age 7–8		
Digits reversed	10	0
Left-right	86	79
Polysyllables	24	21
Subtraction	86	62
Tables	90	71
Months forwards	90	38
Months reversed	95	71
Ages 9–12		
Digits reversed	80	48
Left-right	78	42
Polysyllables	56	24
Subtraction	58	19
Tables	96	51
Months forwards	60	13
Months reversed	86	28

Table 7.3 *continued*

	Dyslexic subjects	Control subjects
Ages 13–18		
Digits reversed	94	52
Left-right	65	53
Polysyllables	66	21
Subtraction	63	10
Tables	85	53
Months forwards	35	3
Months reversed	79	13

The figures given in Table 7.2 confirm that at all three age-levels the dyslexic subjects were scoring significantly more 'pluses' than the controls.[9] Those given in Table 7.3 confirm that all 7 items were contributing to the discrimination. It is possible that those of higher intelligence grades, both among the dyslexic and the control subjects, score proportionately fewer 'pluses', but this is a matter for further investigation.

The data in this chapter are rough and ready. For reasons of time it was possible to obtain control data in respect of only 7 items in the dyslexia test and 'matching for intelligence' has been only approximate. The results, however, are so decisive that one must conclude that this particular attempt to 'knock down' the dyslexia concept has been unsuccessful. 'Plus' scores on items purporting to be indicators of dyslexia were found to be far more common among those believed to be dyslexic than among controls; and had this not been so the claim that these items are indicators of dyslexia would have become very difficult to defend.

CHAPTER EIGHT

Reading

If the central thesis of this book is correct the difficulties experienced by dyslexic subjects over reading should be regarded as manifestations of a wider problem, viz. a limitation in the ability to process symbolic material. The presence of such a limitation, however, does not mean that success at reading is totally ruled out. Indeed, as will be shown in Chapter 19, there is reason to believe that, in society as it exists at present, difficulties over reading are appreciably more likely to be overcome than difficulties over spelling, and far more likely to be overcome than difficulty in remembering digits.

The extent to which my subjects had made progress in reading at the time of the assessment varied considerably and was no doubt in part a function of the amount and quality of the help which they had received. As an initial step I judged that it would be helpful to note how many subjects had reading ages of less than 80% of the bottom point of the range for their chronological age[1]. There were in fact 101 of the 223 subjects who satisfied this criterion[2].

When the remaining 122 records were examined, however, there was clear evidence that large numbers of the subjects had experienced problems over reading. In exactly half of the cases (61) there was independent evidence of an early history of reading difficulty, either from the letters of referral or from reports by the subject or his parents made during the assessment[3]. When the scores for the remaining 61 were examined it was found that 29 of them were below the bottom of the range for their age (see note 8.1), 24 were within the range, and eight were above it[4]. In this context it seemed justified to take into account the subjects' intelligence ratings. The frequencies were as follows:

Category	Below the range	Within the range	Above the range
Z	8	7	4
Y	3	10	3
X	8	6	0
W	8	0	0
V	1	1	1
U	1	0	0
Total	29	24	8

As was made clear in Chapter 2, intelligence test grades are not easy to interpret; and indeed one has no right to expect that intelligence level and reading level, as judged by standard tests, will be highly correlated.[5] It is significant, however, that 7 out of the 8 'above the range' subjects were in the two highest intelligence grades. Moreover even at the level of category W there was no one who was within or above the range for his age, and in category X there was no one who was above it.

In very few cases was there significant evidence of the *absence* of a reading problem. S 203 and S 213 were said not to have been late readers, and it was reported that S 183, 185, 204, and 223 did not now have a reading problem (though this does not establish that there was no problem at an earlier age). The most convincing negative case among the 223 subjects was S 74, who was stated by her parents to have been a fluent reader at the age of 6. Even in her case, however, it is possible that high intelligence had enabled compensation to take place at an earlier age than usual[6].

In general, it seems best to say that in the very great majority of cases where the dyslexic pattern of difficulties is found the subject's performance at reading is affected but that there are occasional cases where reading difficulty does not appear to have been a major problem.

It is also regularly reported that dyslexic subjects even when they have achieved some degree of proficiency still tend to read slowly. This indeed is what one would expect in view of their slowness at naming digits which are exposed for a brief presentation time (see Chapter 17); and for what they are worth I have some incidental observations which support this view. Thus S 252, despite a score of 93 on the R_1 test, said to me, 'Mum was always trying to speed my reading up', and when I asked if this worked she said, 'It didn't – I couldn't do it'. S 137, who scored 89 on the R_1 test, said 'Most people would read two lines on the board when I'd done only half a line', while S 141 said 'If it's a long word on the board I have to have three looks at it'. A letter from the parents of S 221, who by the age of 27 had become a successful business man, mentioned that 'it still takes him longer than others to keep up with the figures'. Similarly S 257 reported that if he was handed a balance sheet he would either ask his subordinate to summarise it or 'hedge' by saying that he would look at it later.

In addition it is widely agreed among those who have worked with dyslexic pupils that reading aloud continues to be difficult even when they are reasonably proficient at reading to themselves. Although I did not investigate this particular problem systematically, it received specific mention in quite a number of cases and I suspect that it is widespread. Thus S 159 said 'I don't like reading aloud though I'm not a shy person', while S 240 said, rather cryptically, 'In reading, it sounds OK by myself, but when I say it to the teacher I get words wrong'. S 209 said that she did not like reading aloud; S 91 said, 'I can read to myself but when I read aloud I make a lot of mistakes', while, according to her father, S 218 had 'never liked reading aloud'. Even the highly successful business man, S 257, reported that he was totally taken aback when, as part of a ceremonial, he was without warning called upon to read the rules of the guild to which he had just been elected as president. There seems no doubt that if a dyslexic person is asked to read aloud this often puts him under considerable strain.

One possibility, of course, is that when he reads to himself he reads inaccurately, but because there is no check by means of the spoken word he 'gets away with it' and his inaccuracies are not detected. It should also be remembered, however, that 'finding the right word' is itself a source of difficulty[7] and that when a situation requries word-finding, understanding, and appropriate intonation the 'load' may be so heavy that at least one of the three is affected. It is interesting in this connection that S 169 said, 'When I read aloud in class I didn't hear a word of it; the others did'.

Even when dyslexic subjects read to themselves they appear to have difficulty in 'holding in mind' any large quantity of material. For example, in a discussion of examination questions, S 166 said, 'I can read it but I can't understand it if it's a long question – I've forgotton by the time I've read it'. Similarly S 186 said, 'Long questions are more difficult. They take time to read, especially questions about quotations'. S 169 said that any form of reading took him a long time, and he added, 'I read it once, and I read it again to understand it'. In view of the evidence in Chapter 18 it seeems likely that a dyslexic person can 'process for meaning' when material is presented auditorily, even though verbatim recall is difficult; when visual material has to be turned into words, however, there is a risk that 'processing for meaning' will become less efficient.

Very occasionally I have met subjects who rely in reading on the visual shape of the word rather than on memory for letters. This strategy is well documented in the case of S 95. In her initial letter to me his mother wrote: 'His remedial teacher. . . believes that he reads almost entirely by remembering the shape of the words. . . I can endorse this myself'. I myself noted that after a particular error on the R_1 test he said, 'I can see the shape of the other word – I realise it's not the shape it should be. They call me "awkward (Brian)" if I don't remember'. There is in fact good reason to believe that in visual matching tasks where no symbols are involved dyslexic subjects are as quick as controls matched for age and intelligence[8], and in a sense, therefore, this subject had chosen a procedure at which he was strong. Unfortunately in most reading tasks the combination of shapes is so complex that it is impossible to remember a sufficient amount of detail for accurate recognition, let alone reproduce it correctly in spelling. To be able to symbolise is a way of reducing complexity, and even for those whose ability to symbolise is limited a spelling strategy based on memory for visual shapes is scarcely likely to be effective. It is possibly an example of the same phenomenon when someone who is unsure of the spelling of a word tries out the 'look' of that word on paper. He is in effect asking, not 'Are the symbols correct?', but 'Is the shape correct?' Since their visual matching is adequate it is not surprising that dyslexic subjects occasionallly adopt this strategy, despite its relative inefficiency.

With regard to methods of teaching reading, the evidence in my files is by no means conclusive, but neither the ITA ('initial teaching alphabet') nor the method of 'look-and-say' come out with any credit. Admittedly it is impossible to be sure in a particular case whether other methods would have made things better, or worse, or no different, nor can one say how many potentially dyslexic subjects might have come for assessment had not ITA been of help to them. The comments made, however, were alike in being unfavourable. For example, the mother of S 7, who was an experienced Primary School teacher, explained that at the age of 5 John had been introduced to ITA. She continued:

'Not only could he not relate and remember the symbols; he developed an overwhelming sense of complete blanketing failure. . . We indicated our concern at his school and our story was listened to with care and concern. They didn't think it was anything to do with ITA and suggested I learn the ITA script, and help him at home. From January until his 6th birthday in July I spent a deliberately relaxed and happy hours each evening with (John) in which he drew and I wrote in ITA underneath – this he copied. We did some reading together. By the July and after one year and one term at school no progress had been made at all with ITA. . . Mental stress and state even worse'.

His R_1 score when I tested him was in fact 32 (the range for age 7 being 20-30). Like his sister, S 74, therefore, he had scored above the age-norm, but there is no reason for doubting his mother's view that he had made progress in spite of, not because of, the use of ITA. Critical references to ITA were also made in the case of S 8, S 76, and S 160, while 'look-and-say' was adversely criticised by the parents of Ss 76, 112, 136, 159, and 164. In the last-mentioned case the report was of 'four years of failure'.

In the light of the above evidence the following conclusions about the reading performance of dyslexic subjects appear to be justified:

(1) Dyslexia is not *primarily* a reading difficulty: many dyslexic subjects learn to read with a fair degree of success.
(2) In almost all cases, however, there is a history of early difficulty in *learning* to read.
(3) Most dyslexic subjects remain slow readers.
(4) Reading aloud continues to present problems.
(5) In a few cases they rely on trying to identify the visual shape of the word instead of thinking of the letters as symbols.
(6) Neither ITA nor the look-and-say method of teaching are likely to be successful.

This last conclusion is, of course, a negative one and gives no positive guidance as to how dyslexic subjects can best be helped. If one considers reading in isolation from other language skills, however, it is scarcely possible to avoid being negative; and before one can come up with positive suggestions it is necessary to examine in some detail the spelling errors and other types of confusion which dyslexic subjects regularly display.

CHAPTER NINE

Spelling

I begin by quoting a letter written to me by a boy aged 11:

> Dear Prassr Mails
> Will you plesas see me my name is --- and I am 11 years old.
> My techere sase that my I.Q.   is norml put I fandit difeclt to rout a can read Falley wall naw But not is wuk as my Frans and I have been going to reading sclooy for to years.
> Mummey came to her you tuk in Bolton Be For Chustomas and we wandr iF I am diclacktic X if you code see me phaps you cude say if this is so ~~ples~~
> PS pleses see me cowikley becars I have my 11 plus soon

I have in fact managed to collect large quantities of spelling by my subjects. In almost all cases they were given the Schonell S_1 test, and in addition I regularly made a point of asking for samples of written work to be brought. This meant that it was possible for me to examine school exercise books and occasionally letters home and other spontaneous pieces of writing. In some cases I was able to retain the originals or have them photocopied, while in other cases I made a record in my own writing of mistakes which seemed to me of special interest.

One of the things which impressed me ever since the early stages of the research was what I have called elsewhere[1] the 'bizarre' character of dyslexic spelling. I have come to realise, as I shall indicate at the end of this chapter, that such spelling is not in fact *limited* to dyslexic subjects but is characteristic of anyone who is 'out of his depth' in the sense that he needs to spell words that are too hard or sophisticated for him (for example a culturally deprived child, a slow child, or, indeed, a bright six-year-old child attempting to spell words in a spelling test that are set at the eleven year level). It remains true, however, that bizarre spelling is a common characteristic of younger dyslexic subjects, as I shall try to show by means of the examples which follow; and indeed this makes sense, since because of the discrepancy between their intelligence level and their spelling performance they are, of all people, among the most likely to be 'out of their depth'.

I shall begin this chapter by indicating some of the differences between bizarre spelling and what, by way of contrast, may be termed 'plausible' spelling, and to make this comparison I shall offer a scheme for characterising and classifying bizarre errors. I shall then give examples of single words or short phrases, written by my subjects, which exemplify the different types of error; these will be followed by longer passages (similar to the one quoted at the start of this chapter) so as to show what bizarre spelling is like in context.

If we look at a sample of errors on the S₁ spelling test we are likely to find such errors as 'discription' for *description*, 'asist' for *assist*, and 'wellfair' for *welfare*. In contrast, we may also find 'aviod' for *avoid*, 'instistuns' for *instance*, and 'lquied' for *liquid*. It seems plain to me from inspection that the last there are odd or bizarre spellings, in contrast with the first three which are wrong but plausible.

How, then, are the two groups of spellings different? Perhaps the most helpful general formula is to say that plausible spelling involves a relatively more sophisticated knowledge of sound-letter correspondences (that is, the ways in which the sounds which we say are represented by different letters or combinations of letters in the English alphabetical system). A misspelling is plausible if it *might* be spelled in that way but in fact is not (where the word 'might' implies conformity with some sort of rule or principle which makes such a spelling possible). In contrast, in the case of bizarre spelling, many of the 'rules' or 'principles' (if they merit the term) are highly idiosyncratic, and the knowledge of sound-letter correspondences is much less sophisticated. Indeed, one continually notices the number of things which the speller has *failed* to pick up, for example that words are divided into syllables and that each syllable must contain at least one vowel. This is not to suggest that the ordinary speller knows these things explicitly in the sense of being able to verbalise what the rules or principles are, but once he has reached a certain level of sophistication he implicitly follows such rules and can tell that there is something wrong if they are broken.

The difference is no doubt one of degree. Even in bizarre spelling one can recognise attempts within certain limits to make use of sound-letter correspondences, and there is thus a limited degree of plausibility, while in plausible spelling there are errors which could be avoided if the speller had some highly sophisticated knowledge, for example that of the latin derivation of 'description'. It therefore seems to me incorrect to say that there are hard and fast dividing lines between the bizarre and the plausible. It is rather that there is a gradual grasping (whether implicit or explicit) of the way in which the English spelling system works, and the more bizarre-looking spellings arise if the person has not acquired a knowledge of certain rules or principles yet attempts spellings which require such knowledge.

The expression 'bizarre-*looking*' is important. It is, of course, the fluent reader who notices that bizarre spelling is bizarre, and it is he who is likely, both when he reads and when he checks spelling, to identify the word as a whole rather than depend on sounding out individual letters. Indeed, it is safe to assume that to the dyslexic subject and other poor spellers there is no distinction between what is bizarre and what is not since they lack a knowledge of the phonic rules which would enable them to carry out the appropriate monitoring.

In view of the total evidence cited in this book it seems to me quite impossible to go along with those who say that all the spelling problems of the allegedly dyslexic child would disappear if the teaching methods used in the early stages were adequate. The basic dyslexic handicap, however, is not such as to *preclude* the learning of adequate spelling[2]; and I do not doubt that bizarre spelling can progressively be eliminated as the pupil's knowledge of the English spelling system becomes more sophisticated. The direction of causality I believe to be as follows: as a result of a constitutional limitation the dyslexic child does not learn characteristics of the English spelling system which in a normal environment the non-dyslexic child simply 'picks up'. Suitable specialist teaching can compensate for this, and thus in a sense absence of such teaching is a causal factor in producing the poor spelling; but it has an effect only if superimposed on the initial constitutional limitation[3].

What is it, then about bizarre spelling which makes it bizarre? In an attempt to answer this question I undertook the difficult task of attempting a re-classification of spelling errors. I say 're-classification' because various attempts in this direction have been made already[4], and I think it is fair to say that different classifications are suitable for different purposes.

One of my difficulties was that when a word is misspelled there may be several different things wrong with it. Thus when S 80 spelled *non-existent* as 'nonxextant' one could say that the x-sound had been duplicated, that the combination of letters 'xex' is impossible, and that the word, if pronounced as he wrote it, would have contained the wrong number of syllables. In some cases, therefore, I have indicated alternative error-categories to which the word might equally or near-equally belong. In this particular case 'nonxextant' is in fact classified as a 'false match for order', but I indicate that it could also be classified as an 'impossible trigram', as a misrepresentation of the number of syllables, or as the 'duplicating of a sound' (for a description of these categories, see below). Indeed there are a number of occasions where the 'omission of a sound' and an 'impossible trigram' go together: if a sounding vowel is left out an 'impossible trigram' regularly results.

A second difficulty is that in classifying, one is not merely giving a factual report: in putting two misspellings into the same category one is implying the same theoretical explanation, and this is a matter where one may be in error. In some cases, indeed, one needs to know the context in which the mistake was made. Thus, to cite an example given by my wife[5], if an attempt to spell *write* comes out as 'witer', one may misclassify this error if one considers only its visual appearance – correct letters in the wrong order – and overlooks the fact that the child originally wrote w-i-t-e- and later added the 'r'. In other cases a particular theoretical approach may encourage a classification of a particular kind. For example someone in the tradition of S. T. Orton might take the view that the writing of 'was' for *saw* should be classified along with b-d confusion as a special kind of 'reversal', whereas my own classification places it along with 'forgein' for *foreign* – an attempt to rely on memory for the recall of the correct letters coupled with the inability to remember or deduce their order[6].

My central purpose in adopting the classifications which follow was to make sense of my subjects' misspellings in terms of the theory offered in this book. Because of the weakness of his internal 'lexicon' there are certain things which the dyslexic child in the early stages of learning to spell simply does not pick up, for example that the letters on the page are representations of what we say and that certain combinations of letters, for example 'lqu', cannot arise. It is this failure to 'pick things up' which makes sense of the first four of my categories (see i to iv below). Another six (v-x) are accounted for in terms of weak immediate memory for verbal material and 'losing the place', while a further two (xi and xii) can be seen as attempts to compensate. The final category (xiii) is that of b – d confusion, to which I return in Chapter 12.

A second, incidental, effect of the classification is to try to show what it is about so-called 'bizarre' spelling which makes it bizarre; any spelling that can be fitted into one of the thirteen categories can be regarded as to some extent bizarre, in contrast with mistakes such as 'discription' for description, cited earlier, which count simply as 'plausible'.

A third effect, perhaps more important, is that by classifying in this way one is to some extent calling attention to dyslexic weaknesses *which can be put right by teaching*. Thus if the pupil writes down a combination of letters which, if pronounced according to the normal rules of sound-letter correspondence, would give the wrong number of syllables, this is evidence that he is unaware of how both written and spoken words can be divided into syllables – an important feature of English spelling which can then be shown to him.

Finally, an incidental advantage from the classification is that one can check whether certain types of misspelling are more common in dyslexic than in control subjects. This may well turn out not to be the case, but if one simply goes by the number of words correctly spelled all possibility of comparison is lost.

For convenience of reference each category has been given an abbreviation of two or three letters or thereabouts. I begin with a description of the first four.

(i) The first category is what I call the 'impossible trigram' (IT). This involves a combination of three letters which are impossible in normal English spelling because they would represent something unpronounceable, for example starting to spell *liquid* with the letters 'lqu'. As I see the situation, the normal reader picks up, even if not explicitly or consciously, the fact that certain combinations of letters cannot go together; he picks up certain 'rules' of spelling much as the fluent speaker picks up the 'rules' of grammar. Thus it will be plain to most readers of this book that 'sha', 'tep', 'spr' and 'tho' are possible combinations of letters in English words, whereas 'spk', 'wll', 'qww', and 'hja' are not. My suggestion is that a knowledge of sequential probabilities is something which normal spellers simply 'pick up' in the process of learning to spell; for the dyslexic person, however, because of his limitations of immediate memory, there is too much going on, and this kind of knowledge is therefore 'squeezed out'. The result is that he cannot appropriately monitor what he has written and does not therefore recognise that it comprises an impossible combination of letters.

(ii) The second category is what I call 'misrepresentation of sounds' (MoS). Most dyslexic children show by their spellings that they have recognised in general that sounds can be represented by letters. Because of their weak lexical system, however, there may be a failure in making the representation accurate, particularly in the case of sounds or vocal movements which are similar; and when this happens the word as spelled may contain one or more 'wrong' letters in place of the correct ones, for example 'cet' for *get* (S 8) or 'bugger' for *buzzer* (S 142)[7]. In addition the difficulty in accurate matching prevents them from monitoring what they have written or appreciating where they have gone wrong.

There is a complication here in that some teachers have supposed – somewhat uncritically in my opinion – that such errors can be described as 'auditory'. I do not dispute that hearing loss can be associated with dyslexic manifestations (compare Chapter 20) nor that as a result of hearing loss there are people who, for instance, fail to distinguish 'p' and 'b' or hard 'c' (or 'k') and 'g'. In my experience, however, a child who has written 'pat' when asked to spell the word *bat* can often recognise perfectly well that 'pat' and 'bat' are different when the two words are spoken; and I suspect that often the error is not auditory at all but one of memory. It is well established that auditory confusability hinders recall[8], and it therefore makes sense that dyslexic subjects, whose recall is weak anyway, should not be wholly secure in knowing which to use of two auditorily confusable letters; this is quite different from being unable, as a result of some weakness in the auditory system, to discriminate that two sounds are different. Moreover, the position is sometimes made more complicated by the fact that the same letter is pronounced slightly differently according to what other letters are near it, for example the letter s in 'sister' has the effect of making the sound represented by the t almost a d-sound. In this case it would be very rash to say that a person who wrote 'sissder' for *sister*, as did my first dyslexic pupil[9], *cannot hear* the difference between 't' and 'd'. Similarly, as my wife has pointed out[10], the Welsh for 'skirt' is 'sgyrt', and a child in a Welsh area who, when asked to spell the English word, writes 'sgyrt' may be confused between the two languages but certainly cannot be assumed without further evidence to have a specifically auditory deficiency. In general I suspect – though I am not sure – that most of the errors in this category made by my subjects are memory errors resulting from auditory confusability; this certainly coheres with the idea that dyslexia involves some kind of limitation of immediate memory.

(iii) The third category of error is that which I call 'wrong boundaries' (WB) between words. The error can take two forms: either a single word is written with a space between the parts as when S74 put 'a nother' for *another*, or separate words are written together without a space, as when, among my early subjects, a young man of 14 (who later went to university) instead of writing *chest of drawers* wrote 'chesetofbrours'. It seems that most of us learn to deal with boundaries between words without much difficulty, but, to judge from their spelling errors, this is one of the things which may become 'squeezed out' in the case of dyslexic subjects.

(iv) The fourth category is that which I call 'wrong syllabification' (WS). In this case the written word comprises a collection of letters which, if pronounced according to normal English sound-letter correspondence, would result in a word with the wrong number of syllables. Thus if *avoid* is written as 'aviod' and these letters were then pronounced as written, the sound would be approximately 'avvi-od', which, unlike 'avoid' contains three syllables and not two; similarly 'instistuns' for *instance* (S97) would contain three syllables instead of the requisite two. These WS errors seem to me to be evidence that the subject has not picked up some of the more sophisticated kinds of sound-letter correspondence. Thus in the case of 'aviod', he is displaying lack of awareness that 'oi' is a digraph, i.e. represents a single sound (or almost so), whereas 'i' followed by 'o' involves two separate syllables. Dyslexic subjects can, of course, be taught to divide words into syllables, and indeed this is an important part of their training, but it is a skill which they sometimes do not acquire unless they are explicitly shown how to do so.

All four of these error-types appear to be the direct consequence of the dyslexic subject's weak lexical system. If entries in his lexicon are not easily established, then it is not surprising that he should fail to notice characteristics of the English spelling system which become obvious to the non-dyslexic child within the setting of a normal classroom. There is, however, a further consequence of this weakness; immediate memory for symbolic material is known to be impaired in a dyslexic person[11] and the next six error-types seem to me to be a direct consequence of this impairment.

(v) The fifth error-type may be termed 'inconsistent spelling' (IS). This description is used when the same word is spelled differently within a few lines. I believe that in the majority of cases subjects do not notice the inconsistency and that this, once again, is because too much is going on.

After all, what is needed is both to find the right words and then write them correctly on paper; each of these on its own is hard enough for a dyslexic person, particularly the latter, and they are therefore in no position to take account of what has gone before[12].

(vi) The sixth category is 'wrong letter doubled' (WLD), for example 'eeg' for *egg* (S 24) or 'sppeling' for *spelling* (S 107). I suspect that what is involved here is a knowledge that *something* must be doubled but that the person does not remember or deduce which letter it is. I have come on only a relatively small number of such errors, but I believe they merit being placed in a separate category.

(vii) The seventh category is 'mistaken recall of order' (MRO). I am thinking here of situations where the subject draws largely on his memory that certain letters are needed but does not know and cannot deduce the order in which they should occur. Thus he may know that the word *how* contains the letters h-, o-, and w- but may write it as 'who'. I was told that the brother of S 221 (who was also dyslexic) once wrote to his parents, 'Dear Mum and Dad, Who are you?' This was not, I am sure, an expression of existential bewilderment!

It should be noted that in view of the memory limitations of dyslexic subjects this is an inefficient strategy. Indeed it is widely agreed that they would be better advised to pay careful attention to the order of letters in the spoken word – and the number of syllables – and then deduce what the order of the written letters *has* to be if there is to be sound-letter correspondence.

My classification of the controversial 'was' for *saw* as an MRO is deliberate. Undoubtedly this mistake is found, though according to my records it is rarer than one might suppose in view of the frequency with which it is cited in theoretical papers. Orton speaks of it as a 'kinetic reversal' – in contrast with the 'static' reversals, 'b' for 'd' and 'p' for 'q' – and he suggests that in these cases the person is somehow going through the letters of the word in the wrong order. It seems to me more likely, however, that the mistake arises because the speller possesses a limited knowledge of how words are made up: he is aware that three-letter words often have a vowel in the middle and consonants on the outside and this knowledge prevents him from writing 'wsa' or 'asw', but, this point apart, the exact inversion of the order of the letters is of no special significance. Similarly he may write 'on' for *no* simply because he is muddled about order, and it may be coincidental that 'on' and 'no' are mirror-images of each other. Despite my respect for Orton I find it difficult to agree with him over this particular aspect of his theory; indeed, interesting though mirror phenomena are, I am not convinced that they are related to dyslexic phenomena at all, and I find it puzzling that the neurological explanations suggested by Orton to account for dyslexic-type mistakes (non-elision of the mirror-image engrams, or traces, from the two halves of the brain) should generate mirror-images in the case of 'static' reversals (e.g. 'b' for 'd') but inverted order of letters (e.g. 'was' for 'saw') in 'kinetic' reversals. A classification in accordance with Orton's ideas would presumably involve the grouping of 'was' for *saw* along with b-d errors, but according to the present classification it involves a successful attempt to remember the letters but a failure to remember or deduce their correct order.

It follows from the above discussion that the same end-product, viz. correct letters in the wrong order, may conceivably occur for different reasons. Even if one does not accept Orton's view of the matter, this point still raises difficulties of classification. Thus, when I came on 'thrid' for *third* it seemed to me quite likely that the subject was not in fact drawing on his memory but was attempting a phonic representation in which letters and sounds had got 'out of step'; and if this was what happened the correct classification of this misspelling is 'false match for order' (FMO, see below). One would have needed to be present at the time of writing, and possibly even to have questioned the subject. However, the 'reliance on memory' explanation seems to me plausible in most cases; and I have therefore, with hesitation, classified as MRO ('mistaken recall of order') all those misspellings where the correct letters are present, along with a few others where this is true of most but not all of the letters, since in these cases, too, it seems that the 'reliance on memory' explanation is correct. Moreover even if my explanation is wrong, it is, I think, still justified to record these errors as a single group, since the fact that people can sometimes produce the right letters for spelling a word and yet be unable to put them in the right order, whatever its explanation, remains a puzzling and challenging phenomenon.

(viii) The category of 'false match for order' (FMO) is similar to that of 'mistaken recall of order' (MRO) in that in both cases errors of ordering occur. I believe, however, that they occur for different reasons. False match for order is, I suggest, a 'loss of place' phenomenon and in that respect is comparable with the omission and duplication of sounding letters (OmS and Dup S; see below). A typical example of the FMO error is 'aklumpist' for *accomplished* (S 249) where there is a mismatch between the 'l' of the written word and the l-sound of the spoken word, the written 'l' occurring too early. Such mistakes seem to me to indicate difficulties similar to those which occur when dyslexic subjects become 'tied up' in saying polysyllabic words (see Chapter 13). They are somehow 'out of step' as a result of having reached later components of the word sub-vocally before the earlier components have been committed to writing. It is, I believe, a case of what psychologists call 'retroactive interference' (in other words later material hinders the correct reproduction of earlier material), and I suspect that the influence of such interference is particularly great when the components of the spoken word are similar either in sound or in the way in which they are articulated. Thus it is the presence of the labials, l, m, n, and r which make it difficult for some people to say the word *preliminary*, and this difficulty is no doubt reflected in their misspellings (examples of which I have set out separately). There are also parallels, I believe, with the 'where-have-I-got-to?' response which regularly occurs when dyslexic subjects attempt to say their tables (see Chapter 16).

The concept of 'ordering', however, and the related concept of 'sequencing' both seem to me to raise problems. In particular there are grounds for thinking that it is not *any* kind of ordering task which the dyslexic subject finds difficult, but only tasks which involve the ordering of symbolic material[13]. Thus a dyslexic subject might well assemble the components of a lock or other mechanism in extra quick time, even though he would almost certainly take longer if reading a book of instructions (or possibly having to verbalise instructions) was necessary. I am reluctant, therefore, to attribute these FMO errors to a failure at ordering *simpliciter*; they seem to me rather to be a manifestation of weak immediate memory when auditorily confusable symbolic material is present.

Categories (ix) and (x) – the omission of one or more sounding letters (OmS) and the duplication of one or more sounding letter (Dup S) can be considered together. An example of the first is 'Agsea' for *Anglesey* (S 52) and an example of the second 'Cheshshire' for *Cheshire* (S 117). Any of us may make such errors when we are being 'careless', but I suspect that dyslexic subjects are particularly prone to them because there is too much to hold in mind. Like FMO ('false match for order') they exemplify the phenomenon of 'losing the place'. Thus the subject may suppose that he is further forward than in fact he is, in which case he leaves something out, or he may suppose that he is further back than he is, in which case he repeats the same letter or combination of letters twice. The parallels with the 'Where-have-I-got-to?' response which one regularly finds when dyslexic subjects attempt to recite their tables (see Chapter 16) has already been mentioned. It is perhaps worth adding that those who edit texts which contain corrupt passages – for example, writings in classical Greek or Latin – have sometimes found it helpful to restore the sense of a passage by postulating the occurrence of one or other of these errors. To fail to write the same combination of letters twice over when this is needed (e.g. 'rember' for *remember*) is referred to as 'haplography' (literally 'single writing'), while repetition of a combination of letters which should have occurred only once (e.g. 'animimals' for *animals*) is referred to as 'dittography' (literally 'writing twice over'). As has already been suggested, we all make 'dyslexic'-type errors from time to time, and one would not expect mediaeval scribes who copied classical texts to have been in any way exceptional in this respect[14].

The next two types of error seem to me to arise as a result of attempts by dyslexic subjects to compensate for their relatively weak memory for correct letters. Most of them appear to have picked up a small amount of knowledge about sound-letter correspondence which they then try to apply, but this knowledge is inadequate for their needs.

Category (xi), then, is the 'phonetic attempt misfired' (PAM). One can recognise the spellings as phonetic (that is, with letters matching sounds) but the result is incongruous since other necessary conditions for correct spelling are not satisfied. Thus 'whiv' for *with* counts as a case of PAM since the 'w' and 'i' sounds are exactly represented and the 'th' sound approximately so. But the attempt to put the three sounds together has misfired, partly because of the confusion between 'w' and 'wh', partly because of confusion between 'th' and 'v', and partly through ignorance of the relatively sophisticated 'rule' that no word ends in a 'v'.

This particular error could in fact be classified as a misrepresentation of sound (MoS), since it is arguable that there are differences in sound between 'w' and 'wh' (though many people ignore them) and between 'th' and 'v'. One could even classify it as an impossible trigram (IT) since at the end of a word 'hiv' is not possible even though it is found at the beginning and in the middle. As was indicated above, however, the categories which I have proposed are not intended to be mutually exclusive.

Possibly PAM is in any case something of a 'ragbag' category, since attempts at phonetic spelling can go wrong for a variety of reasons. Nevertheless it is convenient to group together those misspellings where some kind of phonetic representation has been attempted but which are incongruous because a more sophisticated knowledge of the English spelling system is lacking. Certainly most of the PAM errors can readily be seen to be bizarre.

Category (xii) could almost count as a sub-group within category (xi). It comprises mistakes where there is an intrusive vowel (IntV), for example the spelling of *swallows* as 'sowollos' which I found among the written work of my first dyslexic pupil[15]. As can be seen, this is in a sense an attempt at phonetic representation which has gone wrong, and indeed it could also count as a case of wrong syllabification (WS) since the intrusive vowel necessarily specifies an extra syllable which is not present in the spoken word. It nevertheless seems convenient to put such mistakes in a category of their own in view of their likely origin. What I suspect has happened, though I have no firm evidence, is that the subject tries to use a phonetic approach and in so doing says the word extra slowly and carefully. Now if one tries to do this in the case of the word 'swallows' one has to say something like 'ser-woll-owes', and it is therefore perfectly logical to try to represent this extra syllable in what one writes.

(xiii) My final category, which I style BD, is that of substitution 'b' for 'd' and vice versa whether in upper or lower case letters. This confusion seems to me sufficiently problematic to be discussed separately (see Chapter 12). If it occurs in conjunction with errors belonging in the other categories the bizarre effect is intensified. 'Chesetofbrours' is a good example.

I now pass to actual examples of spelling errors. I have so many of these that I have had to be selective, and I think the most helpful procedure is to start by citing misspellings of single words or group of words in each of the 13 categories (with possible overlaps and alternative classifications indicated where appropriate) and to follow this by giving full sentences and longer pieces of writing where many different errors are combined.

I have included the symbol '(e)', standing for 'earlier', if I had clear evidence that the misspelling had occurred appreciably earlier than the time of the assessment. This sometimes happened when parents produced school exercise books of an earlier period; and even where the '(e)' is not present this is not intended as a firm assurance that the misspelling was invariably a recent one. In most cases, however, it is safe to assume that it occurred shortly before assessment, and the subjects' ages, which I have included after giving their Summary Chart numbers, are thus an approximate guide as to the age at which the mistake occurred.

There are many points about the misspellings which the reader will notice for himself. Of these, I should like to mention three. In the first place, even short words of two or three letters are not always exempt from error; secondly, the logical nature of most of the spellings seem to me to be an indicator of the amount of effort which went into producing them, while, thirdly, the continuous sentences which follow the single words are often highly sophisticated. This last point underlines the plight of those who have intellectually powerful ideas but who, because of the medium through which they have to operate, viz. the written word, are severely handicapped in communicating these ideas to others.

To make the data as complete as possible I have included quite a large number of misspellings in most categories. I doubt if any valid conclusions can be drawn about relative frequencies of types of error, since there was no safeguard against bias in my selection of what seemed interesting; but it is important to emphasise that bizarre spellings are not just occasional curiosities but are regularly found in the written work of large numbers of dyslexic subjects.

Here, then, are some samples of dyslexic spelling:

Target word(s)	Written as	Subject	Age	Other ways of classifying
(i) *Impossible trigrams* (IT)				
quite happy	qwwht hape	10	8	PAM
swallowed	swlowd	14	8	Om S
through	freuu	14	8	PAM
walks	wrrks	24	8	PAM
park	prkr	24	8	PAM
further	frtr	24	8	PAM
people	pilplla	36	9	FMO

Target word(s)	Written as	Subject	Age	Other ways of classifying
made	mde	36	9	PAM
Scotland	Sctland	36	9	Om S
domestic	dmestkig	232	9	Om S
geography	geogrphy	56	10	PAM
hymn	hmy	63	10	PAM
mechanical	micknkle	63	10	Om S
accordance	acordns	63	10	PAM
barley	brliy	64	10	—
combined harvester	conbiy hrts	64	10	Mo S
crystal	crestl	72	10	Mo S
tidal	tiddl	83	10	PAM
swirling	swrling	83	10	PAM
going	gowing	88	11	—
with	whthe (c)	94	11	PAM
water	watrt	96	11	FMO
usually	uslle	96	11	PAM
started	strted	96	11	PAM
obedient	obetnt	101	11	Om S
marjoram	mreygoron	107	11	PAM
production	prodkshon	108	11	Om S
milk	mlke	112	11	PAM
conquered	cquerd	113	11	Om S
happening	hpaning	113	11	Om S
edge	egn	110	11	PAM
pretend	prtend	110	11	PAM
persuaded	pswaded	110	11	—
wanted	wnntied	110	11	—
different	diffnt	110	11	Om S
successful	succusffl	126	12	PAM, WLD
worry	whre	128	12	PAM
first	frst	136	13	PAM
ground	grwd	140	13	PAM
candlestick	canoll Esneck	142	13	PAM
similarities	smilaartis	145	13	Om S
detergent	dturgent	149	13	—
nothing	nthing	149	13	—
unpopular	uppular	246	14	Om S, PAM
heard	hrad	196	14	PAM
Ephesus	Efusfst	196	(e)	FMO, PAM
write	wrte	210	17	PAM
fought	forght	213	18	PAM

Target word(s)	Written as	Subject	Age	Other ways of classifying
(ii) *Misrepresentation of the sound* (MoS)				
job	jop	8	8	—
bell	pell	8	8	—
live	lif	8	8	—
get	cet	8	8	—
Christendom	chisingdum	23	8	—
during	geuring	34	9	—
needle	megl	72	10	—
paddled	pagelid	103	11	—
exploring	egsbloring	123	12	—
first	firsk	128	12	—
buzzer	bugger	142	13	—
fitted	fidid	152	14	—
nitrogen	nigeragan	163	14	—
hub cap	ubcab	171	15	—
continued	contnderd	177	15	—
negotiations	nocosiatios	253	17	—
(iii) *Wrong Boundaries* (WB)				
together	to gefer	14	8	—
indeed	in ded	20	8	—
a castle	acasul	34	9	—
forget	for get	57	10	—
eiderdown	I dodown	69	10	—
disappear	desu per	—	—	—
another	a nother	74	10	—
get ready	getready	74	10	—
cattle market	catellmacet	87	11	—
employer	in ploner	103	11	MoS
in the foreground	intefregound	111	11	OmS
a tennis court	atenis chort	113	11	—
woken	woa kern	100	11	—
chopper	choa per	100	11	—
a type	atipe	135	13	—
no one	nowon	153	14	—
together	to gether	160	14	—
(iv) *Wrong syllabifications* (WS)				
kittens	kins	36	9	—
oxygen	oschun	72	10	—

Target word(s)	Written as	Subject	Age	Other ways of classifying
watched	wastast	94	11	—
instance	instistuns	97	11	—
sneaked	snecet	113	11	—
next	necese	120	12	—
explanation	explaintion	143	13	—
method	meathered	146	13	—
leaped	leepded	150	14	—
edge	egeg	158	14	—
down	dwonon	160	14	—
assist	asiced	207	17	—
believe	bleav	212	18	—

(v) *Inconsistent spelling* (IS)

Target word(s)	Written as	Subject	Age	Other ways of classifying
Aragon	Arergin Aergon	53	9	—
because	becuss becuce	63	10	—
calculation	calcilation calculation calcilation caculation	100	11	—
Joseph	Josheph Joeph	127	12	—
would	whord whored	136	13	—
echoed	ecode ecoad	138	13	—
fire	fier ferar	145	13	—

(The actual sentence was 'fier to make ferar plasyes')

| dinner | dinner diner | 151 | 14 | — |

(The actual sentence was 'It is dinner time he goes and has diner)

suddenly	sunndy sunndly	162	14	—
ladies (lady)	laides laydey	191	16	—
Ephesus	Efusfst afess, efese	196	16	—

(vi) *Wrong letter doubled* (WLD)

Target word(s)	Written as	Subject	Age	Other ways of classifying
egg	gee	24	8	FMO
spelling	sppeling	107	11	—
freeze	frezze	162	14	—

(vii) *Mistaken recall of order* (MRO)

Target word(s)	Written as	Subject	Age	Other ways of classifying
else	esle	6	7	FMO
are	aer	23	8	—

Target word(s)	Written as	Subject	Age	Other ways of classifying
snow	sonw	25	8	FMO
each	aech	27	9	—
two	tow	32	9	—
after	afrte	28	9	IT
fuel	fule	31	9	—
window	windwo	33	9	Dup S
went	wnet	33	9	FMO
cavalry	cavaryl	33	9	FMO
metal	meatl	47	9	PAM
park	pakr	52	9	—
two	tow	52	9	—
to	ot	57	10	FMO
in	ni	58	10	FMO
to	ot	64	10	FMO
who	how (with crossings out)	65	10	—
army	amry	69	10	FMO
died	deid	69	10	—
drawing	darwing	70	10	FMO
edge	egde	71	10	—
how	who	73	10	—
third	thrid	83	10	FMO
argument	agrument	84	10	FMO
reading	raeding	111	11	—
acid	aicd	237	11	FMO
garden	graden	85	11	—
night	nigth	103	11	—
four	fuor	107	11	FMO
draw	darw	110	11	FMO
Florence	florenec	110	11	Dup S
search	sreach	117	11	FMO
bridge	bigder	117	11	FMO
goes	gose	241	12	Possibly PAM
question	qusetion	241	12	IT Dup S
goes	geos	126	12	WS PAM
cloud	could	126	12	FMO
golden	gloden	126	12	FMO
basin	baisn	126	12	—
built	biult	127	12	WS
your	yoru	128	12	WS

Target word(s)	Written as	Subject	Age	Other ways of classifying
two	tow	132	12	—
colour	coulor	139	13	—
hair	hiar	143	13	—
nasturtium	nasturtuim	165	15	—
quietly	quitely	171	15	WS
believe	belevie	171	15	WS
soldiers	soilders	178	15	—
tired	tierd	178	15	—
fields	feilds	183	15	—
how	who	189	15	—
poem	peom	192	16	—
avoid	aviod	192	16	WS
arguing	agruing	192	16	FMO
would	woudl	202	16	—
David	Daivd	202	16	WS, IT
of	fo	202	16	—
else	eles	206	17	WS
field	feild	209	17	—
piles	plies	209	17	—
diary	dairy	210	17	—
dairy	diary	216	18	—
again	agian	216	18	WS
prologue	prolouge	223	23	—

I found 'saw' for *was* in the case of S 82 and 'was' for *saw* in the case of Ss 73 and 227; in the case of S 21 her mother reported that she had written 'was' for *saw* in the past.

I also came on the following errors which I believe should be classified alongside the above, since they comprise *almost* 'the correct letters in the wrong order': 'sied' for *said* (S 20), 'tsaion' for *station* (S 51), 'hoow' for *who* (S 64), 'unfarirly' for *unfairly* (S 94), 'geuse' for *guess* (S 160), and 'Jeuses' for *Jesus* (S 246).

(viii) *False match for order* (FMO)

remembered	remberded	228	9	—
farmer	framer	52	9	—
sister	sitosr	52	9	—
country	cronty	52	9	—
Tower Bridge	torw brigde	57	10	—
readily	rediyl	62	10	—
mileage	milgeag	70	10	—

Target word(s)	Written as	Subject	Age	Other ways of classifying
ferrous sulphate	efrors sulphate	72	10	WS
percolate	pecrlous	79	10	—
non-existent	nonxextant	80	10	IT, WS, Dup S
terrible	terrilb	82	10	—
screamed	creemded	82	10	Dup S, WS
Jerusalem	jlosolam	84	10	—
themselves	them sleves	85	11	WB
against	agents	94	11	—
writing	wtihing	96	11	—
people	pelpe	96	11	—
domestic	desimce	98	11	—
especially	epesley	99	11	—
estimate	estnamat	101	11	—
bicycle	biciksl	108	11	—
because	beacs	113	11	—
pressure	persure	126	12	—
ill	lile, changed to ile	132	12	—
your	uoy	132	12	—
referring	ferering	139	13	—
knew	wnew	162	14	—
ignorance	ogronence	167	15	—
ill	li, changed to il	2	15	—
accomplished	aklumpist	178	15	—
topic	popic	189	15	—
domestic	dismostite	197	16	—
entered	enadt	202	16	—
foreign	frogin	210	17	—
exceptionally	expotinaly	210	17	—

Attempts at preliminary

S74 plrinary
S136 primalery
S148 plimenery
S152 pritiremy
S155 plimiary
S179 plirimonery
S177 premanarly
S185 prelimerlary
S206 preremeanally
S208 primalily

Target word(s)	Written as	Subject	Age	Other ways of classifying
(ix) *Omission of one or more sounding letters* (Om S)				
father	fther	26	8	IT
suddenly	suddly	32	9	—
Scotland	Sctland	36	9	IT
amount	amt	52	9	—
didn't	dedt	52	9	—
Anglesey	Agsea	52	9	WS
treason	teson	53	9	WS
protestant	prostent	56	10	—
preparation	prepartion	79	10	PAM
effect	efek	84	10	—
drainage	drange	237	11	—
immediately	imeadialy	90	11	—
protestants	proestats	90	11	FMO, WS
exceptionally	explunaly	90	11	FMO, WS
conquered	concert	110	11	WS
imagination	imaduntion	134	13	MoS
didn't	din't	139	13	—
conclusion	caclason	141	13	—
successful	susseful	143	13	—
deficiency disease	defiences diase	244	13	—
mosquito	mositow	145	13	—
malaria	miara	145	13	WS
atmosphere	aterfere	146	13	—
melancholy	melokoly	150	14	—
occurred	occed	153	14	WS
introduction	introdutan	155	14	—
conversation	convistion	159	14	—
attendance	etedents	165	15	FMO
assist	esete	165	15	—
carbon dioxide	cobondox	165	15	—
decision	dession	168	15	WS
attendance	attendce	169	15	WS
marriage	marge	170	15	WS
criticised	critized	175	15	WS
irresistable	erestabl	177	15	WS
pre-historic	prestorick	178	15	WS
interested	intressed	180	15	WS
attendance	adence	180	15	WS
domestic	demstick	180	15	WS

Target word(s)	Written as	Subject	Age	Other ways of classifying
different	diffet	181	15	WS
inorganic	iorganic	185	15	—
decision	dession	187	15	WS
especially	espally	196	16	WS
irresistable	irresable	197	16	WS
syllabus	slabols	199	16	WS
conditions	condions	200	16	—
happened	happed	200	16	WS
anniversary	anvissary	203	17	FMO
exceptionally	exepthaly	207	17	WS
mechanical	mechinal	208	17	WS
different varieties	diffent varites	209	17	WS
mechanical	mechinal	210	17	WS
excessively	excively	213	18	WS

(x) *Duplication of one or more sounding letter* (Dup S)

Target word(s)	Written as	Subject	Age	Other ways of classifying
language	languaguage	23	8	—
damage	damageage	32	9	—
their	theirir	46	9	—
square	sqaurare	47	9	—
damage	damiamge	56	10	—
day dream	day dremeam	79	10	—
Eglwswrw	Eglwswrwrw	83	10	—
edge	egegar	91	11	—
geography	gagragphy	114	11	—
doesn't	dosesant	99	11	—
Cheshire	Cheshshire	117	11	—
exceptionally	exececep-titonally	148	13	—
tree	trere	167	15	—
talk	tokok	167	15	—
forty	fortyᶠy	169	15	—
won	onene	202	16	—
collapsed	collazaped	204	17	—
signature	signinature	208	17	—
financial	finacical	223	23	Om S, WS

(xi) *Phonetic attempt misfired* (PAM)

Target word(s)	Written as	Subject	Age	Other ways of classifying
witch	wij	8	8	—
with	whiv	14	8	—

Target word(s)	Written as	Subject	Age	Other ways of classifying
remain	rmen	20	8	—
used	yost	23	8	—
squeezing	scweecing	23	8	—
choir	cwioer	27	9	—
beautiful	byotiful	27	9	—
ash tray	ach traie	32	9	—
piano	pinou	33	9	—
skidded	sckided	34	9	—
few	fyoow	37	9	—
changing of the guard	chejing out the gord	37	9	—
they	tha	36	9	—
rope	roaps	47	9	—
cousin	coisn	47	9	—
goes	goase	47	9	—
assist	asisd	47	9	—
baby	baybiy	47	9	—
other	uvr	49	9	WS
our	aor	49	9	—
rice and curry	ris and kurc	49	9	—
owns a pub	ons a pud	49	9	BD
experts	eepcts	61	10	—
blue jeans	bluw jens	71	10	—
squirrel	scwirel	71	10	—
blowed	blod	72	10	—
use	yoos	72	10	—
your	yuwer	73	10	—
Alexandra	Alicsandrur	74	10	—
ruin	roowin	75	10	—
jutted	ghutid	75	10	—
carefully	cerfly	75	10	—
people	pepeole	87	11	—
furnace	fernec	87	11	—
driven	driyvur	88	11	—
reasons	resonse	89	11	—
departure	depacher	89	11	—
equaliser	eckerliser	94	11	MoS
during	joring	94	11	MoS
edge	ejeg	98	11	—
sewage	seuge	99	11	—
relief	releeth	100	11	—

Target word(s)	Written as	Subject	Age	Other ways of classifying
potato	ptatow	103	11	—
Europe	urup	107	11	—
educational	egercashonal	108	11	—
highly	hily	108	11	—
squeezed	scwisd	113	11	—
recognise	receynys	127	12	—
radiation	radeasu	128	12	—
next	nexed	135	13	—
injection	ingecshen	138	13	—
decision	disishen	138	13	—
built	byilt	142	13	—
edge	eg	146	13	—
telegraph wires	telegphe whyers	150	14	IT, Om S
area	ereaia	151	14	—
hesitating	hesertaghting	153	14	—
Elijah	iliger	158	14	—
goes through	gos thoow	169	15	—
immediately	amejitley	174	15	—
baggage	bagidgsh	174	15	IT
examined	igzamind	174	15	—
exhausted	egsorsted	178	15	—
furniture	farnichare	181	15	—
cautious	cuitious	188	15	—
hedge	heag	191	16	—
poaching	potshing	191	16	—
edge	ajd	193	16	—
toes	tows	193	16	—
actual	atchial atchel	204	17	—
eventually	avenchuly advencherly	204	17	—
syllabus	scyllbus	210	17	—

(xii) *Intrusive vowel* (Int. V)

boil	boyul	27	9	—
millions of miles	melions of miy-yils	108	11	—
twenty	tewenty	241	12	—
exactly	ecacctely	158	14	—

Target word(s)	Written as	Subject	Age	Other ways of classifying
(xiii) *b-d confusion* (BD)				
daughter	borte	23	8	PAM
down	bwon	25	8	MRO
did	bib	26	8	—
daddy	baddy	26	8	—
because	deakos	28	9	PAM
down	bwnd	227	9	Dup S
do not	Boo not	57	10	PAM
celebrated	selladratid	64	10	PAM
odd numbers	obd nudners	72	10	Om S
square numbers	spur nudners	72	10	Om S
bubble	budl	72	10	PAM
be	de	75	10	—
bubble bath	dudl dath	96	11	—
February	fadrey	103	11	Om S
alphabet	alferdet	113	11	PAM
bulb	buld	126	12	—
declared	becalad	146	13	WS; Int V
Deuteronomy, Chapter 6	Beut c 6	246	14	—
exhibition	exadtion	177	15	Om S
Bunsen Burner	Bunsen Durner	185	15	—
job	jod	202	16	—
pudding	Pubbing	213	18	—
Scribes	scrids	213	18	—

I pass now to some continuous passages. These will perhaps give the 'flavour' of dyslexic spelling more than does the presentation of isolated words, and in addition they may be of help in indicating to examiners, prospective employers and others that very strange spelling mistakes are not necessarily evidence of lack of ability.

Among the written work of the 11-year-old S 95 I found a letter which contained the following:

> Dear David
>   I got yor letre and by the way am itritid in mchrie (interested in machinery)

Quite large numbers of my subjects were in fact itritid in mchrie, and it does not take much imagination to be aware of the frustration which they must have felt at the discrepancy between their knowlege of mechanical matters and their ability to put their ideas down on paper.

Here is a piece of even more sophisticated thinking from – surprisingly enough – another 11 year-old (S 113). This passage was taken from one of his school books and was written under the title 'My idea of God'.

> I donot beleave in God one reson is that there is no profe that there is such a being as god and a nather is that if you went up to a person that had not herd ether verson and you thold him the siantific verson and the bible he would by most licley to belive in the siantific explanason more than the bible. I do bleave in Chiscianaty but not in god him self. I do not thing that god could make the woarld in six days I thing that plant life was made by serton atoms cuming to gethe but where did the atoms came from?

Here is part of a story by another 11 year-old (S 93):

> All the time that he wut the little butfil sat on the brim of is hat gust a buv the left iea at night full When the Miller Went tiod tied to bede the butfliy folied it wings and slept by the leg of the mills old cher[16].

Here is a passage from a 13 year-old (S 142) which clearly shows both high-level scientific aptitude and difficulty in getting his ideas down on paper:

> We can y~~ds~~ ~~s~~ us the LMF to caclat the same valys

Here are two passages from a 14 year-old (S 157):

> 'I have gust cum from whork I was ran ing rather hard I have just den lowking throw the lowchel cronicul have seen two Descos avertised. I am thinking of starting a Disc~~o~~ it will ~~k~~cost me about 60£ dut my dad will make me the amply fiers and some things els
>
> I whont to de a shef when I leve shcool. when I go to Dacis (dances) evry th~~e~~ing otside I forget my waris and proplems and the sam at Discos'

He also writes:

> 'I like going for walks with gerls I supos it is Becose of my age ~~you~~ I can for get thing and trudes (troubles) when I am with them~~/~~ dut gerls can de trudul sum times. Running is an enegetick hody dut I can think when I am runing like the Book the long lost runner

Here are two very interesting passages from a 16 year-old (S 193), one a dictation from a concert programme, one a piece of spontaneous writing:

> Parvane Op. 50 by Fauré
> Comp. in 1887, a year befor the recweum, but publised after ~~tha~~ that

work ~~fo~~ as op. 50, for smal orchestra and oshonal chorus, Fauré himself dicreted this delicat peas as "carfully n *wrought* (rort) but not otherwise important". It is a seling of a texst by Verlane (meny of whos powems Fauré set: eg the unfogetabel "Clare Dal°ona"), a pasterel conversation of not grat petick valyou; usaly the work is performed without the words. Yet the work is sagnificant in the same wright as some of the Verlane songs sins it is further pro°f of Fauré abilaty shard with somemay French artists of his time, to recreat the past, espeshaly the age the of racoco, without lapsing into ~~on~~ ~~ą~~ an epectadly "peryod" maner of expretion. Not the lest fasanating part of the this littal peas is th ocestration, with it sensative differenshiation of wood-wind tambrers, althou it may not, infact, be by Fauré himself.

One the most difficult thing to wright is something just of the cuff as you literat perent have not ~~p~~ read the letter propely.

The thing which most illiterats peop~~el~~ live perpetual feer of, is by geting into a situation were one has to read or by someone ones slipe of the tong, It get into your soshal circals. Luckerly this seldom hapens becaues as one is always one your tows. You have alway got to be ready to drag your frends ~~of~~ out of the room ~~wh~~ were ~~fom~~ famerly are, ~~U we~~ when the conversation gets to deep into the suject "o" leval.

I may be panting a ~~ver~~ very black picker, but to be quite honest it is not as enerjetick all that becaues it become a seconed sens.

The writing of 'comp' for 'composed' in the first passage is presumably a form of shorthand necessitated by lack of time. The difficulty of having to spell in French as well as English is emphasised by the barely recognisable 'Clare Daloona' for 'Clair de Lune', while the ability to be explicit about how he copes with his literacy problems is striking evidence of the way some dyslexic subjects can describe their difficulties without bitterness.

In general, it is plain from the above passages that dyslexic subjects often have plenty to say but that they may have disproportionate difficulty in writing it down. The relationship between their spelling errors and the general weakness of their lexical system will be discussed further in Chapter 24.

CHAPTER TEN

Confusion between Left and Right

My main source of evidence for confusions between left and right is the responses given by my subjects to the ten left-right (body-parts) items in the dyslexia test. Details of these items are given in Appendix I and methods of scoring in Appendix II. For ease of reference, however, the items are repeated here, along with their code letters. They were as follows:

(a) Show me your right hand
(b) Show me your left ear
(c) Touch your right ear with your left hand
(d) (Putting hands on the table) Which is *my* right hand?
(e) Touch my left hand with your right hand
(f) Point to my right ear with your left hand
(g) Touch my right hand with your right hand
(h) Point to my left eye with your right hand
(i) Point to my left ear with your left hand
(j) Touch my right hand with your left hand

For convenience I have divided the material into two sections. In the first I cite evidence which indicates the existence of a general uncertainty on the part of many of my subjects when they were presented with tasks involving use of the words 'left' and 'right'; in the second I cite some of the many examples of compensatory strategies which they had evolved in order to circumvent their difficulty.

Many of the subjects were fully articulate about their difficulties. For example S 139 said, 'I once gave my friend directions. I said the right-hand side when it should have been the left-hand side'. S 143 said 'I get muddled up sometimes . . . On a horse they say go round to the right and I am liable to go to the left'. S 241 said, 'There's a game called "Lifeboats". I call out "starboard" when it should be "port". I'm told which side is which at the start of the game but I forget it'. The mother of S 110 said in a letter that her daughter 'had to give up dancing class because left and right were too confusing'.

Fortunately it is possible for many subjects to laugh at mistakes of this

Dyslexia

sort which are seldom disastrous. Thus S 181 said to me 'People say, "Which way?" I say "right" when it should be "left" and that will take them into a ditch!'

In some cases, however, mistakes were made without the subjects being aware of the fact. For example, when I asked S 1 which hand he wrote with, he said rather scornfully 'My left hand, of course', but at the same time held up his right. Similarly S 128 gave the following account of his difficulties: 'I spent a lot of time learning it' (sc. the difference between left and right). 'I remembered, "Which hand do I write with?" I learned it securely when I was around 6'. Yet despite his use of the sophisticated word 'securely' he in fact made two errors, one on item (h), one on item (j). S 148, whose intelligence rating was Z, said: 'Sometimes I get mixed up, not often. I thought of which hand I write with – it becomes automatic'. Yet even after appreciable pauses he had to correct his responses on items (h) and (i). Asked to show me his right hand S 70 showed me his left hand, explaining, 'I was going to put my left up; I wasn't thinking'. (By implication the hand which he in fact put up was his right). To instruction (e), 'Touch my left hand with your right hand', S 114 said, '*Your* right with *my* left? Wait a minute; let me see . . .. Did I get it wrong or right?' He in fact 'correctly' touched *my* right hand with *his* left; this corresponded with what he had said but not with what he had been asked.

The following are further examples of uncertainties. S 54 was described in my notes as having 'paused and looked down at his hands', while S 232, after correctly pointing to *my* right hand in item (d), said, 'No, this is *my* right' (showing his left), 'no, this' (showing his right), and for all the remaining items was correct for his own side and incorrect for mine. After completing the series S 197 said, 'I don't know if I'm doing it right or wrong.' S 160 said 'I kept getting "right turn" and "left turn" mixed up'. When S 83 was asked to point to my left eye with his right hand (item h) there was a long pause, followed by a sigh (which appeared to indicate how difficult he found the task), after which he said 'This one' and pointed to *his own* right eye. S 71 correctly showed me his right hand but instantly added 'It's a guess', while S 73 incorrectly showed me his left hand but then gave a laugh and said 'This', showing his right. S 65 said simply 'I find I get a bit mixed up', while S 108 said 'Sometimes I can; sometimes I forget'. S 162 hesitated and finally showed me his left hand, saying as he did so: 'I think I've got it wrong – that's left. I always get muddled up'. S 4 stopped to think, and after correctly showing me his right hand said 'Is it right?' S 44 incorrectly showed me his left hand, saying as he did so, 'I've forgotten'. S 135 said, 'If you walk along and someone says "Put your right hand up" you think "Which one?"' Even the highly intelligent and mature S 218 reported that 'she sometimes got confused' in giving directions.

An interesting phenomenon was the existence of errors which were consistent. Here is a record of the behaviour of S 6 (which I wrote down while a colleague did the testing). Asked by the tester to show her his right hand he showed his left hand; when asked to show his left ear he pointed to his right ear, and when asked to touch his right ear with his left hand he touched his left ear with his right hand. Asked which was the tester's right hand he pointed to her left hand; and he then correctly touched her left hand with his right hand and pointed to her right ear with his left hand; but he then indicated that he thought this was a mistake and changed his policy so that thereafter his own right and left sides were correctly given but those of the tester were consistently incorrect. This degree of consistency must clearly have called for very considerable intellectual power (he was only 7 years old), and the picture is clearly not that of a person who fails to distinguish right and left through being too young or insufficiently intelligent.

Similar 'consistent' errors also occurred in the case of S 7, S 23, S 32, S 49, S 53, S 54, S 75, S 158, S 201, and S 240, while S 26 gave the 'consistent mirror image' answer to all items except (j) (where she 'correctly' touched my right hand) and S 111 gave the 'consistent mirror image' answer to all items except (g) (where she was 'correct' in pointing to my right hand but incorrect in using her left hand in order to do so). It is almost certain that these 'correct' responses by S 26 and S 111 were in fact mistakes by their own standards – something which they would have changed if they had had the opportunity and been alert enough to do so. In this connection the performance of S 41 is of sufficient interest to be quoted in full:

Tester: 'Show me your right hand' (Subject shows his left hand) 'Are you sure?' (Subject looks puzzled) 'Show me your left ear' (Subject shows his right ear) 'Touch your right ear with your left hand' (Subject touches his left ear with his right hand) . . . 'Point to my right ear with your left hand' (Subject *correctly* points to tester's right ear, though with his own right hand). In the notes taken at the time I wrote: 'I think this is a *double* error. He's got his own side wrong; so by getting my side 'wrong' he ends up by getting my side right![1]'.

In passing, it is worth noting how unsatisfactory from the point of view of dyslexia research are those large-scale studies which record simply the *number of correct responses*. If the record had merely shown, for instance, that S 6 made 2 correct responses out of 10, the really interesting aspects of his behaviour would not have been recorded, and he would have been classified among those whose 2 correct responses out of 10 occurred for quite different reasons.

The existence of these 'consistent' errors, then, is additional evidence that the subjects were not simply being 'careless' or 'stupid' since in that case the errors would have been purely random. Inconsistency is easy to achieve; consistency in getting the wrong answer is not[2].

In another respect, however, it seems likely that there is a greater degree of *in*consistency among dyslexic subjects. Such is their uncertainty that one cannot be sure that they will necessarily give the same answers if the various test items are repeated a second or third time, and I found that in some cases they did not. My normal practice was to give the test items only once, but occasionally I gave them more than once, and the following table shows the inconsistent performances of S 89, S 127, S 134, S 137, and S 145 on their 1st and 2nd trials. (R = right, L = left; all questions were of the form, 'Touch my .... with your .... hand'. Correct responses are underlined; a stroke indicates a changed response).

	Correct answer	S 89 1st	S 89 2nd	S 127 1st	S 127 2nd	S 134 1st	S 134 2nd	S 137 1st	S 137 2nd	S 145 1st	S 145 2nd
(d)	R	R		L	R	R		R		L	R
(e)	LR	LR	RR	RR	LR	RR	RR/LR	LR	LR	LR	LR
(f)	RL	LL	LL	RL	LL	LL/RL	RL	LL	RL	R	RL
(g)	RR	LR/LL	RR	RR	RR	LR	RR	RR	RR	RL	LR
(h)	LR	LR	LR	RR	RR	RR	LR	LR	LR	RR	LR
(i)	LL	RL	RL	LL	LL	LL	LL	LL	RL/LL	LL	LL
(j)	RL	LL		LL	LL	LL	LL	LL/RL	RR/RL	RR	RL

In reply to (i) S 134 said 'Left to right, did you say?' but gave the correct answer! In the first trial S 137 originally responded LL to (j) but changed to RL; the correct answer to (g) in the second trial was given only after a pause, and in reply to (i) he responded RL but immediately added, 'No, that's wrong' and corrected to LL, while in reply to (j) he corrected from RR to RL.

S 60 was consistent in giving the wrong answer on my side (i.e. RR, LL, LR, RR, RL, LL), and when I tested him again after explaining what was needed he made five mistakes out of six on *his own* side (LL, LL, RL, LL, RL, LR).

Sometimes the uncertainty is reflected in unusual comments. Thus S 201, when asked which was *my* right hand, pointed to my left and said, 'That is your really right hand . . . To me that is . . . oh, lor!' At this point he seemed to realise something, as he then said: 'If I was sat that way' (turning in his seat) 'that would be your left but to me it's your right'. On the first time through he gave the consistent mirror image of the correct answer (see above); on the second time through, he was correct on all the items, the only 'positive' indications being a hesitation and a request for repetition over item (j). S 193 reported an experience which is familiar to many of us when the task is more complicated: 'If suddenly you think, "Which is your right hand?", you can't say'.

There is a further phenomenon which some of my subjects mentioned and which appears to be another exemplification of difficulty over left and right, viz. difficulty over laying the table. Thus S 119 said, 'I still set the knives and forks wrongly', while S 241 said 'I get knife and fork the wrong way and put the plate on the wrong side'. Similar difficulties were reported by their parents in the cases of S 75, S 141, S 171, and S 244, and the mother of S 90 said, 'He sets the table the wrong way round, and one of his problems is that he can't see it!'

(ii) A large number of my subjects made use of mnemonics and compensatory strategies. One of the ones most frequently cited was that 'you *write* with your *right* hand'. This was used, so they told me, by S 28, S 48, S 54, S 63, S 75, S 76, S 82, S 93, S 125, S 130, S 132, S 135, S 148, S 157, S 177, S 194, S 202, and S 244. S 76 said 'If my teacher says "Put up your right hand" I quickly say "Which hand do I write with?"' Asked to show me his right hand S 220 said ' I know because I had my pen in it'.

A number of subjects had learned that their watch was on the left hand. S 52 said, 'I wear my left hand with my watch on' (sic). 'If I don't have a watch I'd get mixed up . . . If I'm swimming and haven't a watch I have to copy off other people'. S 237 said 'I know my watch is on my left hand; that makes it easier'. S 17 said, 'Normally I wear my watch on the right, so I was thinking which hand I had my watch on . . . I can recognise it a bit as I have a feeling I have my watch on'. At the start of the left-right test S 126 immediately looked at his watch, and when tested with his watch off he reported that he 'had to think'; he also said that he was liable to become confused in physical education classes when he had to take his watch off. S 181 said, 'I write with my right hand and have my watch on my left hand – that's how I used to work it out'. Others who referred to their watches were S 112, S 114 and S 195, the last two reporting that they wore their watches on the right hand.

A few subjects had undergone some minor injury on one side of their bodies. Thus S 12 said, 'This arm was hurt in rugby so that's how I know sometimes'. S 170 reported that she used both her watch (on her left hand) and a scar on the right of her face. S 158 said he knew which was his left hand because of an accident to his little finger. S 141, after hesitation, correctly showed me his right hand; when I asked him if he had had any difficulty over right and left he said, 'I only know it as it's the one I kick with. I hurt my left knee – they said "Which?" I couldn't tell, but from then on I knew it was my left knee as it was always hurting'.

Other subjects had their own idiosyncratic methods which they were quite willing to talk about. S 119 said that he learned left-right at the age of 10 because of scar on his right hand; 'I always used to get mixed up'. S 146 said, 'I think of the piano in front of me'. S 248 said 'I paint one toe red and one toe green . . . I've got a lump on my finger . . . I have to think, for example at crossroads.' S 234, who came from a Roman Catholic family, had learned that his right hand was the one with which he made the sign of the cross. S 208 was reported by her mother as having to mark her gloves 'left' and 'right'. S 205, in reply to 'Show me your right hand', said 'The only reason I know is I have a lump on my finger'; S 212 said 'My left thumb is double jointed so I go with that', while S 217 said, 'I wear that ring on my right hand'. S 131 said she knew which was her right 'because there's a freckle on my left hand' (my notes record that in response to item (f) and (g) she 'looks at her right hand and works it out'). S 102 reported a technique which he did not make fully clear: in reply to 'Show me your right hand' he said, 'I know it because it's the way I sit'. As far as I could make out the technique involved imagining himself in class and also imagining a boy next to him who presumably was known to be on his right or left. S 169 said, 'I had to write "left" and "right" on my bike and on the back of my hands'. S 67 said 'I always had to turn left to go to school', and S 165 said 'I remember the wall outside my house'. S 129 said, 'I learned that my blazer pocket was on the left'.

Another common strategy adopted by my subjects was that of asking for the question to be repeated or echoing it themselves under their breath (hence my use of the symbols 'RR' and 'EQ'; see Appendix II). For illustration purposes here are some examples. When S 165 was given item (e) she said, 'Will you say it again?'; when given item (f) she said 'Your right ear?' as a question, and when given item (j) she said 'Will you say it again?' (I in fact did so, and even then she touched my *left* hand with her left hand when it should have been my *right* hand). S 197 in reply to item (f) said 'Did you ask for right ear?' (Other comments included, 'My sister says they were ages trying to teach me . . . I still don't know if I'm doing it right or wrong'). S 80 in reply to (c) said semi-aloud, 'My right ear with my left hand?' and responded correctly; in reply to (g) he said, 'Could you say that again please?'; in reply to (h) he said to himself, 'Your left eye with my right hand?', and in reply to (i) said 'Your left ear with my left hand?. . . so it's that one'. S 59, in reply to (e) said 'Your left hand with my right?' and in reply to (f) said 'My right with your left?', on both occasions responding correctly; in reply to (j) he touched my *right* hand with his left, but when I queried this he repeated the question to himself and finally gave the correct answer.

Now it is, of course, the case that anyone, whether dyslexic or not, needs such 'prompts' from time to time, and since in our society the request, 'Could you say it again, please?', is socially quite acceptable it is not surprising that dyslexic subjects should have learned to make use of it. If my interpretation is correct, however, one would expect this particular series of test items to generate more 'RR' and 'EQ' responses in dyslexic subjects than in controls. This is an idea which requires further investigation[3].

For some of my subjects the tasks were made easier because of their ability to verbalise what was required; that is to say, they realised that, since I was sitting opposite them, what was on the left for them would be on the right for me and vice versa. For example S 109 shut his eyes and thought hard, saying, 'I've got to remember your left is my right'; S 145 said, 'I try to work it out by pretending I'm sitting where you are'; S 181 said, ''cos your right hand's opposite – on the other side – to my right'; S 67 said, 'It's always the opposite', while S 220 said, 'Your watch is on the left; I can judge from that watch which side of you you are on' (sic). Part of my intriguing conversation with S 141 (reported in full below) shows that he was attempting to formulate the same idea, while S 95 in reply to (e) said, 'My left with your right? You twist round; your right hand changes'.

Finally, I should like to mention a strategy which has always seemed to me both strange and interesting. Some of my subjects, when given the instruction 'Show me your right hand' or 'Touch my right hand with your left hand', carried out actual movements of their bodies. For example, to determine their own right hand they would go through the motions of picking up a pen and pretending to write and to determine which was my right hand they would turn or half-turn in their seats. In some cases the movements were so slight as to be barely noticeable, and indeed some subjects reported that it was sufficient to *pretend* to be carrying out such movements or to imagine themselves doing so.

S 51 explained the position to me as follows: 'I was told I was a left-handed writer. . . I think I'm writing a letter – if its "left" I put up the hand I'm pretending to write with'. S 39 was less articulate but said, 'I have to hold the pen in my hand' (the implication being that this would give him a clue as to right and left because he knew which hand he wrote with). Asked which was *my* right hand S 46 turned in his seat and then gave the correct answer, while S 37 said, 'If I was turning round I'd *know* which hand'. S 52 who used the 'watch' strategy, turned round in answer to this question but still pointed to my left. S 242 said, 'It took me ages to learn it and even now I have to pretend I'm writing. . . I pretended I had a pen so it was opposite to you'. S 209 explained the position as follows: 'I can't do ballroom dancing. When the teacher says "Stand on your right foot" I have to work out which side I am in relation to the road'. S 199 said 'I pretend I'm using a knife and fork'; S 147 turned in his seat, while S 143 had asked for item (j) to be repeated and as a check began to turn round in her seat. S 114, when given item (e), said 'Your right with my left?' (It should in fact have been, 'my left with your right'.) 'Wait a minute, let me see'; he then 'correctly' touched my right with his left. In response to (f) he said, 'Wait a minute – I've got to turn round because you're on the opposite side'. S 117, without actually turning round, said 'I had to think myself round first'. In response to 'Point to my right ear with your left hand' (f), S 100 made a half-turn in his seat and said 'Point to my left ear with your right hand' (attempting to repeat my words). Asked which was my right hand S 83 gave the correct answer and then said, 'I turned round'. (He had not in fact done so, except, presumably, in imagination. But he then demonstrated the point by actually turning round). S 61, after struggles with the earlier items, said in response to (i), 'Is it all right for me to turn round', after which he did the remaining two items correctly. Asked which was her right hand S 82 gave the correct answer after a pause, and when asked if she found it difficult, said, 'Yes, I remember which hand I write with; I pick up a pen to see'. S 81 also paused, and then explained, 'I had to find my kicking foot. . . I kick a ball with my right or have to lift my leg' (presumably he had been imagining himself kicking a ball). S 59 said, 'I have to do this', making a cub salute (presumably he knew that the hand with which he saluted was his right). S 67 said 'I always had to turn left to go to school' (meaning, I think, that he had to *imagine* himself on the way to school and that he knew that the side to which he turned was his left). S 177, after explaining that he knew his watch was on his left hand, said 'If someone asked me, I used to think "Oh, this"' (meaning, presumably, that he had to direct his attention towards his watch). S 187 made several turns, accompanied by the comment, 'I always have to think'. S 183 gave a twitch to his left thumb and said 'My right hand is the other one'. S 159 said 'I used to turn round and go like that' (movement) 'but I've got it now'. S 168 had said 'I have to think which one I write with' and, when asked which was my right hand, turned in his seat; in reply to item (f) (my right eye with his left hand) he pointed to my left eye with his right hand, then said 'No', turned round to check, saying, 'Let's think', and finally gave the correct answer.

As I have indicated elsewhere[4], I believe that a helpful account of this behaviour is to be found in the formula 'Doing is a substitute for naming'. It is because the lexical system of these subjects is relatively inefficient that a procedure which reduces the naming requirements of the situation is sometimes found to be helpful. The American investigators, Spring and Capps, are, I think, making a similar comment when they say that dyslexic persons 'evidence no dramatic inability to function in an environment of concrete stimuli'[5].

I have also suggested[6] that these difficulties are not necessarily the outcome of a difficulty over direction as such. It is not the case, for example, that when dyslexic subjects want to leave a room they sometimes walk away from the door instead of towards it (as Alice found was necessary in Looking-Glass World). It seems rather that it is the *words* 'left' and 'right' which cause the difficulty. Whether this is a complete explanation I do not know; but it is possible that when dyslexic subjects show uncertainty over direction, whether between left and right, between east and west, between 'b' and 'd', between the correct place for the knife and the correct place for the fork, or in other ways, all these problems are the consequence of a weakness at labelling. Similarly it is possible that their uncertainty over times and dates (see Chapter 13) should not be described as a 'sequencing' difficulty *simpliciter,* since there are some tasks, such as assembling the parts of a radio, which a dyslexic person can perfectly well do in sequence. It is rather that labelling is sometimes an aid to sequencing and therefore when labelling is inefficient the likelihood of faulty sequencing is increased.

If the criterion for showing 'uncertainty over left and right' is taken to be a 'plus' on the left-right test as specified in Appendix II, then 149 out of my 223 subjects (76%) showed uncertainty over left and right. Alternatively, if we take only the 132 dyslexic subjects who were matched with the controls (see Chapter 7) the figure is 87 (65%), compared with 36% of the controls. Although this result is highly significant[7], it is clear that one should think in terms of tendencies rather than certainties.

CHAPTER ELEVEN

Confusion between East and West

The main source of evidence about my subjects' awareness of 'east' and 'west' was an adapted version of the 'Direction' items in the Terman Merill intelligence test. Direction I contains five items, of which I quote the first two as examples: (i) 'Which direction would you have to face so that your *left* hand would be towards the *east*?' (answer, South), and (ii) 'Suppose you are going *west*, then turn to your *right*; in what direction are you going now?' (answer, North). Direction II involves five similar items, while Direction III involves a series of statements, which the subject is allowed to have in writing in front of him, about the distance and direction of travel; he then has to say both the direction in which he is finally going and the distance from his original starting point when he stops.

Direction I is regarded as suitable for the average 14-year-old, Direction II is set at 'Average Adult', and Direction III at the top grade of 'Superior Adult'. Most of my evidence is therefore derived from the performance of my older subjects, since many of the younger ones would have found such items too difficult. Occasionally, however, it was possible to give Direction I and Direction II to 9-, 10- and 11-year-olds.

I did not use the tests in precisely the way in which the original authors recommended, but adapted them instead in order to make them as meaningful as possible from the point of view of assessment for dyslexia. According to the instructions the subject is not permitted to use pencil and paper, but when I initially allowed my subjects to do so it was clear that a wealth of interesting material was emerging; and I therefore continued with the practice, even though this debarred me from using the results to produce an IQ in the standard sense (compare Chapter 2).

Now it was plain in many cases that my subjects knew the kind of response that was needed, viz. the name of one of the points of the compass, even though they did not necessarily come up with the correct one. In contrast there may be younger or slower subjects who either look blank or perhaps reply '*That* way', pointing in some direction, and occasionally there have been subjects who have said, 'But I don't know which way east is from here'. In these cases one can say that the subject has failed to understand the point.

It follows that the tasks involve at least three components, viz. (i) understanding the point, (ii) working out left and right, and (iii) working out east and west. Typically the dyslexic subject, provided he is of suitable age and ability, is successful at (i) but appreciably handicapped over both (ii) and (iii).

Here are some examples. In response to (i), where the correct answer is 'south', S 204 said 'north'. It was apparent, however, when I talked to him afterwards that he had confused 'east' and 'west', and a little later he said, 'If I'd got east and west the right way round I'd have done better'. Similarly, in response to Direction III, when the correct answer is 'west', S 179 said 'east', but when I corrected his diagram, in which east and west were interchanged, he immediately said, 'Then it's west'. When I returned to Direction I, which he had earlier failed, he succeeded over item (i) but said 'south' for 'north' in item (ii), turning left with his pencil as he said the word 'right'; when I pointed out his mistake he immediately said, 'The north'.

Now the confusions which my subjects showed over the points of the compass, and particularly those over east and west, reminded me very much of the difficulties over 'left' and 'right': there were mistakes, hesitations, echoing of the question, requests for the question to be repeated, and special compensatory strategies (including turning in their seats) which were quite often successful.

The following, for example, drew diagrams in which east and west were interchanged: S 94, S 95, S 126, S 137, S 170, S 202, S 219, S 228 and S 244. There were three subjects (S 50, S 81, and S 167) who drew their diagrams as

N

W   S

E

In each case they started at 'north' and proceeded in a clockwise manner, presumably because they were familiar with the commonly used order, 'north-south-east-west'. Even S 221, who was an undergraduate, showed hesitation over his diagram, and although it was in fact correct he turned to me as he drew it saying 'This is east, isn't it?' S 175, in response to the first Direction I item, said, 'Could you say it again? Your *right* hand?' When I said 'No', she then drew a diagram in which west was on the left and east on the right. Next, however, she crossed out 'east' and 'west' and substituted 'east' on the left and 'west' on the right. She then asked, 'Have I got it right? I think it's "west – east"' (indicating west on the left of the page); and, as if thinking out loud, she then said, 'If my left hand faced the east. . . don't know'. In response to the second item she echoed the question and said, 'East, no south'. With encouragement from me she drew the points of the compass again and said 'Am I looking on to north like that or to the back of it?' I did not understand this question but I had the impression that somehow she was not thinking of *herself* as being at the centre of the diagram even though this is something which is taken for granted by most subjects of this level of ability. I in fact put my pen vertically on the page and placed the cap as its 'left hand', after which she correctly answered all the items both in Direction I and in Direction II.

There was also the same need for mnemonics. S 239 said 'Mum told me "WE" so I remember,' while S 217 said 'I learned it was "WE" across'. S 151 said 'I say "Never Eat Shredded Wheat"' (but he nevertheless confused east and west), while this mnemonic was also used by S 135 (see below). There were also cases where the subject turned in his seat: thus S 212 did so in the case of Direction I and S 127 in the case of Direction III, while in response to Direction II, S 158 said 'It's much easier with your body'.

S 135 not only turned in his seat but actually stood up and turned around the room, these actions being combined with the Never-Eat-Shredded-Wheat mnemonic. It was one of these occasions where I particularly wish the behaviour could have been telerecorded. As a second best I have tried to record what happened as accurately as I could. The whole procedure took an appreciable time, but each stage was purposeful and intelligent. He started by rising from his seat to face the wall on the right, saying as he did so, 'Suppose that's north. . . You have north, then east. . . Never eat shredded wheat; so that's south. . . my left hand (pause) towards the east. . . so I would be facing south'. This was in fact the correct answer. His performance seems to me typical of the dyslexic subject in that it shows the ability to make a step-by-step series of deductions and the ability to combine these deductions with use of the appropriate mnemonic. One is also left with a sense of surprise that such strategies are needed at all, since there seems little doubt that in a similar context a non-dyslexic person of the same ability and background would have come up with the answer instantly. Similar compensatory strategies will be referred to in Chapter 15, where an 'instant' answer to 'nineteen take away seven' was impossible for some of my subjects but where a similarly slow step-by-step process often led to the correct answer. The process does not, of course, involve any memory overload; it is rather that a single, *non*-overloading procedure needs to be used several times over. It is also worth noting that S 135, like most other dyslexic subjects, was perfectly capable of 'supposing' that a particular direction was the north. It is symbols which present difficulty, not concrete objects whether real or imagined.

On some occasions there were subjects who went wrong because of a left-right error. For example, in reply to the item 'Suppose you are going *east*, then turn to your *right*, in what direction are you going now?', S 81 went through the motion of turning *left* on his diagram and 'correctly' said 'north'.

In response to Direction III S 185 drew the following diagram, starting at the point X.

The original wording is 'turned to my left and drove east 2 miles', whereas he turned to his *right* and drove *west* two miles! He then *turned the paper upside down* and started again! S 193 said, 'You go south and then turn to your. . . ' at which he became confused, muddling up north and south; and at this point he, too, turned the paper upside down.

In reply to the first item of Direction I S 81 started by saying 'That way' instead of naming a point of the compass. When I asked if he would like to write anything down, he wrote:

N

W   S

E

and when I asked him to try again he wrote:

S

E   W

N

Here the four points of the compass are correctly placed in terms of relationship but the normal viewer would complain that they were upside down! Finally this subject produced the correct diagram, after which he had no difficulty in giving the correct answer. When given Direction II he used the same diagram, and then, in reply to 'Suppose you are going *east*, then turn to your right; which direction are you going now?', he turned left and consistently but wrongly said 'north'. S 179 and S 174 also drew the points of the compass correctly in terms of relationships, with south at the top and east on the left, and S 174 tried to solve Direction III by means of a grid, as shown in Fig.1.

When I queried this he, too, turned the paper upside down! (The other writing in Fig.1 shows the very logical way in which he worked out the answer to the Terman Merrill 'tree' item; see Chapter 15).

A further east-west confusion is worth recording, though in fact it did not occur in response to any of his Terman Direction tests but in response to a Wechsler test item where the subject has to say what part of a picture is missing; in this particular case the sun is drawn directly behind a tree and

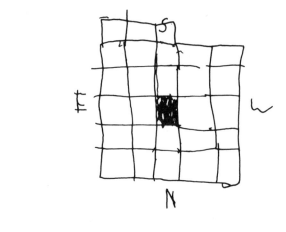

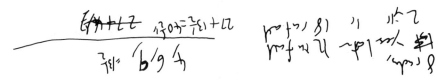

Fig.1   Grid to aid calculation of east and west.

yet the tree gives no shadow. S 67 said: 'If it's rising from the wrong direction – it rises from the west, no, east, and that sun's rising from the west. That's north' (pointing as if the picture were a map). I did not find this statement fully intelligible, but it should be noted that he made the correction from 'west' to 'east' and also (perhaps more interestingly) that he seemed to be under the impression that one could say which were the points of a compass by simply examining the picture. This response is perhaps comparable with that of S 175, mentioned above: in both cases there is some ground for supposing not merely that these two subjects were confusesd over east and west but also that there was something lacking in their under-standing of how points of the compass are represented on a two-dimensional surface. Although this lack came to light only in these two cases, it is possible that they are examples of a more general 'uncertainty over spatial relationships' which appears to be part of the dyslexic picture. Factors in the situation which the rest of us take for granted may not have been understood.

CHAPTER TWELVE

Confusion between 'b' and 'd'

It was plain, even in the early stages of the research, that many of my subjects, including some of the older ones, were confusing 'b' and 'd'. This was clear not only from their performance on the R_1 and S_1 tests but also from an inspection of their school exercise books: they might make a b-sound for a d-sound (or vice versa) in reading and write the letter 'b' for the letter 'd' (or vice versa) in spelling.

There was first-hand evidence of such errors in 75 out of the 223 subjects and reported evidence (which there is no reason to doubt) in a further 71 cases. As an estimate of the incidence of b-d confusion in a dyslexic population this figure (146, or 65%) may be too low, since in the case of some of the older subjects, particularly those unaccompanied by their parents, difficulties at an earlier age would not necessarily have been remembered.

In some cases the confusions were extremely persistent. Of the 47 subjects aged 12 to 14 no less than 14 were scored as 'plus' on this item (that is, they were still making b-d errors at the time of the assessment[1]), and a further 7 out of the 59 in the age range 15 to 18 were also scored as 'plus'. Only recently I was shown a piece of written work by S 126, five years after his original assessment at the age of 12, in which *probably* was written as 'probadly' and *problems* as 'prodlems', both being afterwards corrected[2]. Such confusions are of course not the norm for older subjects, but in view of the apparent easiness of the task by ordinary standards it is remarkable that they occur at all.

It would, I am sure, be a mistake to suppose that dyslexic subjects are the *only* people who confuse 'b' and 'd'. It is a matter of common experience that so-called 'slow learning' children do so and there is evidence from a study by Bottomley that a small number of children with spelling ages under 9 did so even though they were probably not dyslexic[3]. A great merit of Bottomley's study was that the 50 dyslexic subjects were compared, not with age-matched controls but with younger children of the same spelling age; and from this it follows that any differences in respect of b-d confusion are not simply a manifestation of spelling weakness in general. From the data which Bottomley provided it has been possible to take the first 9 words from the Schonell S₁ test which begin with 'b' or 'd' and compare the relative number of confusions by dyslexic and by control subjects. Other types of spelling error were, of course, discounted. The results were:

Interchange of 'b' and 'd'

Word	Dyslexic Subjects	Control Subjects
doll	3	2
bell	2	2
by	1	1
brain	1	0
dancing	3	0
damage	1	0
daughter	2	0
domestic	1	0
duties	1	0
TOTAL	15	5

It is interesting that in the case of the control subjects the confusions were limited to words early in the list. It is possible that by the time these subjects were at a level where they could attempt the later words any tendency to confuse 'b' and 'd' had been outgrown. Occasional b-d confusions among non-dyslexic subject have also been reported by Pollard[4]. In general it seems to me likely that children who show b-d confusion in the early stages do not invariably present the typical dyslexic picture but that in dyslexic children the confusion sometimes persists until an older age and that even at a younger age it is relatively more common.

Now it is usually supposed that mistakes over 'b' and 'd' are basically errors over direction. I am not myself convinced that the subject's handedness is a relevant factor, since I found no evidence that the left-handers or mixed-handers were more prone to b-d confusion than the right-handers (see Chapter 21). It is still possible, however, that b-d confusion is 'of a piece' with other typical dyslexic-type errors – confusion over left and right, writing 'ot' for *to*, working from the 'wrong' end in arithmetical calculation, and so on.

'b' and 'd' are not, of course, the only pair of letters which are liable to confusion. Mistakes over 'p' and 'q' (S 4 and S 11) and over 'p' and 'b' (S 94) were reported; S 13 was said to have written 3 back to front and S 28 to have done the same in the case of 5 and 9. S 12 wrote ι for J; S 6 was reported to have written 'letters and figures backwards' and similar expressions were used in the case of S 51, S 54, S 62, S 197 and S 198. It was not always clear, however, how recent such mistakes were, and it is possible that the parents of non-dyslexic children might sometimes have remembered similar difficulties. S 58 'corrected' 'cap' in his S$_1$ test to 'caq' but this is the only first-hand evidence which I have of p-q confusion in anyone aged 10 or more. There was clear evidence of Ss (and many other letters) being written the wrong way round by S 208 (for example CARBOИIƎⱯROUƧ LIMEƧTOИƎ), but she appears to be a very exceptional and severe case[5], and in none of the 223 records of the Schonell S$_1$ test is there a single example of an inverted S. Any attempt to explain b-d confusions in terms of mirror-images needs also to explain why p-q confusions do not persist so long and why, after the very early stages, inverted Ss are relatively rare.

My tentative suggestion is as follows. I do not believe that it is mirror-images as such which are the main source of the dyslexic person's difficulty. If objects, pictures, or patterns are mirror-images of each other all of us may need longer time to distinguish between them. Where the dyslexic person has difficulty, because of his weak lexical system, is with symbols. This means that in the case of *mirror-image symbols* some extra difficulty is to be expected; and this makes sense of the fact that some dyslexic children do indeed, if only for a limited period, confuse 'p' and 'q' and write Ss and some numerals the wrong way round. 'b' and 'd', however, are a unique pair of symbols in that they are both auditorily and visually confusable[6]. There is therefore a situation where visual processing gives an ambiguous result and where the possibility of an auditory cross-check is reduced. On a 'bad day' any of us may make seemingly 'careless' mistakes[7]; in the case of a dyslexic person, however, an initially weak lexical system may be even weaker if it is a 'bad day', and if in addition there is absence of cross-check between the visual and the auditory, the probability of error may be disproportionately increased. I do not know if this account of the matter is correct, but some such account is needed if one is to make sense of the relative persistence of b-d confusions in dyslexia when other similar confusions have disappeared.

CHAPTER THIRTEEN

Confusion over Times and Dates

The confusions described so far – between left and right, between east and west, and between 'b' and 'd' – are alike in that they all involve errors over spatial relationships. To touch a person's right hand instead of his left or to move eastwards on a map instead of westwards is to go to the wrong point in space; and similarly to read a 'b' as though it were a 'd' or to write 'b' for 'd' is to be in error about the spatial lay-out of one or both symbols.

In this chapter I shall show that there can be similar uncertainties over times and dates. This, indeed, is not surprising, since successive points in time are sometimes represented by adjacent points in space[1], and if spatial representation is in some way faulty it makes sense that temporal representation should be faulty also. However that may be, difficulties connected in various ways with awareness of time were relatively common.

Thus it was reported by his parents that S 114 might sometimes say, 'I'll just go down to the shops' even though it was evening and shops were shut! Still more instructive is the record of my conversation with S 130, which went as follows:

Q. 'What day of the week is it?'
A. 'I think it's the 17th.' (It was in fact the 27th)
Q. 'Yes, but what day of the week?'
A. 'Tuesday. Oh, no, Thursday. I remember, as we came yesterday, so it must be Thursday'.

In the case of S 215 I recorded the following remarks: 'It's Wednesday, at least I hope it is; no, it's Tuesday – Thursday, rather. I think at school I used to tell what day it was – we did things in phases, so I remembered what we did on Thursdays – we did art on Thursdays'. It was reported by his mother that S 143 could not tell the time until the age of 10½ and left out 'Monday' from the days of the week until he was 10. Among others, S 57, S 149, S 154, and S 175 were said to have been late in learning to tell the time.

S 164 said he did not remember what year it was but knew that he would be fifteen next September. I was able to look at the history note book of S 214, where I saw on successive parts of the page the dates 1804, 1805, 1806, and

1807, after which 1809 had been changed to 1808 and there were crossings out or corrections for 1810 and 1811. When I asked S 10 the date of his birthday he said it was in March but could not give the exact date. He then added: 'But I find Christmas and my birthday move on one day, Saturday this year, Friday last year'. When I asked him the date of Christmas, however, he made no reply.

Uncertainty over dates was specifically mentioned by the parents of S 76 and also by the parents of S 258 whom – not without some hesitation – I placed in Group II, though I would certainly have placed her in Group I had more supporting signs of this sort been forthcoming. When S 171 was asked his date of birth he said, 'Five six - no, hang on; six five nineteen, er - , forty nine', the correct answer in fact being 6.5.1959. I also had occasion to ask S 233 the year of his birth. He replied, 'I've been told it a lot of times'; and when I suggested he should work it out (he was 10 and the year was 1972) he said '1862 - no, 1962, - no, 1862'. S 204 said that he 'thought' his year of birth was 1957 (which it was) but that he 'couldn't associate dates with events'. 8 years after her initial assessment I was talking to S 246, who was taking a degree in embroidery, about the Bayeux tapestry; when I asked if its date was known she said 'About forty years after the original events in 1666' (instead of 1066).

The recognition by S 10 (see above) that his birthday 'moved on one day' each year is particularly interesting. Once again this appears to be a situation where understanding the behaviour of abstract concepts – in this case the use of the days of the week to symbolise the passage of time – is in no way impaired. Similarly it was interesting that some of my older subjects, for example S 174, S 204, S 205, and S 218, were successful at the difficult item in the Terman Merrill test where it is asked how 'beginning' and 'end' are alike. S 205 said that they were both 'to do with time' yet when asked to say 'two five nine' in reverse order she said 'nine two five'. Understanding the concept of time is clearly quite different from being able to reproduce symbols in the correct temporal order.

This moment is perhaps a convenient one in which to discuss a related set of difficulties, viz. those experienced by my subjects in repeating words such as 'preliminary', 'anemone', and 'statistical'. The evidence from Chapter 7 shows that difficulties over these words were very much more frequent in dyslexic subjects than in controls, and, quite apart from evidence derived from the administration of the dyslexia test, it is noteworthy that a number of parents spontaneously mentioned similar difficulties. Thus the speech of S 118 at the age of 6 was said by his mother to be full of 'Spoonerisms'[2], and among my younger subjects the following mispronunciations were reported: 'proshifency' for *proficiency* (S 20), 'Jackercrack' for *Crackerjack* (S 25), and 'dikkifult' for *difficult* (S 5). Among my older subjects I noted that S 188 became 'tied up' in trying to say the word 'susceptible' in the Schonell R$_1$ word recognition test and that S 217 had difficulty in saying the word 'corollary'. S 218 reported that she got tied up with words' and that 'people laugh at me about it', and her father reported that at a younger age she had said 'tee-sit' for *sittee*.

I suspect that auditory confusability can sometimes be an important source of error, and that this may be a more significant causal factor than the length of the word as such. As was pointed out in Chapter 3, there is anecdotal evidence of dyslexic children who say 'par cark' for 'car park' (where length of word cannot be a decisive factor), and, although I have not so far carried out a detailed statistical analysis, I suspect that there have been fewer errors over the longer, six-syllable word, 'contemporaneous', than over 'preliminary' which has five syllables and over 'anemone' and 'statistical' which have four. Whether or not this is correct, there is no doubt that dyslexic subjects are more liable than the rest of us to become 'tied up' when asked to repeat certain words, and this appears to be a further example of their weakness at certain tasks involving temporal ordering.

CHAPTER FOURTEEN

Recall of Months of the Year

One of the items in the dyslexia test consists of the simple instruction, 'Say the months of the year'. If the subject makes a reasonable attempt at this he is then told, 'Now say them backwards'.

The patterns of responding are in many ways like those which occurred with the left-right test. In some cases there are actual errors; often there is confusion, and at times there is the conscious working out of compensatory strategies. Detailed documentation seems to me worth while, since the task, at least in the case of 'months forward' is likely to strike a non-dyslexic person as being relatively easy, and indeed the evidence from Chapter 7 shows that 106 out of 132 control subjects scored 'minus' at it, 9 of the remaining 26 being under age 9. In contrast only 57 out of the 132 matched dyslexic subjects and only 101 out of my total pool of 223 dyslexic subjects scored 'minus'[1].

The following are examples of responses when the subject made actual errors. S 188 omitted 'May' and when asked to have a second try omitted it again. S 210, who was aged 17 and was in the highest (Z) intelligence group, proceeded correctly as far as August and then said, 'October, September, November, December'.

There were also many subjects who named some of the months but failed to name all of them. For example S 62 said, 'February, March, June, May, September, August, November, December' – a total of eight months. S 25 gave only four months, S 43 nine, S 52 eight, S 62 eleven (but in the wrong order), S 124 five, S 125 eight (though he claimed to know that there were twelve), S 128 ten, S 162 five, S 164 five, and S 236 six. Sometimes the same month was repeated twice over, as when S 7 said 'November, December, October, November, December, March, April, May, June, July, November, December'. S 20 was correct up to September and then said, 'November, December, October, November. No, I can't. I get mixed up'. S 38 was correct up to September and then said 'November, December, October, November, December, October, March, April, May, June'. S 140 said 'June, where do you start from? June, July, August, September, August, September, August, September, January. July - oh, I forget -

February, August, September – I'm all muddled up'.

In addition to the actual errors there were many corrections and signs of uncertainty. S 138 said 'January, February, June, no, March, April' and then proceeded correctly. S 141 gave the months correctly as far as August, and then said, 'This is where I get stuck – September, November. . . October I've missed out'. At this point he went back to January and started with his fingers; my notes say that he was 'just about successful'. S 159 after responding correctly said, 'Have I missed out August? I usually do'. S 158 said, 'Oh, dear! that is hard. April, May, June, July, August, September, December, November – the rightest I've ever said it. It sounded right – normally I get them in an awful muddle'. S 157, after a long pause, produced the correct answer but added at the end, 'That's the first time I've done it right'. S 173 said, 'January, March, April – or was it February? After that its May, June, July, August'. Then, slowly, 'October, November, December'. S 183 was correct as far as October but then said 'I've missed one out'; he then went through quite correctly but still said 'I've missed one', and after a further correct recitation said, 'Ah! there's twelve that time'. S 232 said 'Blimey!', and when after a pause I had prompted with 'January' he said 'February I think it is, March, April, June, July, August, September, October, November, December' (pause), 'April, June, July, August, September, November, December, um – I've finished, haven't I?' S 47, after omitting May and October, said, 'I know there's one after November before December'. S 99 said 'March, April, June, July, August, September, November, December', and when I said 'Do you know if you have left any out?' he said 'Yes'; when I asked which he said 'March'.

One of the most noticeable characteristics of many of the responses was the uncertainty over *order*. Here are some sample comments from among the many available. S 162 said, 'Oh goodness! where do I start from? Does it matter?' S 179 said 'Not in order, no; December, November, June, January, April, March, May – have I said January?'. S 44 said 'I've forgotten when it starts', while S 59 said 'Where from? Where shall I say them from? I'm always getting muddled'. When I prompted him with January he said, 'February, March, April' (pause), 'May – is it? – , June – I don't know any more'. S 26 said, 'Could you tell me the first one?', and when I said 'January' she said, 'January, February, May, July – no, I've left some out; March, April, June, then August. . . I know it but I can't say the word right. . . October, the same with this, was the last one I said October? (Yes). Does the next one begin with 'a' – accember?. . . September, October, Devember, how many more? (One) Devember'.

Compensatory strategies and mnemonics are not as easy to find in the case of the months of the year as they are in the case of left/right and east/west. There was one strategy, however, which several subjects used, viz. that of counting with their fingers as they said each month so as to ensure that the number of months came to twelve; this was the strategy of

S 56, S 132, S 133, S 176, and S 232. S 72 omitted both May and September, saying at the end, 'I know there's not twelve there'. In a number of cases there was the 'epanalepsis' strategy (see Chapter 3). For example it was again S 72 who, having said 'June, July', appeared to lose his way and repeated 'June, July' before passing to 'August, October, November, December'. S 94 was correct up to April but then started again; he also repeated 'September' when saying the months in reverse order apparently as a way of reorienting himself. S 121 was correct as far as 'June, July', albeit with a slight pause and tapping of his fingers after 'March', but he repeated 'June, July' before saying 'August, October, November, December'.

I was particularly fascinated by the strategy adopted by S 75, who told me that it was of his own devising. His name was Jason, and he said that he remembered the five months from July onwards because the first letters were given by the letters of 'Jason'. Shortly afterwards I was talking to his teacher, to whom he had proudly said, 'I can do the ones from July onwards', looking, as she aptly put it, like a cat that had got at the cream! More recently still I was at a lecture on teaching methods where the speaker in discussing how to teach the months of the year referred to the 'Jason' months and said afterwards in conversation that this mnemonic was now part of the stock-in-trade of teachers of dyslexic children.

If a person cannot say 'months forwards' in the correct order it seems on the face of it inconceivable that he should be correct on 'months reversed'; and indeed where 'months forwards' was a total failure, or somewhere near it, it was plain that one could score 'months reversed' as a 'plus' without putting the subject through the strain of having to attempt a task on which he was sure to fail. It can be seen from the Summary Chart, however, that very occasionally there was a 'minus' at 'months reversed' despite a 'nought' or 'plus' at 'months forwards' or a 'nought' at 'months reversed' despite a 'plus' at 'months forwards'. This happened in the case of S 30, S 34, S 90, S 93, S 116, S 118, S 122, S 151, S 219, S 237, and S 239. This finding is 'genuine' in the sense that the scoring of 'plus', 'nought', and 'minus' conformed with the criteria set out. Since, however, these subjects were more successful at 'months reversed' than at 'months forwards' one must conclude not that they *could not* have succeeded at the latter but only that they *did not* on this particular occasion. The point is an important one since it underlines the uneven nature of the dyslexic subject's performance and confirms that one should not necessarily think of dyslexic-type difficulties as arising from lack of the appropriate brain mechanisms but from the lower probability of their activation[2].

The failures over 'months reversed' do not require detailed documentation, but here are four typical 'plus' responses which I quote for illustration purposes. S 46 said 'December, October. . . I'm sorry, I can't say any more'; S 80 said, 'Oh, crumbs! December, November (pause) September', while S 153 said, 'December, November, August, October, June . . .

cor!. . . July, June, April, May. . . cor!. . . May, April, March, February, January'. S 203 said simply 'I can't. I get stuck'.

Several of the subjects reported compensatory strategies, the most common of which was to say a small number of months in forwards order to themselves and thus 'group' the months for saying in reverse order. For example S 222, an undergraduate, said 'I thought of the month, then worked in threes, and S 155 said, intelligibly if not clearly, 'The ones I know in sequence – you go back to the beginning and get a few more'[3].

At times the difficulties in saying 'months forwards' and 'months reversed' appeared to be similar to those which occurred when my subjects attempted to say their tables. For example, in the case of 'months reversed' S 131 said 'December (pause) November, October, September (pause), August, July, June, May (pause), April – no, I've gone wrong, I think. . . What was the last one?' This response indicates 'loss of place' in much the same way as do the responses over 'tables' which will be reported in Chapter 16.

In view of the number of 'minus' scores, particularly among my older subjects[4], it follows that the months of the year can be learned, and indeed from the figures in Chapter 7 it is clear that to dyslexic and non-dyslexic subjects alike they are easier to learn than tables. It was plain, however, from their comments that several subjects had assumed without question that the task was one which required conscious effort. For example, when given the instruction, 'Now say them backwards', S 114 said 'I haven't learned – I'll try', while S 94 said, 'I only learned the months at play group; I didn't learn them any other time', as though it would be quite natural for something learned so long ago to have been forgotten. Similarly S 29, after saying 'June, July, August, September, August, September, June', explained his uncertainty by adding, 'We didn't learn them'. S 208 said 'I've learned these (i.e. the months) recently'. In the Summary Chart this has to be scored as 'minus', though as a clinical judgement one can say that the fact that a 17-year-old of above average ability had only 'recently' learned the months of the year is highly significant. Similarly S 143 is recorded as 'minus' for both 'months forwards' and 'months reversed' but her mother reported that in fact she had gone through them with her many times. After successful completion of 'months forwards' S 181, with almost a sigh of relief, said 'And *that's* taken a bit of practice'.

Finally, it is interesting to compare saying the months of the year with other tasks where nameable items have to be arranged in series. I seldom asked my subjects to give me the days of the week since in many cases I had found that they could do so with no difficulty. But there were occasional reports that this knowledge had not come easily. Thus S 28 was said by her mother to have only recently 'sorted out' the days of the week, while S 41 (who was a minister's son) explained that he 'didn't know the order of the days of the week . . . but Saturday it was bionic man and Dr. Who . . . I got to know it was horrible church on Sunday'. (This was said in front of his father who fortunately had a sense of humour!) S 7 could not say the date of his birthday but knew that it was the start of the summer holidays, while S 37 when asked to say the days of the week backwards replied, 'Saturday, Friday, Thursday, Tuesday, Wednesday. . . I forget'. Such uncertainties, however, were rare, and one can be reasonably confident that most dyslexic children of the same age and background as my subjects will show no difficulty in saying the days of the week, at any rate in forwards order.

I found greater uncertainty over knowledge of the four seasons. This again was something which I did not investigate very systematically, but from time to time I came on errors which had a distinctly dyslexic flavour. Thus S 83 said 'Winter is first, autumn, summer, winter again'. After S 14 had told me that December came in winter I asked if he knew the other seasons, to which he replied, 'Yes, winter, summer, autumn'; and when I asked, 'Do you know any more?' he said, 'Yes, summer'. Another curious phenomenon which I sometimes found was an uncertainty about the difference between seasons and months and some unwitting slips from one to the other. Thus when asked to say the months of the year S 1 said 'January, February, March, April, June, July, August, autumn', while S 9 when asked to give the names of some of the months said 'October, November, summer, winter'. Asked if he could say the months of the year S 58 said, 'No. . . Spring, autumn, winter. . . I've remembered – spring, autumn, winter', and when I asked 'What's the right order?' he said, 'What do you mean?'[5].

It seems to me that learning overlay is possible in the case of the days of the week because few children, whether dyslexic or not, can avoid being exposed to them. In that respect they are similar to the lower numbers in the number series. The same names, Thursday, Friday, etc., keep appearing, as we say, week after week; this happens fifty two times a year, compared with once a year in the case of the months and once a year in the case of the seasons. It is likely, too, that a child needs to know that it is, say, Thursday more often than he needs to know that it is, say, January or spring, particularly if his school has a regular time-table; and even if he learns certain associations – for instance that one plays cricket in summer – the idea of a *sequence* of months or seasons is not necessarily something which will occur to him. It should be noted that length of the series does not appear to be the only relevant factor; otherwise the 4 seasons would be more readily learned in sequence than the 7 days of the week.

CHAPTER FIFTEEN

Subtraction and Addition

In this chapter the subjects' responses will be classified under three heads, viz. (i) those which suggest a basic weakness over calculation in general, (ii) those which suggest a specific uncertainty over the direction of the number-series, and (iii) those which exemplify the use of compensatory strategies. The sources for the data will be the subtraction items in the dyslexia test (see Appendix I), and a number of items from the Terman Merrill intelligence test which require addition and/or subtraction.

(i) Just as a dyslexic subject does not easily 'pick up' the details of how words are spelled, so he may also be at risk when required to make seemingly simple calculations with numbers. Thus S 42, when asked $9-2$, replied '8, I mean 7', and when asked $6-3$ replied '4, no, 3'. In response to $19-7$ S 124 said '2 - I mean 12', while S 44 said '13' giving as his explanation, 'I took 9 away from 7, leaves 3' (sic) 'and added 10, makes 13'. (This response indicates not only a weak number sense, since $9-7 = 2$, not 3, but a confusion over order since he clearly meant 7 from 9, not 9 from 7). When given $43-8$ he replied '44. . . I added 10, and take 8 from 13 leaves 4, then 44'. As I understand the situation he had correctly added 10 to 3 but had both made a mistake over $13-8$ and forgotten to subtract the 10 afterwards. Once again, as with the answers to the left-right items given in Chapter 10, it is the method of working which is of interest rather than the question of whether the end product is right or wrong.

Similar uncertainty is reflected in the response of S 113, who, in reply to $6-3$, correctly said '3' but added: 'I knew that one. . . I know some of the harder ones but I get most of the easy ones wrong'. When given $9-2$ S 95 said 'Is it 8? No, 7' and when given $6-3$ he said '3; I think two threes are six'. When S 100 was given $9-2$, there was some long muttering during which he counted forwards from 1 to 7 and finally said '7'; when I asked, 'Are you sure?', he said 'About 50-50'. When S 87 was given $19-7$ he said 'I knew 9 take away 7 is 3 so I made it 13', and when given $43-8$ he took a piece of paper and said 'I make it 5. . . I don't know how I did it'; when I asked, 'Can you tell if it is *nearly* right?' he said, 'No', and when I explained that the answer was 35 he said 'So you bring that down there?'

(meaning the 3). This response suggests that he was an intelligent boy who was willing to learn certain rules of calculation, such as bringing down a number into a different row, but that he had not picked up a basic knowledge of how the number-series behaves. I do not doubt that the properties of the number-series can be taught, just as correspondence betwen letters and sounds can be taught; what is important in the case of the dyslexic subject is that one cannot take for granted that he will acquire such knowledge, as other children acquire it, during the course of ordinary experience at home and school.

In two cases the parents had noticed a similar basic lack of understanding. Thus in the case of S 60 his father reported that he 'hadn't got the concept of what dividing etc. are', while in the case of S 232 his mother said, 'He has little idea of the relationship of one number to another; for example he would have difficulty in saying whether 282 was greater than 268'.

The following record of the behaviour of S 104 is evidence of high reasoning power and, indeed, of some verbal fluency in describing this reasoning, which was nevertheless coupled with uncertainty over an elementary number relationship. When first asked $19-7$ he replied '8', and when asked how he got it he said that he did not know. He then made another attempt and said '13', giving the following explanation: 'I put one on the 19 to make 20, and 7 and 4 make 10 so after that I. . . when I add 4 to make it. . . instead of having 4 you knock off one so it comes to 13'. I have been able to reconstruct what I believe to be his argument, which runs as follows: 'Bring both terms to the nearest 10: 19 becomes 20 by adding 1 and 7 becomes 10 by adding 4 (sic). One therefore adds 4 to $20-10$, which gives 14, and one 'knocks off' the one needed to bring 19 up to 20, thus ending up with 13'. This reasoning is entirely correct, and the only mistake is that 10 is $7+3$, not $7+4$. What is remarkable is that a boy of this reasoning ability should not have known that $7+3=10$!

In contrast I was defeated by the explanation of S 86 as to how he arrived at 11 for $19-7$. 'I went up to 10; another 10 would make 19, so I did 11'. If there was any logic here I did not discover it. Possibly his 'logic' was the same as that of S 162, who in reply to $44-7$ said '32', which he said was 'mainly a guess and mainly a bit of working out'. This was similar to S 99, who in reply to $52-9$ said '42. . . I think it was in the 40s and then I did a guess'.

Sometimes errors and corrections seemed to have been generated by the memory-load which some of the subtraction tasks involved. Thus S 63 gave $52-9$ as 46 and explained afterwards 'I remembered it as 55 and took away 9'. In reply to $43-8$ S 155 said '35, sorry, 34 - no, 35', while S 154 said '37' and then said '53, was it? No, 43, take away 8; no, it was 36; no, I was right, 47; no, 37'.

Sometimes the subjects' spontaneous comments indicated the strain under which their handicap placed them. Thus S 114, in reply to $9-2$, said '8 - I mean 7. I make slips in my exam but I check it. When someone's racing me against the clock I'm fast saying it in my mind but when I get it down I make slips. When I'm being timed I feel I must beat the clock – I came top but didn't get in Set I'.

Even the relatively mature S 201 showed uncertainty when I gave him $6-3$. He first echoed the word 'three', as if to repeat to himself that this was the number to be taken away, and then said 'No! Minus three'. Without the explanatory concept of dyslexia the failure by a bright 16-year-old to answer this item instantly would be truly astonishing.

There was also an interesting comment from S 96 who said that when he had to write 'a thousand and fifty' he had started by putting 1000[1].

Further evidence of uncertainty over numbers is to be found in the many requests for repetition made by my subjects when some calculation was required. For example, S 182, in response to $19-7$, said '8, no 9. You said 18. . . You said 19 take away what?'. Both S 203 and S 58, in response to the same question, said '19, was it?. . . 12', while in reply to $44-7$ S 96 said, Was it 40 take away 7?'. S 99 echoed the question when given $6-3$ and S 131 did so in the case of both $52-9$ and $44-7$, while S 93 asked for both $19-7$ and $44-7$ to be repeated.

S 175, in reply to $44-7$ said 'Thirty, oh, heck! – What was it? 44?', and when I repeated '$44-7$' she said '36. . . I got lost again'. S 185 gave 33 as the answer to $44-7$ but corrected it to 36; when I asked, 'Are you sure?', he said, 'I think so; what was the number again?' S 159 when asked $52-9$ said 'Forty. . . ' followed by an s-sound, as if he was about to say 46 or 47, and then said, 'I'm sorry; what was it again?'; when I told him he gave the answer as '44' and, showing signs of crossness with himself, corrected this to 34.

In general there can be no doubt that many dyslexic subjects show a basic uncertainty over number which is often strikingly at variance with their ability in other directions, not least their ability to grasp some quite abstruse mathematical ideas.

(ii) The difficulty, however, is not simply that of remembering symbols as such (including the number-symbols in particular) but of remembering the direction in which to move when numbers have to be arranged in order. Uncertainty over left and right is no doubt a contributory factor here; but when an instruction such as 'x take away y' is given orally (with values for x and y supplied) and the subject wonders if the instruction was 'y take away x' it appears that there is a confusion of temporal order in addition. It is, of course, a tiresome complication that in some arithmetical operations it is necessary to go from right to left and in others from left to right; and indeed there are some tasks, including parts of long multiplication and, in certain contexts, the presentation of graphical data where there is initially a choice of direction even though it is necessary to be consistent thereafter.

If he has to express, say, the number 'fifty nine' in figures the non-dyslexic child very quickly learns to put the 5 on the left and the 9 on the right. He also learns that in the case of the 'teens' the order is the other way round[2]. The dyslexic child, on the other hand, because of his uncertainty over directions, may fail to 'cotton on'to this characteristic of the number-system unless he is specially taught, and even then he may become confused or make mistakes. For example S 227 was reported to have written 24 for 42, while S 232 was said by his mother 'sometimes to tackle sums from the left-hand column'. According to his father S 135 used to put '3 × 9 = 72', while S 167, when travelling with his parents, had said 'That petrol's reasonable – forty seven' when in fact the figure on the petrol pump (long years ago, it now seems!) was 74.

S 70, during his assessment, needed to write the number 18; to achieve this he wrote an 8 and then added a 1 on the left, saying, 'I don't know which I do first', while S 57 said, 'I used to get them all wrong – all double numbers; I sometimes put them the wrong way round'. S 4 said the number 'ninety two' and wrote 29. Sometimes there appears to be a muddle over the actual words 'backwards' and 'forwards' (possibly because there is no 'permanent tag' for backwards and forwards in the number series, since to reach any number one has to go backwards from a higher number and forwards from a lower one). Thus S 5, when given 24 – 2, said 'Easy – I went backwards and found out that number – 24, 25, 26, 27'. He then hesitated, as though he had made an error, and said 'Did I go back three?'. It seems that by implication he meant that the correct answer should have been 26, which in his terminology would have been 'back' two. When I asked the leading question, 'Did you go forwards?' he said 'Backwards'.

It is also possible for dyslexic subjects to 'get things the wrong way round' in time as well as in space. For example S 140, in response to 9 – 2, said, '9 take away 2. . . 2 take away 9. . . I thought you meant take away 9 from 2'; and in reply to 52 – 9 he said, 'Is it 9 take away 52?. . . 47, I think. . . 43'. In reply to the same item, S 90 said, '47, no, 57' (taking 2 from 9 instead of 9 from 2); S 56 asked, 'Is it 8 from 43 or 43 from 8?', while in reply to 9 – 2 S 45 said '2 take away 9? 7'. S 143, in reply to 19 – 7, paused for a long time and finally said, '16. . . 9 from 7 and I added 10 on'. I do not follow her logic here but in any case she should have said '7 from 9'. In reply to 52 – 9 she said, '55, no, 45. Take 2 from 9 and add 4 on'. Here, I suspect, she had in fact correctly taken 9 from 2, despite the incorrect verbalisation, and if, like some of the other subjects (see below), she had incorrectly reached 41, the adding of the 4 would explain the 45 (though I am still not clear how she arrived at the 4 in the first place). In reply to 19 – 7 S 208 said, 'Can you say it again, please? I thought you said "7 take away 9"'.

For 52 – 9 a common response was '41'. This was given by S 107, S 112, S 127, S 133, S 138, S 144, S 150, S 160, S 162, S 174, S 177, and S 201, while S 185 and S 212 both said '41' and corrected it to '43'. The most likely explanation seems to be that they took away 10 from 52, correctly reaching 42, but *then moved in the wrong direction*, i.e. downwards to 41 rather than upwards to 43.

I should like at this point to cite two pieces of evidence reported by Griffiths[3], both of which illustrate directional errors. In one case a dyslexic boy, aged 13, of above average intelligence, had been shown how to multiply 176 × 6 by the Egyptian 'duplatio' method (which calls only for addition and for multiplication by 2). He correctly set out:

1	176
2	352
4	704

knowing that he had to add 352 and 704 for the correct answer, but in fact he added 253 and 407. Another boy was given the exercises:

Ex. 1	79	Ex. 2	304	Ex. 3	5927
	56		275		7246
	90		493		3193
	+ 85		+ 629		+ 6455

His comments were recorded on tape. For Exercise 1 they were: '80 and 90, 170, 220, 290, 299, 305, 305, 310'; he then, correctly, wrote 310 as the answer. These comments show that he was adding the numbers in the left-hand column first, working upwards and 'correctly' ending at 290; he then worked *down* the right-hand column, adding 9 and 6 to get 305, staying at 305 because of the 0, and correctly ending at 310. In the case of Exercise 2 he said, '1000, 1200, 1500, 1570, 1660, 1680, 1684' (which he repeated twice, presumably as an epanalepsis in order to keep his place), '1689, 1692, 1692, 1701'. The reader who follows his logic will see that he started in the left-hand column and went upwards, went down the middle column, and finally went down the right-hand column. It is interesting to note that despite these directional oddities the correct 'place values' for thousands, hundreds, and tens were fully understood. For Exercise 3 the method was too difficult for him to operate. The end product was:

5927
7246
3193
6455
177
21228

He started, as usual, with the left column, which came to 21, wrote down the 2 and added 1 to the next column; since 1 + 9 + 2 + 1 + 4 comes to 17 he wrote down 1 and added 7 to the third column; thus $7 + 2 + 4 + 9 + 5$ gave 27, so he wrote down 2 and carried 7 to the right-hand column which he then wrote as 28. Working from left to right can still give the correct answer if suitable safeguards are observed, as is shown in the case of Exercises 1 and 2; in Exercise 3, however, instead of observing these safeguards, he transferred the 'carrying number' from left to right instead of from right to left and this led him into error.

One must conclude, therefore, that uncertainties over order and over left and right are a regular source of difficulty for dyslexic subjects when they attempt calculation.

(iii) Finally, there were all kinds of compensatory strategies as a result of which the subjects sometimes reached the correct answer, albeit in a laborious – and often highly idiosyncratic – way.

Before describing the evidence in detail I should like to make some tentative suggestions as to why these strategies were necessary and what they were designed to achieve. For this purpose it will be helpful to distinguish between arithmetical tasks where the answer can be given instantly and arithmetical tasks which call for counting or deduction. If, for example, the task is $19 - 7$, one can be confident that the great majority of readers of this book will say that they 'just know' that the answer is 12.

Now it seems likely that the range of items which the dyslexic subject 'just knows' is severely limited. The great majority of my subjects were able to give the answer to $24 - 2$ instantly, but $19 - 7$ presented them with much more difficulty. It is possible, of course, even in the case of $24 - 2$, that some of them did a rapid count, but this was certainly not apparent. In contrast, even those who arrived at the answer 12 for $19 - 7$ often used aids, for example their fingers or marks on paper. The suggestion was made in Chapter 10 that in some contexts, for a dyslexic subject, doing can be a substitute for naming; and I think it likely that the tapping of their fingers or the writing of marks on paper are further examples of such 'doing'. Once the rule has been grasped that one finger-tap or one mark on paper represents each number in the number series, the subject can proceed indefinitely, and there is no need for him to rely on 'just knowing' the answer to any calculation. I suspect – though this is by no means established – that there is some kind of threshold value, perhaps around 4[4], and that when the number to be added or subtracted is less than this – as in $24 - 2$ – an 'instant' response is sometimes possible. When larger numbers are involved, however, the units have either to be counted out one by one or else to be grouped as sums of smaller numbers. For example, if the question is $44 - 7$, the 7 can conveniently be split into 4 and 3; $44 - 4$ is immediately seen to be 40, and $40 - 3$ (which may well not be known instantly) can be worked out, with only minimal risk of error, by means of finger-taps. As in in the case of reciting tables (see Chapter 16), the multiples of 10 are in an important sense 'anchor points'.

The main strategies were in fact the use of fingers, the use of marks on paper, and the breaking down of larger numbers, in particular 7, 8, and 9, into smaller units so that two short calculations were possible in place of one longer one. The first of these two calculations would normally be chosen so as to bring the subject to the most suitable 'anchor point'.

Among the subjects who noticeably used their fingers as an aid to calculation were S 8, S 9, S 23, S 24, S 38, S 43, S 47, S 59, S 65, S 68, S 79, S 83, S 96, S 99, S 100, S 111, S 113, S 117, S 124, S 135, S 145, S 157, S 158, S 165, S 175, S 181, S 197, S 205 and S 212, and this list is almost certainly not exhaustive. S 12 told me that he used his toes! I have no exact data on the extent to which non-dyslexic subjects use their fingers in similar tasks, but I am doubtful if any appreciable number do so beyond the age of 9 or 10, whereas some of my subjects were doing so at age 14 and later.

The following are examples of the use of marks on paper as an aid to calculation. S 3, when asked to solve $19 - 7$, drew a line consisting of 19 dots arranged vertically; he then drew a line under the seventh dot and counted up the remainder. S 232 used strokes for the first three items ($9 - 2$, $6 - 3$, and $19 - 7$) but not for $24 - 2$. S 230, when given $19 - 7$, wrote as follows:

```
                    1  2  3  4  5  6  7  8  9 10 11 12
        1  2  3  4  5  6  7  8  9 10 11 12 13 14 15 16 17 18 19
```

This enabled him to give the correct answer. S 40 used dots on paper even for $6 - 3$.

Similar 'concrete aids' were used by some of my subjects when they attempted items from the Terman Merrill intelligence test. For example, in the third 'cans of water' item[5] S 95 made 9 marks, each about 1 cm long, vertically downwards on the paper, and placed 5 further marks alongside the bottom 5, while S 94 drew two rectangles, one with 9 bars across, one with 5 bars across. Figure 2 shows the 3 diagrams used by S 175 for all three items.

A number of my subjects also needed concrete aids in order to solve the 'boxes' item[6]. For the fourth item S 158 put a rectangular figure down 21 times, while S 162, for the third and fourth items, wrote

```
        1               1
        3               4
        3               4
        3               4
        3               4
```

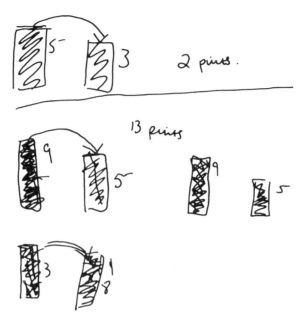

Fig.2 'Concrete aids' for numerical calculation.

S 109 and S 178 spontaneously drew the boxes while S 137 produced the drawing shown in Fig.3.

Fig.3 Similar 'concrete aids' for the Terman Merrill 'boxes' item.

Many of the subjects were able to be quite articulate about their compensatory strategies, and in most cases it was possible by means of suitable questioning to understand the logic of what they did. S 7, when given $19 - 7$, explained 'I started to think nineteen, eighteen, seventeen, sixteen counting in my head how many numbers I took away'. In response to the same item S 46 echoed the question subvocally, murmured 'no . . . nineteen . . . twenty two . . . no, not twenty two . . . twelve . . . What do you call it?' (He appeared to be searching for the word 'add'). He then explained: 'Add three on to make it ten, then take away by ten, then' (pause, as if stuck), 'add three to the other one – it makes what do you call it, twelve'. (In other words, he turns the 7 into a 10 by adding 3, so has to turn 'the other one', 19, into 22 by adding three and then subtracts 10 from 22). S 61 said, 'I put down nineteen, take-away sign, and seven; I took seven off nine, counted seven, eight, nine from seven to nine missing out the seven, it made two, and one for nineteen made it twelve'. (In other words he gets the difference between 7 and 9 on a 'one-by-one' basis and then correctly retains the 1 in the tens column). S 64 said, 'Nineteen – there's ten in. From ten I took seven and added the other nine'. S 179 said, 'I put seventeen, and there was two more to nine, so it had to be ten and two'. S 249 said, 'It's rather complicated. I added the seven to itself, which is fourteen, and added the remainder to the seven'. S 164 said that his method was to 'count up from seven to nineteen and note how many counts', though because of a slip in counting he gave the answer as 'eleven' instead of 'twelve'.

It was clear that some of the more sophisticated subjects tried to look for logical procedures which would make calculation easier. This point was made explicit by S 193, who, when asked $9 - 2$, said, 'Five, yes. . . no, seven. I was looking for a pattern; I have one or two patterns for taking away'.

In reply to $52 - 9$ S 84 said, 'What was the question again?'. After calculation he gave the correct answer, and explained that he was 'self-taught': 'Take the two away, this leaves you seven, and see how many are left from seven, so it's forty three'. (This seems a good example of the ability to use multiples of 10 as 'anchor-points'). S 100 and S 111 both did the same sum by working backwards on their fingers, until nine fingers were used up. S 100 also said that he could do $6 - 3$ because he 'remembered three is half of six'. When I gave him $9 - 2$ for the second time he muttered to himself, counting forwards from 1 to 7, finally saying 'seven'; and when I asked him if he was sure he said 'About fifty-fifty'.

In reply to $44 - 7$ S 169 said 'Thirty. . . five; no, thirty eight, thirty six, thirty seven; four, no, four minus seven minus three, so minus three from forty gives thirty seven'. The reasoning here is not fully clear, but once again it appears to be an attempt to divide 7 into 4 and 3 and make use of 40 as a multiple of 10.

In a number of cases I have seen complex reasoning co-existing with elementary difficulties over calculation. Thus it was plain, in the Terman Merrill cans-of-water item, that S 109 was fully clear as to the kind of solution that was needed, but only after careful working out was he able to discover that $9 + 4 = 13$! Similarly S 201, when given the Terman 'tree' item[7], produced some fully coherent arguments, marred only by the fact that he believed the difference between 18 and 27 to be 11! (For the paper-work which led to the correct solution of this item by S 174 see Fig.1).

When one looks at the attempts of dyslexic subjects to do subtraction and addition, the overall picture is often that of a highly sophisticated person, well capable of quite complex logical reasoning, who is nevertheless severely restricted in his ability to give instant answers, and who therefore has to resort to strategies – often of his own devising – which are time-consuming and may sometimes involve considerable risk of error.

CHAPTER SIXTEEN

Reciting Tables

When I started to use recitation of tables as a test for dyslexia it was immediately obvious that almost all my subjects were having difficulties, often very severe ones. The following were some of the characteristics which were particularly noticeable: (i) loss of place, as exemplified by questions such as 'Was it six sevens I was up to?'; (ii) consistent errors in which a correct deduction is made from a faulty premise, for example, 'Two eights are fifteen; three eights are twenty three'; (iii) a variety of slips such as changing to the 8 × table during the course of reciting the 7 × or saying 'eight eighties' for 'eight eights'; (iv) the adoption of compensatory strategies, for example the use of fingers, the use of epanalepsis (i.e. taking up what one said earlier as a means of getting back 'on course', see Chapter 3), and the saying of the table without the 'preamble' ('one six is. . . , two sixes are. . . ', etc.).

These mistakes are by no means uncommon in children who are not dyslexic (see Chapter 7), but a distinction should certainly be drawn between those who have not spent much time learning or practising their tables (whether because they are still young, because they were absent from school, or because in their school tables were not taught) and those who still fail despite long and hard efforts.

These tendencies are so widespread that detailed documentation would be monotonous. I shall therefore limit myself to citing a small number of examples from each age level.

Age 7

It appears that at this age the number sense in a dyslexic child can sometimes be extremely confused. When asked to say the 3 × table S 5 said: 'Two threes are four; four threes are five; five threes are six; six threes are seven; seven threes are eight; eight threes are nine; nine threes are ten'. S 6 said: 'I know all the answers but I hate saying it'. He said his 3 × correctly up to 'four threes are twelve', and continued, 'Six threes. . . no, five threes are fifteen. . . no, fifteen; six threes are eighteen; nine threes are twenty; three threes are twenty three – which one am I on now?' When asked to say his five times he said, 'I can give the numbers, five, ten, fifteen, all right'.

Age 8

The picture is not all that different at age 8. When asked to say his 3 ×, S 26 responded 'One two is two; two twos are six; three twos are nine; four twos are eleven; five twos are fourteen; six twos are seventeen; seven twos are. . . no'. S 12, when asked to say his 4 ×, was correct up to 'three fours are twelve'; he then said 'Four fours are fifteen and – um – five fours are nineteen and five – six – fours are twenty three and – um – seven fours are. . . what did I get up to? Thirty three, did I?'

S 20 said, 'Do I have to say "one three is" as I can't do it like that?' When I said that he need not, he started 'Three, six, nine' etc. and continued correctly up to fifty-one when I stopped him. When required to include the 'preamble' he said, 'One three is three; two threes are six; four threes are. . . no, I've missed one out; four threes are twelve; five threes are fifteen; six threes are seventeen – eighteen; eight threes are twenty one, nine threes are twenty four; seven – um – ten threes are thirty'.

When asked if she could do her tables S 8 said, 'I can do some, but I forget half way through'. Asked to say his 2 ×, S 11 said, 'One two is two; two twos are four; three twos are six; seven twos are nine; eight twos are ten; nine twos are thirteen; ten twos are fourteen; eleven twos are fifteen; twelve twos are twenty four'.

Age 9

At this age I sometimes tried the more difficult 6 × and 7 × tables, but some of my subjects were still unsure over the 3 × and 4 ×.

S 43 said his 3 × correctly up to 'five threes are fifteen; he then said 'Six threes are twenty one; seven threes are twenty four; eight threes are twenty seven; ten threes are thirty; eleven threes are thirty three. Twelve threes are thirty six.' On the 4 × he was correct up to 'three fours are twelve', after which he said, 'Five fours are sixteen; seven fours are twenty one – I'm stuck!'.

The performance of S 38 was extremely curious. She said, 'I did tables once – I keep getting them backwards'. She wrote '02' and asked if that was the way to write 'twenty'. When I started her off with 'One two is two' she said, 'Two twos are four' (pause); 'eight and eight is' (long pause) 'seventeen; three and three are six; six and six is twelve; ten and ten is twenty.' When I indicated that she could write down her 3 × table and said 'One three is three' she wrote

20	20	20
30	30	30
40	40	40
50	50	50
60	60	60
70	70	70

S 46 said his 7 × correctly up to 'four sevens are twenty eight'; he then said, 'five sevens are thirty two; six sevens are thirty eight, thirty nine. What am I up to? Was it six sevens? Seven sevens are forty two – that's wrong. Forty two, yes, I think it is. . . forty nine, fifty six, sixty three. What do you call it? I must have got some of them wrong. Seven sevens are forty two; six sevens must be wrong'. (My notes say, 'Fascinating sub-vocal speech – too fast to take down').

Age 10

Even some of the 10-year-olds had difficulty with the 3 × and 4 ×. S 61 said 'One three is three; two threes are six; three threes are. . . three threes are twelve, no, three threes are nine; four threes are twelve; five threes are fifteen; four threes – have I just done four threes?. . . Five threes are eighteen; six threes are twenty one. . . which one am I on?'

S 58 produced the following strange series (though it is one that is not wholly lacking in logic): 'Two threes are six; six threes are twelve; twelve threes are twenty two; three twenty twos are thirty six'. When I tried him on the 4 × he said, 'Four twos are four; four fours are eight; eight twos are sixteen; sixteen twos are twenty six; twenty six twos is forty six; forty six twos is seventy six – sixty. I mean sixty six'.

S 83 said his 2 × correctly, but without the preamble, as far as thirty six. He then murmured 'thirty seven' *sotto voce* before saying 'thirty eight' and, later, after saying 'forty two' he murmured 'forty three' sotto voce before saying 'forty four'. I stopped him at 50, and, not surprisingly he did not know how many twos it was. When he was asked to include the preamble he said, 'One two is two – there's two twos in every two; two twos are four; three twos are six; four twos are ten; five twos are two – four, six,. . . um. . . twenty – oh, twenty two, twenty four, twenty six. . . oh, twenty six, thirty'. (I did not follow his logic over the last part).

Similar uncertainty was shown by many of those who attempted their 6 × and 7 ×. For example, S 75 recited his 6 × correctly up to 'three sixes are eighteen'; he then paused and said 'three' as an epanalepsis, and continued 'Four sixes are twenty four; five sixes are thirty; eight – six eights are thirty six; seven sixes are forty two; eight sixes are forty two; eight sixes are fifty eight' (pause); 'nine sevens are. . . um. . . fifty one. . . um. . . eleven, ten sixes are sixty; eleven sixes are sixty six; twelve sixes are seventy two'.

On a few occasions there was the substitution of a similar sounding number for the correct one. Thus S 74 said her 6 × table correctly up to 'nine sixes are fifty four' and then said, 'ten sixties are sixty; eleven sixties are sixty six; twelve sixties are seventy two'[1].

Age 11

Even some of the 11-year-olds were have difficulty with the 2, 3, and 4 ×. Thus S 105, when asked to say his 2 ×, responded 'Once two is two; two twos are four; two, no three twos are six; four twos are' (pause) 'eight; five twos are ten; six twos are twelve; seven twos are fourteen; eight twos are sixteen; seven twos. . . eight twos are twenty' (long pause); 'ten twos are twenty two'. S 107 said his 4 × correctly up to 'seven fours are twenty eight' and continued: 'Nine fours are thirty two, twelve. . . eleven. . . have I had nine fours? Nine fours are thirty two; ten fours are thirty six; eleven fours are forty; twelve fours are forty four'.

S 91, when asked to say his 3 ×, said: 'One three is three; once threes are four – no, one threes are six; three threes are nine – no, I get all muddled up'. S 92 said his 3 × correctly as far as 'four threes are twelve' but continued. 'Five threes are sixteen; seven threes are eighteen; nine threes are twenty one; eleven threes' (pause). . . 'ten threes are thirty four; ten threes are thirty seven; eleven threes are forty; twelve threes are forty three'.

S 98 could say her 4 × correctly as far as 48 provided she did not include the preamble. When she was asked to include this she was correct as far as 'seven fours are twenty eight' and then said 'Where am I up too?' When encouraged to 'have a go', she said, 'Four sixes are twenty eight; seven sixes are. . . seven fours are thirty two; eight fours are thirty six; nine fours are forty; ten fours are forty four; eleven fours are forty four; twelve fours are forty eight'.

S 111 was able to get as far as 'five fours are twenty' using her fingers. She then said, 'Five fours are twenty four; six fours are thirty; eight fours – seven fours. . . thirty four; seven, oh!, have we done seven fours? – thirty eight; eight, er, nine fours are. . . ' (counts on fingers) 'forty; ten fours are forty four'.

There were many typically 'dyslexic' responses over the 6, 7 and 8 ×. When asked to say his 6 × table, S 95 said, 'One six is six; two sixes are twelve; three sixes. . . oh, gosh!' (pause); 'I know. . . no, I don't, eighteen'. He then proceeded correctly as far as 'eight sixes are forty eight'. He then said, 'What's next? Nine sixes are fifty. . . oh, gosh, fifty four. What's next? That's nine sixes; ten sixes are sixty; eleven sixes are sixty six; twelve sixes are seventy two – must be seventy two as I know two sixes are twelve'. His 7 × was correct up to five sevens are thirty five;. . . 'I usually say five sevens are thirty six. What's next? That's *five* sixes; six sevens are forty-two; eight sevens – now, let's see; ah! it's fifty six; five, six, seven, eight, so seven eights are fifty six. Where am I? I've forgotten where I am. I was on seven – five, six, seven, eight; seven nines are sixty three; seven sev . . ., no, seven tens are seventy; seven elevens are seventy seven and seventy twelves – seven twelves – no wonder I'm getting all confused – are fourteen, so eighty four using the same system'.

S 74 had clearly learned to use the 'ten times' as an aid. He said his 7 × correctly as far as 'seven sevens are forty nine'. He then said, 'Eight sevens are fifty five – I've gone wrong somewhere. I was adding the seven and I knew the next number wouldn't go on. If it had got to sixty five I knew it couldn't go on like that . . . If it's seventeen times nine I put ten nines are ninety and I say, Nine sevens, that's sixty three; then I add them together'.

S 90, so his mother told me, had pinned his tables up in his bedroom and eventually learned them, 'but they were very hard work'. When asked to say his 7 × he was correct as far as 'seven sixes are forty two'; he then said, 'Eight sixes are fifty four . . . oh, dear! – gone wrong . . . ten sixes are sixty; eleven sixes are sixty six; twelve sixes are eighty four'. It seems that even hard work in learning tables does not guarantee success, at any rate in a context where one has to recite them aloud.

Age 12

At least three of my twelve-year-olds (S 120, S 124, and S 131), out of a total of sixteen, were still having difficulty in reciting the 4 ×, while of those who were given the 6, 7, and 8 × only one failed to satisfy the criteria for a 'zero' or a 'plus'.

S 120 said his 4 × correctly up to 'seven fours are twenty eight', after which he said, 'Nine fours are thirty two, no, seven fours are thirty two; eight fours are thirty six; nine fours are forty – no, nine fours . . . *ten* fours are forty; eleven fours are forty four; twelve fours are forty eight'. S 124 was correct up to 'three fours are twelve' after which he said, 'Four fours are fifteen, no, twenty; five fours are twenty four; six fours are twenty seven; six fours are twenty eight; nine fours – no, seven fours are thirty two; eight fours are thirty six; nine fours are – I don't know; I'm lost'. S 131 was correct up to 'four fours are sixteen, after which she said, 'Five fours are eighteen . . . Can I just say the numbers as it gets me muddled up?'

Here are two typical performances with the 7 and 8 ×. S 125 said his 7 × correctly up to 'five sevens are thirty five' and then said, 'Six sevens are forty five, no forty three – forty two; seven sevens are forty nine; five sevens are fifty six; six sevens are forty – no, fifty three' (the intonation of the 'forty' suggesting that a number in the forties would have followed and that he did not simply mean the number forty) 'and then – what is it now? I've got them muddled. Nine sevens are . . . um . . . sixty; ten sevens are sixty seven'. S 133, when attempting his 8 × said, 'One eight is eight; two eights are sixteen; three eights are twenty eight; four eights are thirty six; five eights are forty; six eights are forty eight; what am I on? Seven eights are sixty four; eight eights are . . .' (pause) '*eight* eights are sixty four', after which he finished without further error. S 127 said his 6 × correctly up to 'nine sixes are fifty four', but then said 'Ten sixties are sixty; eleven sixties are sixty six; twelve sixties are –, no, twelve sixes are seventy two'.

Age 13

Even at this age there were still subjects who had difficulty with the 3 × and 4 ×. Thus S 147 said his 3 × correctly up to 'three threes are nine', after which he said, 'Four threes are eighteen; five threes are twenty one; six threes are twenty four; seven threes are twenty seven; eight threes are thirty; nine threes are thirty three; ten threes are thirty six; eleven threes are fifty nine; twelve threes are forty two'. From 'eight threes' onwards he was overtly using his fingers. S 143 said her 3 × correctly up to 'eight threes are twenty four', and then said, 'Five – no, where are we? Nine threes are twenty seven; ten threes are thirty; six tw . . .' (as if she had been about to say 'twelve' but had stopped herself); 'eleven threes are thirty three; twelve threes are thirty six'. S 142 said his 4 × correctly up to 'three fours are twelve', after which he said, 'Four fours are four . . . fifteen; five fours are nineteen; six fours – I can't remember – twenty seven, thirty one; eight fours are thirty one; nine fours are thirty five; ten fours – I've gone wrong'.

Even omission of the preamble does not guarantee correctness. For example, when I asked S 141 if he had had any difficulty over tables he said, 'I had to go through a lot of this. I could say "Two, four, six, eight" but not "once two is two", like that'. I asked if he would like to say his 6 × 'the easy way', to which he responded, 'Six, twelve, eighteen, twenty four, thirty, thirty eight, forty two, fifty, fifty six . . . no, that's not right; can I start again?' On the next attempt he went through correctly to 72, though with a slight pause at 42. I then asked if he would like to try it 'the hard way'. He was correct as far as 'five sixes are thirty' but added 'I'm on six, am I?'. He continued, 'Six sixes are thirty six; seven sixes are forty two; eight sixes are forty eight; nine sixes are fifty four – sixty; seven sixes are sixty six; eight, no – where am I on? Eleven sixes are sixty six; twelve sixes are seventy two'. It is possible that the substitution of 'seven' for 'eleven' is another example of an error arising from auditory confusability comparable with those already mentioned[2].

Age 14

Among my 14-year-olds there was still one subject (S 162) who failed at the 2 ×. The following is a record of my discussion with him. I started by asking him to say his 4 ×, to which he replied, 'One four is four; two fours are eight; three fours are sixteen or something – I never can remember them'. I then asked him to try his 2 ×, to which he responded: 'Two twos are four; three twos – I'm all mixed up – two twos are four; three twos are six; four twos are nine; five twos are eleven; six twos are thirteen; seven twos are fifteen; eight twos are eighteen, I think; nine twos are twenty; ten twos are twenty two; twelve twos are twenty three'.

S 158 also had difficulty with his 4 ×. His responses were: 'One four is four; two fours are eight; three fours are sixteen; five fours are eighteen; five fours are twenty two; six fours are forty – um – forty six; seven fours are fifty two – how could they be? Oh, help! I'm all lost now'. When I gave S 152 what I thought would be an easy task, viz. that of saying the 4 × without the preamble, his response was: 'Four; eight; twelve; twenty four; thirty six; forty two'.

When I asked S 156 if she had had any trouble with her tables she said that they were 'a nightmare'. Her 6 × was correct up to 'five sixes are thirty', after which she said, 'Seven sixes are thirty six; eight sixes are forty two; nine sixes are forty eight; ten sixes are sixty; eleven sixes are sixty six; twelve sixes are seventy two.'

When I said to S 164, 'Did you have any trouble with tables?' he replied, 'I still have'. On the 6 × his responses were: 'One six is six; two sixes are twelve; two twelves are twenty four; three twelves are forty eight'. When I asked him to try the 4 × he said, 'One four is four; two fours are eight; three fours are sixteen; three fours' (sigh) 'no – twenty two; four fours are forty . . .' (pause, with intonation implying a number in the forties to follow) . . . 'I'm lost again'.

Age 15

S 181 had difficulty with her 2 ×. With a slight pause after 'two twos are four' she was correct as far as 'seven twos are fourteen'. She then said, 'Oh, I've lost count. Eight twos' (using fingers) 'are fourteen; nine twos are sixteen; ten twos are eighteen; ten twos' (said not as a correction but as if she was saying the next number up) 'are . . .' (pause for use of fingers) 'twenty'.

S 166 said 'I can do it on paper but I can't do it aloud.' He said the 2 × correctly up to 'five twos are ten'; he then said 'Eleven twos are twelve; twelve twos are fourteen.' I then suggested that he sould write out his 7 ×, and he wrote:

$$
\begin{array}{ccccc}
1 & \times & 7 & = & 7 \\
2 & \times & 7 & = & 14 \\
3 & \times & 7 & = & 21 \\
\cancel{3}4 & \times & 7 & = & 28 \\
8 & \times & 7 & = & 56 \\
9 & \times & 7 & = & 61 \\
10 & \times & 7 & = & 68 \\
11 & \times & 7 & = & 75 \\
12 & \times & 7 & = & 92 \\
\end{array}
$$

Writing down, however, was usually an aid. S 177 had got into serious difficulty over his 6 ×. When I gave him 'one six is six' he continued, 'Two sixes are twelve; three sixes are thirty eight. I can't do the rest; what was the last one I said?'. However, when I allowed him to write down the answers, he wrote '44, 50, 56, 62' etc. all 'correctly' at intervals of 6 as far as 98.

S 179 said his 4 × correctly up to 'three fours are twelve' and then said, 'Four fours are fifteen; five fours are nineteen; six fours are twenty three; seven fours are twenty six; eight fours are thirty; eight fours are thirty four; nine fours are thirty eight; ten fours are thirty; eleven fours are thirty three; twelve fours are thirty . . .' (pause, indicating that a number in the thirties was to come) ' . . .six – thirty seven'.

I did not normally ask my subjects to say the 9 ×. This was because, more than the 6, 7, and 8 ×, it allows for learning overlay. In the early stages of the research I had met subjects who had been told either to 'drop one each time' (the second figure being successively, 9, 8, 7, 6, etc.) or to check that the two figures in conjunction added up to nine – 1-8, 2-7, 3-6, etc.; and if either strategy has been taught there was the possibility that the dyslexic handicap would be masked. When S 170 was asked to say her 9 ×, however, she made the typically dyslexic responses of using her fingers and 'skipping' to the wrong table: 'One nine is nine; two nines are eighteen; three nines are' (pause) 'twenty seven; four sevens are . . . four nines are thirty six; five nines are' (uses fingers) 'forty five; six nines are fifty four; seven nines are' (pause, uses fingers) 'sixty four; eight sevens are seventy three; nine sevens are eighty two; ten sevens are seven—are ninety; eleven nines are ninety nine; twelve nines are a hundred and eight'.

Age 16

This is the first age-level at which none of my subjects had difficulty with the 3 × or 4 ×. The overall picture, however, though sometimes more sophisticated, is not basically different.

Here are three typical efforts. S 191 was correct over his 6 × up to 'six sixes are thirty six'. He then said, 'Seven sixties are forty two; eight sixties are forty eight; nine sixes are fifty two; ten sixes are sixty; eleven sixes are sixty six; twelve sixes are fifty eight – I get lost, I get muddled'. S 200 was given 'one seven is seven' to start him off; he then said, 'Two sevens are fourteen; twenty one; twenty eight; thirty five'. This omission of the preamble was his own choosing. When I asked him to put in 'how many sevens' it was, he was correct up to 'three sevens are twenty one' and then said, 'Seven fours are twenty eight – no, yes, twenty eight; five sevens, no, seven sevens are thirty five; eight sevens are forty two; nine sevens are forty nine; ten sevens, um, what am I doing? It can't be. What were . . .? I'm a bit confused. I was on ten sevens and got to forty nine'.

S 193 gave an interesting account of his difficulties. 'I never learned my tables but I have a number of numbers which I can do easily; for example, three sevens multiplied by two is forty two . . . they made me learn them but I never did'. When he attempted his 6 × he was correct as far as 'four sixes are twenty four', after which he said, 'Six sixes are thirty six; seven sixes are thirty two; eight sixes are thirty eight; nine sixes is for-' (as if it was to be a number in the forties) ' . . . what was the last one? Fifty four; six sixes – no, ten sixes are sixty; eleven sixes are sixty six; twelve sixes are seventy two'.

Age 17

It is still the same story at this age. In attempting her 6 × S 205 was correct as far as 'eight sixes are forty eight'. She then said, 'Nine sixes are . . .' (laughs) 'I've got to add it up. What am I on . . .? Fifty four; ten sixes are sixty; eleven sixes are – eleven – eight sixes are seventy two'. ('Are you sure?') 'Oh, sorry! Twelve sixes are seventy two'.

S 209 said her 6 × correctly up to 'six sixes are thirty six' and then said, 'Seven are forty two; eight are forty eight; nine are' (pause) 'fifty four; ten are sixty; sixty six, eleven; seventy two are twelve'. This appears to be an attempt to make the task easier by reducing the time-interval over which the multiplier has to be held in mind.

S 204 muttered inaudibly to himself some of the time. When I started him off with 'one seven is seven' he said, 'Two sevens are fourteen – no, – twenty, no, fourteen; three sevens are twenty one; four sevens are twenty eight' (pause); 'thirty six; I think; five sevens are thirty five – that's wrong – oh – yes!, forty nine – good at tables' (said sarcastically); 'forty nine; fifty four, I think – fifty six, I think. What are we up to so far? Next one's forty two, forty nine'.

Age 18

Even among my oldest subjects there is no change in the basic pattern, only an increasing degree of sophistication and in some cases use of compensatory strategies.

S 213 said to me, 'I don't know my tables even now'. She was correct on her 7 × as far as 'four sevens are twenty eight'. She then said, 'Five sevens are thirty – heavens!, thirty five; six sevens are forty two; seven sevens are forty nine; eight sevens are' (pause) . . . 'seven sevens are forty nine; eight sevens are fifty six; nine sevens are' (pause) 'sixty three; ten sevens are seventy; eleven sevens are seventy seven; twelve sevens are eighty' (pause to work out number in the eighties) 'four – no, eighty five'.

S 219 said his 7 × correctly as far as 'four sevens are twenty eight'. He then said, 'Five sevens are thirty six – thirty seven; six sevens are thirty eight; seven sevens are forty five' (uses fingers); 'no, five sevens are forty five; six sevens are fifty two – I've got to make sure it's right – I've got to check up'. He then recited from 'five sevens are thirty five' to 'twelve sevens are eighty four' correctly.

S 220 said his 7 × correctly up to 'four sevens are twenty eight'. He then said, 'Five sevens are' (pause) 'thirty five; six sevens are' (pause) 'seventy two – I've just got to add. Six sevens are forty two; seven sevens are forty nine; eight sevens are fifty six. What are nine . . .? Nine sevens are – seven off ninety which is eighty three; ten sevens are seventy; eleven sevens are seventy seven; twelve sevens are eighty five; thirteen sevens are ninety two; I'd be worse if I didn't play darts'.

89% of my subjects (199 out of 223) scored 'plus' on the 'tables' item of the dyslexia test, or 119 out of 132 (90%) if we take only the dyslexic subjects who were matched against controls. In contrast there were 71 'pluses' in the control group (54%)[3]. Clearly, therefore, difficulties over tables are not found solely in dyslexic subjects, and it seems likely that they occur in anyone who has not had the requisite amount of practice or experience. What is interesting about the dyslexic subject is that in spite of all the opportunities available to him the difficulties persist.

CHAPTER SEVENTEEN

Recall of Digits

I had noticed at an early stage of the research that many of my subjects appeared to be weak at the recall of auditorily presented digits, whether in the 'forwards' or 'reversed' condition. From the norms given in the Terman Merrill test it was plain that a 9-year-old of average ability could be expected to succeed in at least one trial out of three at 'four digits forwards' and a 12-year-old in at least one trial out of three at 'five digits reversed'. Yet even some of my older subjects were making errors over 'three digits reversed' and those who obtained passes at the 'Superior Adult' grades of the Terman Merrill test were consistently failing at 'five digits reversed' even though this is set far lower down the scale. I also found that subjects who scored well above the average on some of the other sub-tests of the WISC were consistently below average on the 'digit span' sub-test. A check on the literature in this area[1] fully confirmed that among poor readers of all kinds a distinctive weakness in the area of 'digit span' was extremely common.

It was during the early 1970s that I first decided to make a study of the responses of dyslexic subjects to visually presented digits. The conditions in such an investigation are different from those of auditory presentation not only because a different sense modality, vision, is involved but also because, if one so wishes, the digits can all be presented simultaneously. We are so made – and this is no doubt a point of considerable theoretical interest –that if digits, or other symbols, are presented to us auditorily they have to occur in succession, whereas if they are presented visually they can be either simultaneous or successive.

It was not a standard part of the assessment to present digits visually, but examination of my records showed that I had usable data in respect of 40 out of my 223 subjects, along with 2 other subjects (S 237 and S 245) from my 'incomplete records' group[2]. As I had data on the performance of all my subjects when digits were presented auditorily, it was possible not only to examine the performance of each of these 42 subjects in the visual condition but to compare it with his or her performance in the auditory condition.

To avoid the dangers of premature grouping I have presented the data for each subject separately in order of age (see Table 17.1). My procedure was to show the subject the tachistoscope (a device for exposing stimulus-material for controlled periods of time[3]), explain what was required (viz. that when the presentation was over he should report the numbers which he had seen on the screen), and then expose about 30 cards at varying exposure-times. These times were decreased or increased according to the subject's success or otherwise in reproducing the correct digits, larger numbers of readings being taken near his 'limits' for correctness. A somewhat complicated method of scoring enabled me to take account not only of whether he had responded with the correct digits but whether he had given them in the correct order[4].

Table 17.1 shows the performance of each subject when six digits were exposed. The first column gives the mean (average) exposure-time for 3 presentations of six digits near the range at which he had just started to make incorrect responses. The second column gives the subject's mean score out of a maximum of 6 for the 3 presentations. In addition, to make possible a comparison between different subjects despite variations in exposure-time, I calculated a figure, presented in the third column, which I termed the 'comparison ratio'; this is the subject's hypothetical score at an exposure-time of 1000 ms (1 second) by extrapolation from the actual score at the specified exposure-time. Thus a score of 4.2 at an exposure-time of 2000 ms would give a comparison ratio of 2.1[5]. Finally, so as to make comparisons between each subject's performance in the visual condition and in the auditory condition, I have extracted from the Summary Chart the highest series-length for which the subject gave a correct response on 'digits forwards' and used this, along with the comparison ratio, as a basis for assigning each subject to a 'visual grade' and to an 'auditory grade'. The grade labels are 'high' (h), 'medium' (m), 'low' (l), and 'very low' (vl)[6].

One of the most striking points about Table 17.1 is the excessively long time needed by some of the subjects to respond correctly in the visual condition. Some data for adequate spellers have been collected by Pollard[7], from which one can infer that the typical non-retarded 9- to 12-year-old will have a comparison ratio of about 6; and, although comparisons are not straightforward because of differences in the experimental conditions, the figures obtained by Ellis and Miles[8] make it highly improbable that the typical normal speller aged 10-14 would have a comparison ratio of less than this amount. Yet 4 subjects in the present study needed over 6000 ms (6 sec.) before they could get somewhere near a correct answer and 24 others needed 1500 ms (1½ sec.) or more. Only 4 subjects had a comparison ratio of 5 or above, and only 1 subject (S 49) produced a result which would have led to a prediction of 'non-dyslexic' had no other information about him been available[9]. Slowness at processing visually presented symbolic material was thus extremely widespread.

Table 17.1 *Comparison of Subjects' Recall of Digits in Conditions of Visual and Auditory Presentation*

Case no.	Mean exposure time (ms)	Mean score	Comparison ratio	Maximum no. of digits forwards	Visual grade	Auditory grade
3	2500	4.33	1.73	5	vl	l
7	1500	4.67	3.11	5	l	l
12	2000	3.67	1.83	5	vl	l
16	6000	4.67	0.79	4	m	vl
20	3000	5.00	1.67	4	m	vl
21	1833	4.67	2.56	6	l	m
33	7000	5.00	0.71	4	m	vl
34	2000	4.00	2.00	8	l	h
40	2500	5.00	2.00	3	l	vl
49	667	5.33	8.42	3	h	vl
50	2000	3.00	1.50	5	vl	l
53	3000	3.75	1.25	5	vl	l
56	2333	4.33	1.86	4	m	vl
60	8000	3.00	0.38	4	m	vl
62	1600	5.00	3.13	5	l	l
69	3667	5.33	1.45	6	vl	m
74	1467	5.00	3.41	5	l	l
79	1200	5.00	4.17	5	m	l
84	1000	5.33	5.33	6	h	m
86	2000	3.66	1.83	5	vl	l
87	1467	5.33	3.63	4	l	vl
88	4000	4.67	1.17	6	vl	m
90	1200	5.00	4.17	5	m	l
237	1000	5.00	5.00	6	h	m
102	2000	5.00	2.50	4	l	vl
104	4667	5.00	0.94	4	vl	vl
107	3000	4.33	1.44	5	vl	l
108	2000	5.33	2.67	6	l	m
112	1833	5.33	2.99	7	l	h
121	3000	4.33	1.44	5	vl	l
136	1500	5.00	3.33	5	l	l
146	1500	5.33	3.55	4	l	vl
245	1333	4.00	3.00	5	l	l
149	2000	4.66	2.33	6	l	m
159	1000	5.33	5.33	5	h	l
165	8000	4.33	0.54	5	vl	l
174	1067	4.00	3.75	8	l	h
193	1200	4.67	3.89	6	l	m
197	1233	5.00	4.06	5	m	l
202	1600	4.67	2.92	6	l	m
208	1000	4.67	4.67	4	m	vl
213	933	4.33	4.64	5	m	l

Now it has sometimes been suggested that a distinction should be drawn between the 'visual dyslexic' and the 'auditory dyslexic'. There are, however, various reasons for doubting the validity of this distinction[10], and it seemed to me that a possible way of throwing further light on the problem was to compare each subject's performance in the auditory condition with his performance in the visual condition. The idea of two types of dyslexia – one characterised by a predominantly visual weakness and one characterised by a predominantly auditory weakness – would receive strong support if most of the subjects could be classified without ambiguity as belonging to one type or the other: a high score in the visual condition and a low score in the auditory condition would suggest 'auditory dyslexia' while a low score in the visual condition and a high score in the auditory condition would suggest 'visual dyslexia'.

Table 17.2 shows no convincing evidence for such a grouping.

Table 17.2 *Numbers of Subjects in Each Grade (Auditory and Visual Conditions)*

		Auditory condition			
		High	Medium	Low	Very Low
Visual condition	High	0	1	1	1
	Medium	0	1	3	6
	Low	3	5	7	3
	Very Low	0	2	8	1

The high scorers in the visual condition were not necessarily the low scorers in the auditory condition, nor vice versa, and indeed 19 of the 42 subjects obtained 'low' or 'very low' scores in both conditions[11]. This finding does not prove that the distinction between 'visual dyslexia' and 'auditory dyslexia' is valueless but it provides no active support for it. I think it likely that most dyslexic persons are slow at processing symbolic verbal material irrespective of the sense modality through which the material is presented[12].

CHAPTER EIGHTEEN

Additional Evidence

This chapter contains a number of findings on topics which it was not possible to investigate fully or systematically. Of necessity, therefore, the evidence is somewhat uneven in quality, but many of the results seem to me interesting and suggestive.

Memory for sentences

In a number of cases I was able to give my subjects the sentence-memory item which occurs in the Terman Merrill test (year xi, no. 4). It runs: 'At the summer camp the children get up early in the morning to go swimming'. This turned out to be an interesting test because it was just marginally too long for many of them, even in cases where they had no difficulty in understanding the gist, and it was often helpful to determine how many trials were needed before they were word-perfect.

The results were very clear. On almost all occasions the main points of the sentence were given, but it was very common for one or two words to be left out. Here are a few examples from the many available: S 63, S 77, S 114, S 120, S 137, S 159, S 163, S 170, S 181, and S 213 left out 'in the morning'; S 176 left out 'early'; S 184 ended up 'early to go swimming in the morning', while S 121 ended 'get up early and go to the baths'. An unusual reproduction, apparently combining an error based on auditory confusability with an error of ordering, was made by S 140, who said, 'The children get up early in the morning to go fishing to the summer camp'[1]. Since this item is regarded in the Terman Merrill test as suitable for 11-year-olds it is highly significant that some of the errors mentioned above should have occurred in subjects aged 13 and over who, with the exceptions of S 163 and S 170, were graded W or higher in intelligence rating.

Particularly interesting is the fact that some subjects needed 5 or more repetitions and were not always word perfect even then. Here is a record of the responses of S 93 over 7 trials, the original sentence being repeated by me between each trial:

(i)   'At the summer camp the children in the morning get up early to go swimming'.
(ii)   'At the summer camp the children get up early to go swimming'.
(iii)   'At the summer camp early in the morning the children go swimming'.
(iv)   'At the summer camp the children get up early to go swimming'.
(v)   'At the summer camp the children get up early in the morning to go swimming' (correct response).
(vi)   'At the summer camp the children get up early to go swimming'.
(vii)   'At the summer camp the children get up early to go swimming'.

Here is a further series, this time from S 49:

(i)   'The little boys get up in the morning and go and have a swim'.
(ii)   'At the summer camp the boys get up early in the morning to have a swim'.
(iii)   'The summer – no, the boys get up in the morning and go and have a swim'.
(iv)   'At the summer camp the children get up early in the morning and go for a swim'.
(v)   'At the summer camp the children get up in the morning and go for a swim'.

I have similar records for S 59, S 75, S 83, and S 99. The conclusion appears to be that a dyslexic subject can be very strong at 'processing for meaning' but is sometimes extremely weak at verbatim recall.

Other memory problems

S 139, according to her mother, 'could never learn nursery rhymes. This struck me as odd'. Difficulty in rote learning was also mentioned in the case of S 25 and S 218. Difficulty in following instructions was regularly mentioned, and the mother of S 110 commented on the fact that instructions often needed to be repeated. Several subjects mentioned the need to 'go back' when they became lost (the epanalepsis strategy mentioned in Chapter 3). For example, in connection with learning the alphabet S 206 said, 'If I want to know what comes after H or I I have to go back to the start'. S 34 said, 'I don't like long stories. They stop in the middle of a page – it gets your turn – you have to begin from the top of the page to get it properly . . . When Mrs _____ reads a story I can remember right back but what's just happened I forget'.

When we arrived at the word 'anxious' in the Schonell S$_1$ test S 209 said, 'That's one of the words Mrs _____ went over with me but I can't remember what she said about it'. An admirably succinct statement was given by S 63, who simply said, 'I'm a quick forgetter'.

In some cases mathematical calculation was affected. For example S 214 said, 'I've never liked mental arithmetic. I'd just work half of it out and I'd have forgotten it before I could work out the rest'. A particularly insightful comment was made by S 155, who said, 'If I have to work something out at maths and have to keep something else in my head I use my fingers. You get confused easily when you try to remember something and keep something else in your head'.

Copying from the board

Difficulty in copying from the board was mentioned on many occasions, for example in the cases of S 4, S 61, S 145, and S 227. A related difficulty was that reported by S 175 who had been studying Macbeth and found it difficult to locate particular passages which she wished to examine.

Learning a foreign language

Difficulty with written French was also commonly reported and for interest a copy of a French dictation by S 115 is given below (Fig. 4). I was told

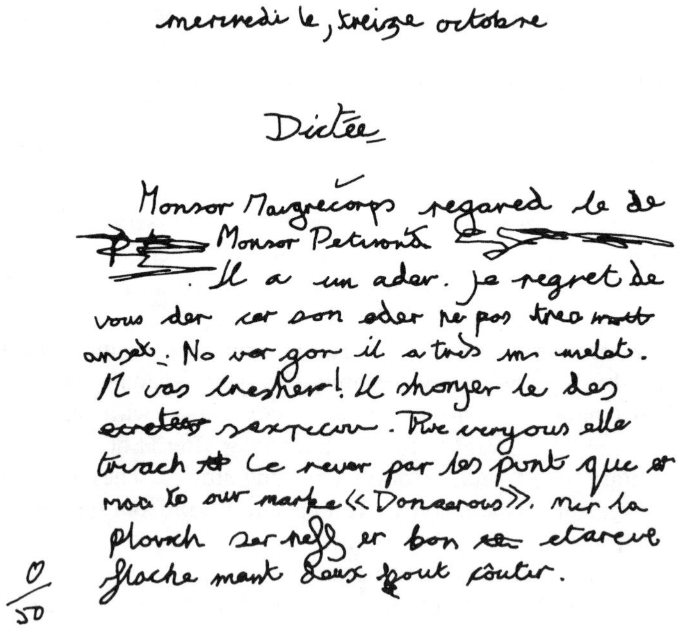

Fig.4 A French dictation

that S 147 had been good at oral French but had had severe problems in learning the difference between acute and grave accents. I think it likely that only a very bright dyslexic subject would be able to achieve 'O' level standard in written (as opposed to oral) French, and my experience was that those who had struggled with it were usually very relieved at the thought of giving it up. Possibly languages which are phonically more regular would present less difficulty – a point made to me by S 168 who, in connection with the polysyllables item of the dyslexia test, said, 'I do a lot of this in Spanish. The words are similar and you've got to pick out the differences'.

Finding rhymes

In some cases I gave my subjects the Terman Merrill 'rhymes' test. This is an item given to 9-year-olds in which they are asked to say (a) a colour which rhymes with *head*, (b) a number which rhymes with *tree*, (c) an animal that rhymes with *fair*, and (d) a flower that rhymes with *nose*. Those who appeared to be having difficulty were given a supplementary test (see Appendix I) in which words were presented in pairs (e.g. 'cat/dog' 'cat/fat', etc.) and the subject was required to say if 'yes' they rhymed and 'no' if they did not.

The number of subjects who displayed difficulty over rhymes was not large; but when they did so my impression was – as with so many other dyslexic manifestations –that in some way they had 'missed out'; in other words it was not simply that the items were too hard for them but rather that they were at a loss to know what was needed.

My records give the following data in respect of S 1:

Stimulus	Response
hit/bit	yes
cat/dog	yes
cat/mat	no
bet/set	no
cat/mat	I've said it before; yes
cat/hat	no
cat/hit	no
bat/sat	yes
egg/bacon	yes – no, it should be bacon and egg

With one subject (S 49) I went over the items a second time because I had serious doubts as to whether he would be consistent. The following table shows his responses:

Stimulus	*Response* (first time)	*Response* (second time)
cat/dog	no	yes
cat/sat	yes	no
mouse/elephant	yes	yes
mouse/house	yes	yes
fish/dish	yes	no
fish/water	yes	yes
butter/gutter	no	yes
butter/jam	yes	yes
egg/bacon	no, yes	yes

S 88 went through the whole list replying 'yes' indiscriminately, and when I asked him, 'What exactly *is* a rhyme?' he replied, 'Something like "Jack and Jill"', without any awareness, so it seemed to me, of the fact that 'Jill' and 'hill' in the next line are similar sounds. S 181 gave 'two' as the number that rhymed with 'tree' and 'fish' as the animal that rhymed with 'fair'. She was able to respond correctly to the pairs of items, but when asked about 'egg and bacon' she said, 'I don't know why – I just don't think they do rhyme. They're always together but I don't think they rhyme'. It is hard to see how a person who had really understood the notion of 'rhyming' could say that she did not *think* that two words rhymed, since the matter is surely one for immediate recognition. Similarly S 75 in reply to 'mouse-house' said 'No—yes' (changing his mind) and in reply to 'egg-bacon' he said 'yes' and corrected this to 'not really'. The responses of S 72 were puzzling and ambiguous. He responded correctly with 'red' as a rhyme for *head*, but when asked for a number that rhymed with *tree* he said, 'Trente – no, that's French', and when I asked if 'trente' rhymed with 'tree' he said, 'No, not really'. He responded 'yes' and 'no' correctly to all the pairs of words, except that to 'egg/bacon' he said, 'Yes, no', and, when I asked which, he said, 'Yes, they do'. Asked to give two words that rhymed he said 'Sit and bit – no, that doesn't rhyme'. When I asked what a rhyme was he said, 'A word that flows into the other one – they kind of flow – they are similar words'. S 179 gave 'red' as the colour that rhymed with *head* but only after a long pause; he gave 'two' as the number that rhymed with *tree*, and failed to give rhymes to either *fair* or *nose*. He said 'yes' and 'no' correctly to all the pairs of words, and when I included 'two and tree' and he said 'no', I pointed out that 'two' could not be right for the earlier item. He then said 'Three – yes, I think so; they've both got "e" at the end'. A subject whom I described in an earlier book[2] was able to do the 'rhymes' test by means of a similar compensatory strategy: if one has not grasped the idea of auditory similarity it is still possible, in the case of older subjects, to spell the two words and note if they end in approximately the same letters.

The existence of a difficulty on the part of poor readers over recognising if words rhyme has also been reported by Bradley and Bryant, whose subjects were required to give the 'odd one out' from a list of words such as *nod, red, fed, bed*[3]. I find it hard to believe that this difficuly arises from any kind of hearing deficiency of peripheral origin, although by analogy with the acquired aphasias I would not object to calling it an 'auditory agnosia', provided one appreciates that even those dyslexic children who display it may well grow out of it. What is involved, I suspect, is the formation of some kind of linkage or association between words such that the person can classify the cat-sat relationship as similar to the hit-bit relationship. If the language system is in some way deficient, as in dyslexia, the development of this particular linkage may not come easily, in much the same way, perhaps, as, for some dyslexic children, the recognition that the letters which we write represent the sounds which we hear does not come easily. It does not follow that such failures are permanent or incurable; the position seems to be that dyslexic children do not invariably 'pick up' various forms of language skill which in non-dyslexic children can be taken for granted.

Bell-ringing

Next I should like to call attention to a curiosity which was mentioned on two occasions (S 244 and S 246). Both had attempted to learn bell ringing and both had had to give it up because they could not keep count! I suspect that this task necessitates holding in mind a verbal record of the number of previous rings which have occurred; the person therefore has to count at speed, and the difficulty experienced by a dyslexic subject is presumably a special case of the 'loss of place' phenomenon which has been described in Chapters 13 and 16.

Driving a car

I am sometimes asked if dyslexic persons are in any way at risk in driving a car. The question is presumably raised because of possible confusions over 'left' and 'right'.

There are occasional references to car driving in my records. Thus S 248, who used a lump on her finger as a mnemonic, said, 'I have to think, for example at crossroads'. S 253 said, 'I do have difficulty in defining left and right; it was terrible when I started learning to drive'. S 205, when asked 'Show me your right hand', said 'The only reason I know is I have a lump on my finger . . . One of my faults (sc. in my driving test) was turning left when he said "right"'.

If, however, as seems likely (Chapter 10), it is the *words* 'left' and 'right' which are a source of confusion for dyslexic subjects rather than the directions as such, there is no reason to think that a dyslexic driver would be more prone than other drivers to cut across traffic, since one can tell that another car is approaching without any knowledge at all of the words 'left' and 'right'. Moreover, if a guide tells a dyslexic person to turn left and he mistakenly supposes that he is being asked to turn right, he would have to be a very incompetent driver before he turned right across a stream of on-coming traffic; if he failed to wait this would be nothing to do with misunderstanding the instructions.

I know of several dyslexic adults who are very good drivers and of none who have been involved in any serious accident.

It therefore seems to me perfectly reasonable that a dyslexic person should learn to drive a car if he believes himself to have the necessary competence. Few, if any, actions in life are totally risk-free, but I do not believe that there is any distinctive risk (certainly not any appreciable one) if a dyslexic person is in charge of a car.

Wetting and soiling

Although wetting and soiling are commonly believed to be signs of stress, the occasions when they were mentioned during my assessments were remarkably few in number. The bed-wetting of S 7 has already been mentioned in Chapter 5. In addition I was told that up to age 8 S 158 was 'still bed-wetting and full of nervous twitches', that S 211 used to wet the bed until age 9, that S 169 soiled until the age of 10, and that S 207 had until recently had a persistent soiling problem. I did not specifically ask questions in this area, and it is therefore hard to be sure that there were no other cases of wetting or soiling among my subjects, but these were the only cases where the matter was spontaneously mentioned. It is interesting that Mrs Naidoo[4] reports no higher incidence of wetting or soiling among her two dyslexic groups than among her controls. Since it is clear that many dyslexic children are under appreciable stress it is possible that the commonly accepted idea that wetting and soiling are signs of stress is itself in need of revision.

Chess

I was told on several occasions that my subjects had been successful at chess. S 62, who came to me at the age of 10, was said to be able to win against his mother; the skills of S 118 were said to have been particularly encouraged at Junior School, and S 179 said that he could beat anyone in the school except for two boys. At first glance it might seem that chess involves calculation and that there is a large amount to remember. It is different, however, from a skill such as reciting tables, since (except in blindfold chess) the information about the position of the pieces is available whenever one wishes to be reminded of it. Moreover a dyslexic person has no difficulty in *imagining* such and such to be the case and there is therefore no reason why he should not pass in his imagination to several moves ahead;

nor does this involve any 'memory overload' since the different moves can be considered successively and do not have to be held in mind all at once. All that needs to be considered at one instant is the piece and the place to which it is moving; even possible threats from the opponent's pieces can be considered successively. I see no reason, therefore, why dyslexic subjects should not be good at chess, and from the above evidence it is plain that some of them are.

Music

Enough of my subjects were gifted musically to convince me that for a dyslexic person success in this area is entirely possible. If there is a draw-back one might expect it to arise from a difficulty in *reading* music not from any difficulty in appreciating it. In particular an orchestral score is so full of symbolic material that one would expect a dyslexic person to have consider-able difficulty with it (though a conductor, if dyslexic, would presumably be able to rely on his musical knowledge), and one would also expect relative difficulty with piano music, where two staves have to be read simultane-ously. On the other hand, since despite early struggles a dyslexic person eventually learns to read a book there seems no reason why he should not also master musical notation in the same way.

The reports which have reached me, though few in number, seem on the whole, to bear this out. Thus S 72 and S 74 had passed Grade Two at the piano, though the latter was reported to have difficulty in reading the bass clef 'even though she knew what was there'. She had also passed Grade Four on the flute. S 193 had been successful at the piano, and when I asked him about reading music he said, 'I read it slowly. I'm less ahead than most people would be for the amount of learning I've done. My sight reading is a bad point; I know it all but it's slow. Then eventually my fingers re-member'. S 147 had been deputy-leader of his school choir and had sung in oratorios, while S 241 had apparently had considerable success on the flute[5]. The only counter-example which I have recorded was that of S 112 who according to his mother 'could not make headway with the piano because of his left-right problem', though it was not clear what exactly this problem was.

I think it probable, therefore, that a dyslexic person is as likely as anyone else to be gifted musically, and that although the reading of music may be something of a barrier, once this barrier has been overcome (as in book reading) there is no reason why good progress should not be made. It is perhaps a pity that young children sometimes equate 'doing music' with learning the names of the notes on the stave (E B G D F, etc.), since any weakness in this area may give them the impression that they will be unsuc-cessful at music; and this may in fact be quite mistaken. The situation is not unlike that when a dyslexic child mistakenly concludes from his difficulties over calculation and tables that he is 'no good at maths'.

Art and craft

It is likely on general grounds that the spread of talents and interests among dyslexic children is as varied as it is among other children. One must also suppose, however, that those talents which are least affected by the handicap will be the ones which tend to flourish. In particular, art is something at which a dyslexic subject can be successful without having too many dyslexic-type problems to overcome. Some of my subjects were in fact extremely gifted in this area. For example S 171 and S 199 were aiming at going to Art School, while S 46, S 54, and S 150, among others, showed me some quite remarkable drawings. S 179 gave me a mosaic comprising small dots of many different colours, which had clearly involved many hours of patient work. S 123 had made beautiful carvings of a rabbit and a stoat, while S 257, despite his lack of success at school in other ways, told me that he had done well at art and woodwork. S 120 had pottery and painting as his hobbies, and S 112 was reported to have considerable talent for technical drawing.

Creative writing

Many of my subjects showed remarkable powers of literary appreciation and expression. For example the school books of S 192 showed some extremely imaginative writing, and his mother when she first wrote to me said: 'He loves poetry, however, and does appear to understand some difficult poems. When I read his own writing I am always amazed at the depth of feeling especially when I consider the almost total lack of reading experience'. In the school books of S 46 I found:

> 'A yellow frightened moon slid itself behind the dark clouds as an owl hooted mornfully from the black woods. It was cold and strangely quiet here'.

Presumably in this case the spelling had been amended. Sometimes, however, the poor spelling can increase the pathos, as in the following line which I found among the school books of S 204:

> 'I feel so much pain in this garbag hiepe called time'

The following was written by S 237 about his memory:

> 'My morey is a Labourinth (crossings out) of passegs with an old sage moveing for on to room to another thats how I rember things when I am not tring'.

To conclude, I should like to quote two samples of written work by S 128, the first a piece of imaginative prose, the second a humorous poem. This is the first:

I am a TT rider about to start the race

I can bearly hear the reving up of the powerful race bikes my mind is dume to everything exept the starters flag the smell of the 5 star 4 stroke petrol the tention wich was bilding up in me was unberable I just had to go sudenly the checked flag droped and I was away among the screming gutsis, BMWs, BSAs and Nortons to name but a few

This is the second:

I am a gnu
Sick of typhoo
But just between you and me
I drink beer, sparkling beer
And so do all the other gnus I knew

But now I've reformed
I drink typhoo
Boo-hoo-hoo
Gnu-gnu-gnu
Sadly gnu.

A weak lexical system appears to be no barrier to creative writing.

CHAPTER NINETEEN

Improvement Over Time

As was indicated in Chapter 6, the Summary Chart provides a large quantity of material for statistical analysis; and although in the present book no attempt has been made to treat the data exhaustively, there is one area, viz. that of improvement over time, where I thought it appropriate to introduce a somewhat higher degree of statistical technicality.

Ideally it would have been helpful to have had longitudinal studies of all the subjects in the sample, so that each individual's changes in performance could be investigated as his age increased. Unfortunately there is only a limited amount of evidence in this area, since relatively few of my subjects came for a second assessment (see the postscript to this chapter). It may still be of interest, however, to compare, not the same subjects at different ages, but different subjects at different ages.

The items chosen for study were reading, spelling, digits forwards, digits reversed, months forwards, and months reversed[1]. The question at issue is whether – or to what extent – the older subjects were more successful at these items than the younger ones[2].

Table 19.1 shows the subjects' reading scores, Table 19.2 their spelling scores, Table 19.3 their 'digits forwards' scores, and Table 19.4 their 'digits reversed' scores, all in relation to age; Table 19.5 shows the percentage of subjects at each age level scoring 'plus', 'zero' and 'minus' on 'months forwards' and Table 19.6 gives the same information in respect of 'months reversed'.

For ease of inspection the scores in the reading and spelling tests have been grouped in tens and in all six tests the ages have been grouped in years. In the calculations which follow later in the chapter, however, the actual scores have been used and the ages were recorded to the nearest month[3].

Inspection shows that the older subjects were considerably more successful at reading than the younger ones, appreciably more successful at spelling, but only marginally more successful in the other four tests.

To express the relationship to age of each of the six tests with greater precision it was decided to make use of the statistic known as the correlation coefficient. This figure (written as 'r') lies between ±1 and indicates the

Table 19.1 *Reading and Age: Table of Frequencies*

Score on R_1	7	8	9	10	11	12	13	14	15	16	17	18
						Age in years						
90-99	—	—	—	—	—	—	—	—	4	1	2	9
80-89	—	—	—	—	—	2	3	1	7	1	4	—
70-79	—	—	—	3	4	3	2	6	4	6	2	1
60-69	—	—	—	—	7	3	4	2	3	2	—	—
50-59	—	—	3	4	5	3	4	2	5	1	—	—
40-49	—	3	6	10	6	—	—	4	2	—	—	—
30-39	1	3	13	6	8	3	1	—	1	—	—	—
20-29	3	7	3	3	3	1	2	—	—	—	—	—
10-19	1	3	4	3	—	1	—	—	—	—	—	—
0- 9	2	3	—	—	—	—	—	—	—	—	—	—
Mean	18.00	24.63	34.93	41.52	49.18	55.56	60.44	63.80	71.19	71.42	85.00	92.11
s.d.	11.61	11.48	11.64	16.07	15.86	21.16	19.35	12.63	17.67	13.86	7.52	6.87

Table 19.2 *Spelling and Age: Table of Frequencies*

Score on S_1	7	8	9	10	11	12	13	14	15	16	17	18
						Age in years						
90-99	—	—	—	—	—	—	—	—	—	—	—	—
80-89	—	—	—	—	—	—	—	—	2	1	1	7
70-79	—	—	—	—	—	—	1	—	5	2	2	1
60-69	—	—	—	—	2	—	4	2	2	2	1	1
50-59	—	—	—	1	3	4	2	2	4	4	3	—
40-49	—	1	—	6	5	4	3	6	6	—	1	—
30-39	—	1	6	8	7	4	3	2	5	1	—	1
20-29	2	8	18	8	14	2	2	3	2	1	—	—
10-19	2	8	5	6	2	2	1	—	—	1	—	—
0- 9	3	1	—	—	—	—	—	—	—	—	—	—
Mean	12.57	20.05	25.62	30.55	34.09	39.06	46.19	43.47	51.88	55.00	63.75	
s.d.	9.50	8.24	5.79	11.28	13.77	13.36	16.76	12.65	17.17	21.56	13.98	

Table 19.3 *Digits Forwards and Age: Table of Frequencies*

No. of digits	7	8	9	10	11	12	13	14	15	16	17	18
						Age in years						
9	—	—	1	1	—	—	—	—	1	—	—	—
8	—	—	2	—	—	—	—	—	1	—	—	—
7	—	1	—	—	1	4	4	3	6	2	—	4
6	—	7	7	10	9	7	3	3	8	4	2	3
5	4	6	12	10	11	4	7	6	10	6	4	3
4	3	5	5	8	11	1	2	3	—	—	2	—
3	—	—	2	—	1	—	—	—	—	—	—	—
Mean	4.57	5.10	5.27	5.20	4.94	5.88	5.56	5.40	6.04	5.67	5.00	6.15
s.d.	0.53	1.05	1.36	1.08	0.93	0.89	1.03	1.06	1.08	0.78	0.76	0.80

Dyslexia

Table 19.4 *Digits Reversed and Age: Table of Frequencies*

No. of digits	Age in years											
	7	8	9	10	11	12	13	14	15	16	17	18
6	—	—	—	—	1	—	1	—	2	1	1	—
5	—	1	1	2	3	3	3	—	6	—	—	2
4	—	5	5	7	5	5	3	3	9	5	4	5
3	5	12	18	18	22	8	8	10	8	6	3	3
2	2	1	5	2	2	—	1	2	1	—	—	—
Mean	2.71	3.32	3.07	3.31	3.36	3.70	3.69	3.07	4.00	3.67	3.75	3.90
s.d.	0.49	0.67	0.70	0.71	0.86	0.79	1.08	0.59	1.02	0.89	1.04	0.73

Table 19.5 *Months Forwards and Age: Percentages Scoring 'Plus', 'Zero', and 'Minus'*

	Age in years											
	7	8	9	10	11	12	13	14	15	16	17	18
Plus	100	89	62	59	33	63	31	67	35	17	25	20
Zero	0	0	14	7	18	0	0	0	0	0	0	0
Minus	0	11	24	34	48	38	69	33	65	83	75	80

Table 19.6 *Months Reversed and Age: Percentages Scoring 'Plus', 'Zero', and 'Minus'*

	Age in years											
	7	8	9	10	11	12	13	14	15	16	17	18
Plus	100	95	83	90	67	62	50	93	73	25	62	30
Zero	0	0	10	0	18	13	25	7	4	8	0	10
Minus	0	5	7	10	15	25	25	0	23	67	38	60

extent to which increase in one variable (for example, reading score) can be predicted from increase in another (for example, age). In what follows age is symbolised by 'a' and scores on reading, spelling, digits forwards, digits reversed, months forwards and months reversed[4] by the letters 'u', 'v', 'w', 'x', 'y' and 'z' respectively. Calculation gave the following results:

$$r_{au} = 0.78 \qquad r_{ax} = 0.30$$
$$r_{av} = 0.73 \qquad r_{ay} = 0.37$$
$$r_{aw} = 0.26 \qquad r_{az} = 0.35$$

These figures indicate in particular the very low extent to which it is possible to predict performance in the 'months' and 'digits' tests from the subject's age[4].

To determine the degree of 'improvability' in the six different tasks regression lines were fitted to the data described in Tables 19.1 to 19.6[5]. These were found to be:

Reading:	$y = -25.05 + 0.52x$
Spelling:	$y = -21.67 + 0.41x$
Months Forwards:	$y = -0.58 + 0.0103x$
Months Reversed:	$y = -0.69 + 0.0078x$
Digits Forwards:	$y = 4.22 + 0.0079x$
Digits Reversed:	$y = 2.35 + 0.0074x$

where y is the score on each test and x the age in months. The slope for reading (given by the formula $\tan^{-1} 0.52$) was found to be 28° and that for spelling 22°; none of the other four slopes was greater than 1°.

Table 19.7 gives the confidence levels for the differences between the slopes of the regression lines, that is, the likelihood that the difference between a particular pair of slopes could have occurred simply as a chance fluctuation.

Table 19.7 *Confidence Levels for the Differences Between the Slopes of the Regression Lines*

	Reading	Spelling	Digits forwards	Digits reversed	Months forwards
Spelling	**				
Digits forwards	***	***			
Digits reversed	***	***	*		
Months forwards	***	***	ns	ns	
Months reversed	***	***	ns	ns	ns

ns	not significant (at 5% level).
*	significant at 5% level.
**	significant at 1% level.
***	significant at 0.1% level.

Caution is needed, however, in the matter of interpretation, since the figures were not based on longitudinal studies but relate to different subjects at the different ages; any reference, therefore, to 'improvement over time' is thus a kind of collective statistical improvement rather than the improvement of a particular individual.

Two explanations, not necessarily mutually exclusive, suggest themselves. One is that there is some kind of 'capacity limitation' in a dyslexic person as a result of which he cannot handle more than a certain amount of information at once; the second is that reading and spelling because of their social usefulness receive a very much larger amount of practice.

In the case of the two 'months' tasks it seems likely that lack of practice is the decisive factor. There is no good reason for supposing that a dyslexic subject could not be taught the months of the year if this was regarded as sufficiently important. That many of them do not easily or naturally 'pick up' this particular series is well established, and it is likely that dyslexic subjects would take longer to acquire it than age-matched controls[6]. Mnemonics are possible, however, for example the 'Jason' mnemonic mentioned in Chapter 14; and in the case of 'months forwards' success was in fact achieved by 101 out of the 223 subjects[7]. Moreover, once 'months forwards' are known a variety of strategies make it possible to say 'months reversed', for example saying two months forwards at a time to oneself and then inverting them.

The relative lack of improvement over the two 'digits' tasks is less easy to interpret. The idea of a 'capacity limitation' is not excluded, but there is no way of knowing how much might have been achieved as a result of practice.

With regard to the other differences, the figures show that progress at spelling in dyslexic subjects falls further behind the norm than progress at reading; this means in effect that they are differentially weaker at spelling relative to controls, over and above their weakness at reading. This is perhaps no surprise, since recognition of the correct word when it is already written is an easier task than creation of the correct letters from nothing, and if one is handicapped an easier task is more likely to be conquered by effort than a harder one. The slightly higher correlation between 'digits reversed' and age, in comparison with that between 'digits forwards' and age, is not easy to explain; it could be due to sampling error (since the difference is only just within the 5% significance level, see Table 19.7) or it is possible that the compensatory strategy of 'saying them forwards first' was marginally easier to acquire than the compensatory strategy of 'grouping' in the case of 'digits forwards'. This latter explanation, however, is speculative, and the factors which lead to improved performance in the two 'digits' tasks require further systematic investigation.

Postscript

A full re-assessment was possible in the case of 21 of my subjects. The results are set out in Table 19.8.

For each subject the information in the first line has been extracted from the Summary Chart (with the data on handedness, eyedness, and 'limits' excluded); the second line then gives the data at the time of re-assessment, viz. age, score on R_1, score on S_1, score on the two 'digits' tests, and the results of the dyslexia test scored in terms of 'plus', 'zero' and 'minus'. A further column gives the time-interval in years and months between the two assessments, the next two columns the gains in 'reading age' and 'spelling age' respectively, and the final two columns the rates of gain in each case, that is, the gains in reading age and spelling age divided by the time-interval between the two assessments.[8]

Now it is clear from Table 19.8 that almost all the subjects showed considerable gains in both reading and spelling, with reading consistently showing the larger gain. Of the 11 subjects who were first assessed at ages 7, 8, or 9 (S 3, S 6, S 10, S 13, S 18, S 19, S 22, S 35, S 43, S 48, and S 53), all had gained at least two years in reading age when they were re-assessed and only S 6 had failed to make significant progress in spelling (gaining 1 year 7 months in spelling age during a period of 5 years 1 month between assessments). Of the remaining 9 subjects (exclusive of S 258, see below) only S 64 had a reading age of under 12 (70 words correct) on re-testing, and 6 had a reading age of 13 (80 words correct) or over. All of them, however, remained relatively weak spellers, 4 having spelling ages of under 11 (60 words correct) and 2 others having spelling ages of under 12 (70 words correct). Whether their reading and spelling would have remained weaker still had they not come for the original assessment is a question that cannot be answered with full confidence; but, for what it is worth, the mean of the 'rate of gain' column for reading is 0.99 (which means that, on average, their reading performance after assessment 'kept up with the clock'), while the mean of the 'rate of gain' column for spelling was 0.78 (that is, a rate of gain of just over 9 months spelling age in any year). The 'slopes' of the two improvements were therefore 45° and 38° respectively, whereas the reading and spelling slopes for subjects of different ages before they came for assessment were found to be 28° and 22° (see above). These results are therefore compatible with the view that the assessment made a difference, a possible 'causal chain' being that the parents were encouraged as a result of the assessment to look for skilled help and that this skilled help was sometimes effective[9].

With regard to performance on the dyslexia test, Table 19.8 shows that 19 out of the 20 subjects (exclusive of S 258) were found to have an index of 4 or more 'pluses' on the second testing, and indeed 11 of them had an index of over 5. Quite independently, therefore, of my first-hand knowledge of their earlier difficulties there would have been grounds for a positive diagnosis in these cases. Even S 13, though his index was only 3 on the second occasion, displayed weakness at digits reversed and typically dyslexic difficulties over tables, and in the context of his high intelligence and relatively weak spelling a diagnosis of dyslexia would therefore have seemed extremely likely[10].

At this point it may be helpful to refer to the case of S 258, who at the time of the first assessment left me uncertain as to whether she was genuinely dyslexic[11]. When I assessed her the second time there were still difficulties over left and right and over tables; her score of 6 on 'digits forwards', though not low enough for a 'plus', was on the weak side, and

Table 19.8 Re-assessment Data

Case no.	Sex	Age	Int.	R₁	S₁	DF	DR	L-R	Pol	Sub	Tab	MF	MR	b-d	Famil	Index	Interval (years & months)	Reading age gain (years & months)	Spelling age gain (years & months)	Rate of reading gain	Rate of spelling gain
3	M	7.6	W	0	3	56	33	+	–	+	+	+	+	0	nk	5½	–	–	–	–	–
		8.1		22	18	56	33	+	–	+	+	+	+	0	nk	5½	0.7	2.2	1.6	3.7	2.6
6	M	7.9	X	21	15	56	33	+	+	+	+	–	+	0	+	7½	–	–	–	–	–
		12.10		64	31	64	43	+	+	–	+	–	+	0	+	7½	5.1	4.4	1.7	0.9	0.3
10	M	8.1	Z	31	24	65	33	+	–	–	+	+	+	+	nk	6	–	–	–	–	–
		12.6		90	66	87	77	+	–	–	+	0	+	0	nk	4	4.5	5.11	4.2	1.3	0.9
13	M	8.4	X	22	18	67	43	+	–	+	+	+	+	+	nk	6	–	–	–	–	–
		15.8		91	78	78	45	0	–	–	+	–	–	0	nk	3	7.4	6.11	6.0	0.9	0.8
18	M	8.6	X	8	16	55	45	0	0	0	+	+	+	+	+	6½	–	–	–	–	–
		10.0		32	29	55	43	–	0	–	+	–	–	0	+	5	1.6	2.5	1.4	1.6	0.9
19	M	8.7	W	40	30	55	43	+	0	–	+	–	+	+	0	5	–	–	–	–	–
		10.8		61	45	65	43	+	+	–	+	–	+	0	0	7	2.1	2.1	1.6	1.0	0.7
22	M	8.8	W	29	23	65	44	+	–	+	+	+	+	0	+	6½	–	–	–	–	–
		15.7		78	77	55	44	+	+	–	+	–	0	0	+	7	6.11	4.11	4.7	0.7	0.7
35	M	9.4	X	19	22	66	34	–	–	+	+	0	+	0	nk	5	–	–	–	–	–
		16.11		77	62	45	34	–	+	–	+	–	+	0	nk	5½	7.7	5.10	4.0	0.8	0.5
43	M	9.7	Y	34	28	65	34	+	–	–	+	+	+	0	0	7	–	–	–	–	–
		12.11		62	58	56	45	+	0	–	+	–	+	0	0	5½	3.4	2.10	3.0	0.9	0.9
48	M	9.9	Z	39	25	45	33	+	–	–	+	0	0	+	nk	5½	–	–	–	–	–
		16.6		87	72	76	43	+	0	–	0	–	–	+	nk	5½	6.9	4.10	4.8	0.7	0.7
53	M	9.11	X	45	34	56	33	+	0	–	+	0	+	0	nk	5½	–	–	–	–	–
		16.2		93	73	66	43	+	0	–	+	–	0	0	nk	5	6.3	4.10	3.11	0.8	0.6
61	M	10.3	Y	70	56	67	34	+	–	+	+	–	–	0	+	5½	–	–	–	–	–
		14.4		95	88	56	34	+	–	+	+	–	0	0	+	7	4.1	2.6	3.2	0.6	0.8
63	F	10.3	Z	56	42	43	33	+	+	0	+	–	–	0	nk	6	–	–	–	–	–
		14.4		82	68	66	43	–	+	0	+	–	–	0	nk	4	4.1	2.7	2.7	0.6	0.6

Case no.	Sex	Age	Int.	R₁	S₁	DF	DR	L-R	Pol	Sub	Tab	MF	MR	b-d	Famil	Index	Interval (years & months)	Reading age gain (years & months)	Spelling age gain (years & months)	Rate of reading gain	Rate of spelling gain
64	M	10.4	Y	26	19	67	43	+	+	0	+	+	+	+	nk	7½	—	—	—	—	—
		16.4		67	56	65	54	0	+	−	+	+	0	0	nk	6½	6.0	4.1	3.8	0.7	0.6
94	M	11.3	Y	37	28	45	53	−	0	+	+	−	+	0	0	6½	3.4	3.5	2.0	1.0	0.6
		14.7		71	48	55	43	−	0	−	+	−	−	0	0	4½					
96	M	11.3	X	32	22	55	34	0	0	+	+	−	+	+	0	7½	—	—	—	—	—
		14.4		88	59	56	43	+	−	−	+	−	−	0	0	5	3.1	5.7	3.8	1.8	1.2
110	F	11.9	X	45	32	66	33	+	+	−	+	−	0	0	+	6	—	—	—	—	—
		16.9		80	58	76	23	0	+	−	+	−	0	0	+	6½	5.0	3.6	2.7	0.7	0.5
118	M	12.0	Z	76	38	66	33	−	+	0	+	+	0	0	nk	5½	—	—	—	—	—
		19.6		94	72	56	34	−	+	−	+	−	−	0	nk	4½	7.6	1.10	3.5	0.2	0.5
143	F	13.6	X	62	61	65	23	+	+	+	+	−	−	+	nk	7	—	—	—	—	—
		17.5		81	75	45	43	+	+	−	+	+	−	0	nk	6½	3.11	1.11	1.5	0.5	0.4
190	M	15.11	V	(58)	(50)	67	55	−	+	0	+	+	+	−	nk	5½	—	—	—	—	—
		19.1		(72)	(64)	78	44	+	+	−	+	−	−	−	0	4½	3.2	1.5	1.5	0.4	0.4
258	F	8.1	Y	32	24	67	55	+	−	+	+	−	0	−	0	4	—	—	—	—	—
		14.6		86	75	66	65	+	−	−	0	−	−	−	0	2	6.5	5.5	5.1	0.8	0.8

there was the further evidence that when digits were presented visually for
$\frac{8}{10}$ sec. her 'comparison ratio' (see Chapter 17) was only 5.0 which again is
less than would be expected in a non-dyslexic person of her age and ability.
If anything, therefore, I would be more inclined to go for a 'positive'
diagnosis of dyslexia than I was at the first assessment, even though the
scoring system showed her as having only two 'pluses'. The truth seems to
be that from time to time one meets people who are only very slightly or
marginally dyslexic[12].

It is also worth noting that 19 out of the 20 subjects (exclusive of S 258)
scored 'plus' on the 'tables' item. Apart from S 53, who showed only minor
hesitations on re-testing, not a single subject went through his 6 ×, 7 ×,
and 8 × tables without some appreciable degree of stumbling.

One additional piece of evidence is worth mention,viz. that 5 of the
subjects on re-assessment did the Raven Advanced Matrices test. Table 19.9
shows the scores and the resultant intelligence grade, with the earlier
intelligence grade given in brackets.

Table 19.9   *Scores on Advanced Matrices Test*

Subject no.	Score	Intelligence rating (with earlier rating in brackets)
13	26	Z (X)
35	26	Z (X)
64	22	Y (Y)
118	26	Z (Z)
143	21	X (X)

These figures are interesting in that in all 5 cases the intelligence rating
obtained at the first assessment either remained the same or actually
improved. Caution is needed, of course, since (i) only 5 subjects were
involved; (ii) from the way in which the grades were determined (see
Chapter 2, pp. 13-14) some degree of inexactness is unavoidable; and (iii)
any attempt to compare later performance on the Advanced Matrices test
with earlier performance on the Wechsler or Terman Merrill tests can only
be an approximation. Despite these possible objections, however, the
figures seem to me to be worth citing. I have sometimes wondered if, in my
anxiety to help and encourage my subjects, I have been guilty, in using the
concept of a 'selected I.Q.' (see Chapter 2), of over-estimating their ability.
In the case of an Advanced Matrices score, however, no 'selection' of items
is possible; and if these 5 cases are in any way typical it follows that there
cannot have been over-estimations on any large scale. In addition the
figures suggest that if tests are used (such as the Advanced Matrices) which
do not involve the dyslexic subject's areas of special weakness, the actual
figure for 'intelligence level' need not decrease; and this confirms the idea

that in their 'good' areas dyslexic subjects mature at the same rate as anyone else.

The evidence contained in the postscript confirms that dyslexic subjects can improve their performance in all kinds of ways as they grow older, and that, even at reading and spelling, there can be appreciable gains if the conditions are right. Even so, however, it is clear that traces of the handicap remain; and it seems that these are particularly likely to show themselves in difficulty over saying tables and difficulty over remembering digits. It is therefore incorrect simply to describe a dyslexic child as 'behind' at reading or spelling and able, or partially able, to catch up; a less misleading formulation is to say that he is handicapped but can achieve considerable success in learning to compensate[13].

CHAPTER TWENTY
Familial Incidence

On some occasions it was possible to assess more than one member of the same family. This was true in the following cases:

Brothers Ss:	Brother and Sister(s) Ss:
2 and 51	6 and 110[1]
14 and 108	7 and 74
16, 88, and 142	12, 82, and 248
22 and 238	18 and 117
24 and 178	34 and 246
55 and 106	72 and 103
92 and 148	129 and 224
189 and 204	122 and 28
	177 and 208

In addition, I had at an earlier date assessed the elder brothers of S 17, S 120, S 170, and S 229 and the cousin of S 116. More recently I had assessed the younger brother of S 23 and S 61 and the sisters of S 39 and S 97[2], while a colleague using the same criteria had assessed the sister of S 68 and the brother of S 221. In all these cases the diagnosis was positive. S 172 was the cousin of S 177 and S 208, and S 104 was the cousin of S 140. In addition I had ample evidence from discussion over many years that the mother of S 219 was dyslexic[3]. These results, taken in combination, gave me an assured 'positive' family history in 50 out 257 cases[4] (see those marked 'plus' in the Summary Chart).

There were in addition plenty of other cases where it seemed *prima facie* likely that another member of the family was affected. In accordance with the procedure described in Appendix II such cases were scored as 'zero', my intention being to make a distinction between those cases where I myself had observed difficulties in another member of the family at first hand and those cases where I had to rely on the reports of others. With regard to scoring, however, the real problem arose when it became necessary to decide whether the reported evidence was sufficient to count as a 'zero' or whether it was not. In general I accepted reports of late reading as meriting a 'zero'; for example the sister of S 1 was said not to have read until age 9, an uncle of S 45 not until he was aged 12, and the father of S 38 not until he was aged 14. Except in the case of late reading, however, I required some kind of twofold confirmation, for example that a particular relative regularly muddled left and right and in addition could not remember telephone numbers. On some occasions one or other of the parents, after listening to my account of their child's difficulties on the reading, spelling or dyslexia tests, reported similar difficulties in themselves; and provided more than one such difficulty was mentioned the result was again scored as 'zero'. This was true, for example, in the case of S 23 whose father reported that he himself was a poor speller and had never succeeded in learning his tables. (When a younger son came several years later for assessment and was also found to be dyslexic the original 'zero' was changed to 'plus'.)

The category 'nk' (= 'not known') was used (i) when there was insufficient evidence for a 'zero', (ii) when no evidence was available either positive or negative, and (iii) when the parents reported that they knew of no relatives similarly affected. Thus S 125 was scored as 'nk' since the only evidence was that his father was a poor speller, and similarly S 62 was scored as 'nk' since it was reported only that he tended to spell phonetically. If I was in doubt I tended to go for 'nk' rather than 'zero', since a critic could argue that in the assessment situation there were social pressures on the parents to 'oblige' by finding dyslexic relatives if at all possible! It may well be that I have overcompensated for this – somewhat speculative – possibility, and I suspect that the number of cases scored as 'zero' (72) is probably an underestimate of the number of cases where there were in fact dyslexic relatives.

Nine of the subjects had been adopted, and in these cases familial evidence was virtually impossible to obtain[5]. In a further 14 cases the subjects were not accompanied by their parents and, not surprisingly, could not answer questions about the family history with any confidence. If these 23 are subtracted from the total of 257, this leaves 234, of whom 122 (50 + 72) almost certainly had a positive family history. If, as is likely, the figure of 71 for the zero category is an underestimate, then in any sample of dyslexic subjects it appears that one should expect familial incidence over 50% of the time.

Does it follow, then, that the familial incidence of dyslexia is something which requires explanation? This question is not as absurd as it seems, for there are clearly plenty of characteristics which occur in more than one member of a family but which in themselves seem to be of no special significance. For example, there could well be two members of the same family who enjoyed swimming, and if this is unimportant and the familial incidence of dyslexia is important, wherein lies the difference?

The answer appears to depend on the relative unlikelihood of certain features occurring in conjunction. If one takes, for example, poor spelling on its own, this is perhaps a somewhat surprising phenomenon in those, like most of my subjects, who had adequate intelligence and the opportunities to learn, and the surprise is therefore the more if two members of the same family are both poor spellers. This, however, could happen from time to time simply as a chance combination of two relatively infrequent events. If a person is dyslexic, however, this involves a combination of weaknesses; and although the control data show that such weaknesses can quite well occur from time to time in those with no spelling problem, yet as the number of positive indicators increases the probability of their occurring by chance in two members of the same family rapidly decreases; and since there is evidence in some families of three, four, or even more members being affected, the hypothesis of 'random spread' (as there might be random spread of the enjoyment of swimming) has to be rejected. For example, unless there had been some familial factor it seems inconceivable that the mother of S 97, along with her son and daughter, and the father of S 55 and S 106, along with his two sons and their elder brother (assessed before 1972), should all have been dyslexic.

Now the most obvious explanation of the familial incidence of dyslexia is to postulate a genetic factor. In other words, because of their genetic make-up certain individuals are predisposed to dyslexic-type difficulties. It is important, however, not to accept this hypothesis without considering alternatives.

A suggestion which is sometimes put forward is that one should take into account the unconscious or 'dynamic' factors in the family situation. For example it is suggested that children sometimes unconsciously identify with a parent or sibling and therefore 'choose' the same things to be weak at. This idea, however, seems to me entirely speculative, and the onus is clearly on those who accept it to present relevant evidence. Moreover it is hard to see how a child of, say, eight could know that his father was a relatively weak speller or relatively weak at recall of digits. In addition, even if he knew, it is hard to see why he should imitate these particular facets of his father's behaviour when there was so much else to choose from, and why children in other families should imitate precisely the same facets of *their* parents' behaviour. There is the further difficulty that where one parent is affected and not the other, it would be necessary, if the 'identification' hypothesis were to be made convincing, for independent criteria to be formulated as to why it was this parent with whom the child identified; and where two siblings were affected one would have to assume that they identified themselves not with either parent but with each other. Finally, if one considers a family such as that which I have described elsewhere[6], where the members visited the U.S.A. and found several second cousins similarly affected, it is hard to see how there could be 'identification' with previously unknown relatives living on the other side of the Atlantic! In general, the 'unconscious identification' hypothesis seems to be psycho-dynamic speculation run wild.

Nor is it convincing to lay the blame on poor teaching, since it would then be necessary to explain why other children, exposed to precisely the same teaching, have learned to read and spell perfectly well.

If, however, it is correct to look for constitutional factors in the causation of dyslexia, then it is also *prima facie* plausible, in view of the incidence of familial dyslexia, to suppose that these constitutional factors are genetically determined. To be strict, perhaps one should speak of a genetic predisposition rather than of a genetically transmitted agent whose effects are 100% certain, since we know, after all, that dyslexic tendencies can to some extent be counteracted by suitable training, and we do not know the limits of such counteraction. The view that some kind of genetic factor is involved has of course received very considerable support[7].

In a number of cases, however, the parents, when carefully questioned, said that they knew of no affected relatives. Although it is hard to establish a 'negative' with complete assurance, since it is always arguable that mild forms of the condition among relatives would have gone undetected, it is hard to believe that these parents were invariably mistaken, and if this is correct it follows that there are at least some cases (the so-called 'sporadic' cases) where dyslexic-type difficulties occur in those whose relatives are all unaffected. In a few cases, too, there was evidence of more gross physical damage – an early history of hearing loss in S 8, S 37, and S 198, a history of convulsions in the case of S 83, a suggestion of very slight brain damage in the case of S 143, a report that S 167 was 'brain damaged and slightly spastic' and a report in the case of S 174 (via his mother) that 'Dr _____ says that in his view there is a physical condition caused by damage at birth which has also caused the dyslexia'. The proportion of such children finding their way to Bangor may well be small since our assessments were known to be educational rather than medical; but the above evidence makes clear that the dyslexic group of difficulties can sometimes be associated with factors of this kind.

In the cases where there is early hearing loss it seems *prima facie* likely that this is a causal factor. Indeed such a causal connection would be in no way surprising since the earliest language for all children except the deaf is *heard* language, and it makes sense that deprivation of heard language should lead to a stunting of the mechanisms for processing verbal stimuli[8]. It also makes sense that slight physical impairments, perhaps sometimes classifiable as mild cases of spasticity or epilepsy, should result in the typical dyslexic picture even though intelligence level is not affected. It seems to me that, at least in the present state of knowledge, these cases, too, should be classified as 'dyslexic' since, as in the sporadic cases, there is no evidence for differences in behaviour pattern or for believing that different teaching methods are needed.

It remains to discuss the puzzling phenomenon of the imbalance between boys and girls. Of my 257 subjects 208 were male and 49 female. This gives a male-to-female ratio of about $4\frac{1}{4}$ to 1, which is in line with those commonly reported[9]. One should be cautious, however, in assuming that where the dyslexia is genetic in origin it is necessarily also sex-linked, since it is well established that boys are more vulnerable to a variety of developmental anomalies which are not necessarily genetically determined[10].

Now if one were sure which were the genetic cases and which were the sporadic ones it would then be possible to check whether the former contained a larger proportion of boys. In my own sample I had 122 cases where I was fairly confident that there was familial incidence, and by going back to the records it was also possible to pick out 80 cases where familial incidence seemed least likely. It is impossible to be sure that these 80 cases were genuinely sporadic, but for what they are worth the results were:

	Male	Female
Familial incidence most likely	98	24
Familial incidence least likely	62	18

These figures provide no justification for supposing that the male-to-female ratio is any greater in the genetic cases than it is in the sporadic cases[11]. The fact that boys are more vulnerable than girls to some developmental anomalies appears therefore to be relevant, though this by no means excludes the possibility that in the familial cases it is a sex-linked gene which is doing the damage.

In brief, the evidence from the present research (i) confirms that dyslexia sometimes runs in families, (ii) confirms that dyslexia is more common in boys than in girls (the actual ratio in this particular enquiry being 4¼:1), (iii) establishes that dyslexia can occur when the evidence that relatives are affected is negative, (iv) gives some support to the view that dyslexic manifestations can occur as a result of a physical deficit such as early deafness. The results make it likely that familial dyslexia is genetically determined but whether it is also sex-linked remains an open question.

CHAPTER TWENTY ONE

Handedness and Eyedness

It is commonly supposed that there is some connection between dyslexia and unusual patterns of handedness and eyedness. Various suggestions have been made about the nature of this connection. The simplest view is that there is an enlarged proportion of left-handers in a dyslexic population; a more sophisticated view is that the dyslexic person shows poorly developed dominance, or in other words is neither strongly right-handed nor strongly left-handed, while a third view is that many dyslexic persons are 'cross-lateral', in other words right-handed and left-eyed or left-handed and right-eyed.

Even in the early stages of the research I had felt doubts as to whether handedness and eyedness were as important in dyslexia as these views implied. The first necessity, therefore, was to obtain more data, and it was for this reason that tests of handedness and eyedness were included in the dyslexia test and given to all my subjects. (For details see Appendix I). In addition, one of my students gave identical tests to 62 local schoolchildren, aged 8 to 11, who had been selected on the basis of adequate scores on a spelling test[1]. This procedure gave a control group with whom the dyslexic subjects could be compared. (For details of the performance of individual dyslexic subjects see the data on handedness and eyedness in the Summary Chart).

In the table which follows, the cross-lateral subjects (right-handed, left-eyed and left-handed, right-eyed) have been grouped together, and, as in the Summary Chart, the abbreviations R (= 'right'), L (= 'left'), and M (= 'mixed') have been used, with the first letter of each pair signifying handedness and the second letter eyedness. The numbers falling into each category, with percentages in brackets, were as follows:

	RR	RL LR	LL	MR ML	RM LM	MM
Dyslexic subjects	122(55)	44(20)	9(4)	35(16)	11(5)	2(1)
Control subjects	36(58)	18(29)	2(3)	6(10)	0(0)	0(0)

If we now pool all those who were right-handed and right-eyed and designate as 'UHE' (= unusual handedness or eyedness) all the others we obtain the following figures:

	RR	UHE
Dyslexic subjects	122	101
Control subjects	36	26

From this table it is plain that there is not a significantly larger proportion of left-handers or UHE subjects in the dyslexic group[2], and indeed, though the result is not statistically significant[3], there is actually a slightly larger proportion of cross-lateral subjects in the control group! This finding is in line with quite a number of other reports[4], and the idea that there is an association between dyslexia and either left-handedness or cross-laterality is one which should be treated with caution. That more sophisticated tests of 'cerebral dominance' (itself no easy concept) could yield different results I do not dispute, particularly in view of what is known about the role of the left hemisphere in speech[5], but if 'handedness' is understood in its popular sense it is dangerous to leap to premature conclusions.

There remains the possibility that there is an enlarged proportion of mixed handers in the dyslexic population. If once again we pool the results into a 4-cell table we get the following figures:

	'Mixed'	Others
Dyslexic subjects	48	175
Control subjects	6	56

Calculation shows that these differences just fail to reach the 5% level of significance[6]. Even if they are genuine, however, the interpretation is not obvious. Certainly they do not permit any comprehensive theory of dyslexia in terms of 'poorly developed dominance', since at most such a theory would be applicable only to a relatively small proportion of dyslexic subjects (22% in this particular sample). Even more important, however, is the consideration that inconsistency of hand or eye preferences in the tasks given is very slender evidence on which to base statements about 'dominance'. Dyslexic subjects show uncertainties in all sorts of ways, and it is not clear that the inconsistencies shown in these two tests by a small proportion of dyslexic subjects are evidence for anything more than typical 'dyslexic muddle'. One of the subjects, incidentally, who was 'mixed' at both the handedness and the eyedness tests was the problematic S 208 (see Chapter 5) who indeed was liable to show confusion in a variety of ways.

There is a further piece of dyslexic folk-lore which seemed to me to be worth examining. Basically it is concerned with the analogy of the mirror.

The suggestion is sometimes made or implied that when dyslexic subjects confuse left and right or 'b' and 'd' the central nervous system somehow signals the mirror-image of the correct answer. Orton's concept of 'strephosymbolia' has perhaps given credibility to this view; and the implication is that it is an important fact about certain errors that the response is the mirror-image of the correct one.

If this were true one might expect there to be more confusions over left and right and more b-d errors in those with UHE or in those of mixed handedness or eyedness than in other dyslexic subjects. The data in the Summary Chart make possible a test of this hypothesis. There were in fact 149 of the 223 subjects who scored 'plus' on the left-right test and 34 who scored 'minus' (40 scoring 'zero'). If these are classified according to handedness and eyedness we get the following table:

	RR	RL LR	LL	MR ML	RM LM	MM
'Plus' on LR test	81	25	8	26	7	2
'Minus' on LR test	20	8	1	4	1	0

If we again pool the results in respect of the UHE and 'mixed' groups we get the following two 4-cell tables:

	RR	UHE	'Mixed'	Others
'Plus' on LR test	81	68	35	114
'Minus' on LR test	20	14	5	29

In neither case is the result statistically significant[7] and indeed the absence of any association is plain from inspection.

Figures for b-d confusion tell the same story. In this case the Summary Chart shows that there were 74 subjects for whom there was first-hand evidence of b-d confusion and 78 where no such confusion was reported (with 71 scored as 'zero'). If these subjects are similarly classified according to handedness and eyedness we get the following table:

	RR	RL LR	LL	MR ML	RM LM	MM
b-d positive	36	16	4	16	2	—
b-d negative	46	16	2	10	4	—

If we again pool the results in respect of the UHE and 'mixed' groups we get the following two 4-cell tables:

	RR	UHE	'Mixed'	Others
b-d positive	36	38	18	56
b-d negative	46	32	14	64

In neither case is the result statistically significant[8]. In other words there is no tendency either for the subjects in the UHE or 'mixed' groups to be more prone to b-d confusion than other dyslexic subjects.

The evidence in this chapter has been almost entirely negative. Dyslexic subjects are no more prone to UHE than are controls; at most the evidence shows slightly more inconsistency of response in a few of them when given particular tests of handedness and eyedness. In addition, the subjects in the UHE and 'mixed' groups are no more prone than other dyslexic subjects to have difficulty with the left-right test or to show b-d confusion.

Indirectly, therefore, the results give limited support for the view that difficulties over left and right and over 'b' and 'd' are labelling difficulties, since in that case there would be no particular reason to associate them with UHE in any form. That some dyslexic responses are in fact the mirror-image of the correct ones is not in dispute. What may be doubted is whether traditional studies of handedness and eyedness or analogies with mirror phenomena will contribute anything significant to an understanding of dyslexia.

CHAPTER TWENTY TWO

Struggles and Misunderstandings

The next two chapters will be concerned with some of the social aspects of dyslexia. I shall try to show (i) that the family's problems can be exacerbated if the child's dyslexia is misunderstood, and (ii) that, conversely, an authoritative diagnosis can give a fresh orientation and new hope.

Much of the evidence in the present chapter is derived from what the parents told me. Not surprisingly, therefore, I have sometimes wondered whether they were guilty of exaggeration and whether, had I consulted the teacher or other official whom they mentioned, I would have received a very different story. On the other hand, there was a remarkable consistency in what I was told, in that the same kinds of cavalier treatment were reported by many different families, and their accounts regularly gave the impression of 'ringing true'. Even, therefore, if there has been some degree of distortion (and I am not convinced even of this), any wholesale discounting of what was said seems out of the question. On some occasions, too, I was able to see written reports where professional workers had put their views in writing, and in these cases there can clearly be no question of any misrepresentation.

As a first illustration, here is a letter from the mother of S 59:

'His headmaster thinks he is below average in intelligence, which I do not accept. After seeing a programme about dyslexia on the television a couple of Sundays ago, I 'phoned an educational psychologist who does not like the term "dyslexia", nor for that matter does T's headmaster. When I asked how T. was going to get on at senior school in a year's time and what facilities would be available to help T. the educational psychologist was very vague and woolly. I have been led to believe T.'s difficulties would gradually disappear, but especially since seeing the TV programme, I am convinced that this is not so. These children have to contend with a great deal of frustration and I feel it would help them to understand themselves better if their true handicap was explained to them'.

Reference to the Summary Chart show that T.'s intelligence rating was given as Y, with scaled scores of 17 and 17 on two WISC sub-tests – figures which scarcely square with the statement that he was 'below average intelligence'.

I received the following further information after the assessment.

'One of T.'s teachers ripped out his work in front of the entire unit (100 children) and made such an exhibition of the affair that T. was reduced to tears . . . When we called to see the Headmaster they defended themselves by saying that T. was too easily distracted, he could do better if he tried harder and his work was inconsistent. When they read your report they shook their heads as if to say "this can't be right". They were willing to accept that T.'s spelling age was 7.6 and his reading age was 9.8 but as for the rest they were not prepared to accept your findings at all. Well, as far was we were concerned the only course was to try and help T. at home and just hope that one day the message would get through to them'.

Here is a letter from the mother of S 109. 'I have been particularly concerned by his present teacher's assessment which described him as lazy, stupid, a child who gave up very easily . . . He has just finished "Watership Down" and declared it brilliant. I feel if he can appreciate and grasp a reasonable level of literature there exists the possibility that it is wrong for a teacher to label him as stupid'. Reference to that Summary Chart shows an intelligence rating of Z, with two passes at 'Superior Adult II'.

Similarly the mother of S 56 said at the start of the assessment: 'At (name of town) he saw a Dr.— who said he's just slow. "He's slow" – we've been getting the story for so long'. In the case of S 118 his mother told me that he had been called 'lazy', 'lethargic', and 'confused' at school, and was gaining a reputation for being 'charming but prone to idleness and scruffy work'. She also told me that although her daughter was said to be 'scholarship material' she herself believed that the boy was the brighter of the two; and this view was partially supported by the results of the intelligence test which I gave him, where he obtained a rating of Y. She herself was a qualified teacher, and at one point – speaking of her own experience – she said: 'At no point in his mother's training course was dyslexia mentioned, and among our many acquaintances who are teachers most know next to nothing about it'.

When S 132 was brought for assessment at age 11 his mother told me that they had been trying to get help since he was aged 8, while the mother of case S 127 said 'It's been running for six years. They said he'd grow out of it'. Similarly the mother of S 53 said 'We are always told not to worry, that it is bound to come in time'. A letter from the father of S 47 said: 'His primary school teachers have for the past two years been advising "Don't worry". But as the problem persists, we feel the time has come to seek further advice. Local channels – family doctor and health visitor – have been explored with negative result'. In similar vein the mother of S 111 told me that her daughter 'has been going to the Local Educational Psycologist (sic) for 4 years with no improvement in her reading'.

Lack of proper help was also mentioned in a letter from the mother of S 163. 'He has been described in all school reports as "lazy", however he is very willing and helpful. He feels inadequate and resorts to irresponsible and anti-social behaviour in order to impress. Last year, because of this behaviour, we consulted the Child Guidance Clinic at ——. Although we asked if he could be Dyslectic, he (the doctor) would not comment on dyslexia. Despite his difficulties he is not receiving any remedial attention at school'. A letter from the father of S 241 underlines the same point: 'At his primary school I mentioned dyslexia to the headmistress who assured me that his reading problems were entirely due to lack of effort and concentration. His form master . . . has told me that there is a definite inherent disability evident from his written work . . . I wrote to the BMA Nuffield Library who sent me 3 books on dyslexia, which further confirm my original diagnosis of my son's problem. Unfortunately I have no idea of a remedy'.

Ironically enough, it was sometimes the parents who – despite not being trained teachers – recognised that the help which was offered to the children was inappropriate. Thus the mother of S 82 wrote to me after the assessment saying 'She (the teacher) suggests that E. must write her spellings out several times and learn them. This I know will not help'.

It was sometimes possible for me to see the teachers' comments in school exercise books. One of the disturbing features was the lack of *constructive* comment. For example, in a book belonging to S 72 I found the following account of a chemistry lesson: 'What we first did was get a fetter funl and some cotter woo and blod the megl and put sand in. Then we got some buy want and put it on the top. Then we wotch it come froo. It come froo clener. But it was not clenunuf'. The comment from the teacher was 'A lot of spellings to correct'. On another occasion the boy wrote: 'Now we got some washud up lquwer and put some water with it. The we bloo budl with it. We bloo the (illegible) of the busn berner . . .'. His teacher's comment: 'Make more effort with your spellings'. Some writing by S 71 was characterised as 'Lazy, untidy work', while S 213 was told 'Very careless. Take more care with spelling', and a comment in the exercise book of S 158 was 'Your work is full of spelling mistakes'.

Sometimes there was evidence not just of adverse comment but actually of cruelty. Thus I was told by his mother that S 43 had been made to sit outside the headmaster's door as a punishment, and that one teacher had threatened him with the cane and made him stand in the corner, saying that he should wear the dunce's cap. A similar lack of sensitivity had apparently been shown by the teacher of S 117: we had reached the stage in the assessment where she had been asked 'nineteen, take away seven' and had given the answer as 'eleven'; when I asked her how she did her calculations she said, 'I usually use my fingers. Mr —— pulls your hair if you can't do it straight away'.

Another disturbing feature was the adverse criticism of parents which I sometimes read in teachers' reports. Thus a teacher wrote of S 162, 'He is an only child and the mother tends to be over-protective . . . Just as lazy about his written work'. I also read that he was 'a spoiled only child around whom home life revolves . . . very difficult to motivate'.

The following is also a distressing example of what appears to be a total misunderstanding of a dyslexic child's needs. The mother of S 232 told me that N.'s class teacher took the view that N. "needed a good thump" to knock some sense into him so he would get on with some work. His difficulties in other aspects of school work, particularly arithmetic became increasingly apparent, but his teachers failed to make any allowance and as a result he became increasingly despondent. He finds memorising of tables quite impossible and has great difficulty in copying or remembering numbers . . . We discovered that his teacher gave up trying to teach him maths and during maths periods gave him a book to read. As you may imagine this was not a success as he found it quite impossible to concentrate sufficiently to read a book whilst a lesson was being taken on an entirely different subject, and he was then punished for being unco-operative'.

One of the obstacles which many parents experienced was the entrenched attitudes of those who insisted that the child's difficulties were due either to tensions within the home or to inadequacies on the child's part such as lack of self-confidence or lack of motivation. The following, for instance, is an extract from a letter written by the mother of S 20. 'The educational psychologist said that C. is not dyslexic but that all his difficulties stem from being jealous of his sister . . . Apparently a remedial teacher has seen C. and reported to the headmaster that he is a very average child with an I.Q. of 100 whose only problem is that he is completely lacking in self-confidence'. The mother of S 159 reported that her son had been said by his teacher to have an 'emotional blockage'. Of S 38 the educational psychologist had written: 'I think this is the sort of child who would learn to read much faster in response to psychotherapy than any form of remedial teaching. She certainly has a major antipathy now to anything connected with the printed word and she also clearly has a very confused sense of identity'.

The following are extracts from an educational psychologist's report on S 14. 'A. has a very low opinion of himself. He is probably naturally reserved and even withdrawn but his lack of animation and poor confidence need not necessarily follow from his introverted personality . . . I have seen his parents who have also consulted me over A.'s brother P.' (S 108). 'I have hinted (sic) to them strongly (sic) that I feel that home attitudes may have contributed to A.'s problems and have encouraged them to do what they can to reassure him and restore his confidence . . . A. will do well in school subjects when his own attitudes and motivation are improved . . . A. needs to know to know that he has nothing to fear in the challenge that reading presents. He knows of his brother's difficulties in this area and his parents have observed that there is a little animosity between them. A. is choosing not to try rather than try and fail which in this family is probably more anxiety provoking than in many others'.

I find it hard to comment on this report. If one regards the two brothers as dyslexic, then clearly the picture is quite a different one. It has certainly been my experience that some dyslexic children 'choose not to try rather than try and fail' and that as a result the impression is given that their 'attitudes and motivation' are at fault. But the way to bring about the appropriate change is to explain to them the nature of their dyslexic handicap, so that 'failure' is not the terrible thing that it seemed to be and the defensive strategy of 'not trying' is recognised as unnecessary. It is not the search for underlying motives, as such, which makes the above report misguided, but rather the failure to recognise that the boy's behaviour was the response to a dyslexic-type handicap. This leads to unconfirmed speculations about the family being less able than some other families to tolerate anxiety and perhaps to the attaching of too much significance to the alleged 'animosity' between the two brothers. Moreover, if one uses the dyslexia concept, this immediately makes sense of the fact that *both* brothers were dyslexic, since the condition is known to run in families, whereas as far as the writer of the report is concerned this important aspect of the situation is totally ignored. Finally, in the absence of any suggestion of dyslexia, A.'s 'low opinion of himself' becomes just an isolated and inexplicable fact (unless indeed one searches for further speculative explanations in terms of sibling rivalry or parental expectations), whereas if both he and his parents recognise that the 'low opinion' is the natural consequence of the dyslexic handicap the way is open for constructive help. This report is therefore an interesting – albeit sad – example of how lack of the dyslexia concept can lead to a wrong view of the situation.

Sometimes the use of the word 'dyslexia' appears itself to have exacerbated controversy. Thus the mother of S 36 told me that when she mentioned dyslexia to her doctor he said 'This is a modern thing like a slipped disc'. Similarly I was told that an educational psychologist had explicitly declared that S 174 was 'not dyslexic', while the parents of S 242 were told that she 'can't be dyslexic' on the grounds that her reading age was the same as her chronological age. They reported, however, that she was regularly in trouble for poor spelling, and that once, when she had taken four hours over some homework the teacher had supposed that she had 'scribbled it off in five minutes'.

An educational psychologist who spoke to me on the telephone about S 226 said that he was very cross with a psychiatrist who had diagnosed the boy as dyslexic and that he 'had no business to do so'. He also spoke of 'emotional pressures' on the boy and asked me not to use the word 'dyslexia' in my report as it might affect his chances of getting help.

Sometimes there was no firm denial that the child was dyslexic, but nothing was done about it. For example, the mother of S 252 wrote to me saying, 'Very little notice was taken when we informed the school she was dyslexic. I doubt whether they believed in such a thing, and she continued to work uncomplainingly, though never reading for pleasure'. The parents of S 147 said that they had been told by T.'s headmaster that he was 'sure there was nothing wrong', but mother added, 'The school did not want to know'.

Sometimes the reactions on the part of the school appear to have been positively hostile. Thus the mother of S 180 told me (and her report was confirmed in a letter to me from a mutual acquaintance) that at school her son was 'pulled out of the class' and made to read aloud, with the comment, 'Your mother says you're dyslexic. You aren't'.

The following is a teacher's report on S 111: 'When D. first arrived at school she quickly informed the group that she was "dyslexic"' (writer's inverted commas). 'She was quite happy to use this as an excuse not to work . . . D. usually takes a long time to start writing with excuses such as her pen having "just broken" or "just run out". On such occasions D. needs firm persuasion, anything less produces further delays. Because of these frequent time-wasting procedures D. rarely leaves herself enough time to complete her work'. A report from the educational psychologist says, 'It is difficult to avoid the conclusion that D.'s problem is any more profound than sheer laziness and lack of motivation.'

Once again it is not so much the facts that are in dispute as the way in which one interprets them. It is of course a common strategy among dyslexic children to resort to 'time-wasting devices' when they are in an unsympathetic environment, and many dyslexic adults will confirm this; but the obvious way to make sense of such behaviour is to recognise that the child is trying to avoid a stressful situation in which his lack of skill will be shown up with resultant humiliation. Similarly it is no doubt the case that some undiagnosed dyslexic children show 'lack of motivation'; but this is understandable if the child is placed in circumstances where he knows that he will fail. To describe a child as 'poorly motivated' *simpliciter* gives no indication of what can be done to bring about a change, whereas to describe him as 'dyslexic' gives a totally new view of the situation: there are in that case all kinds of things which can be done to help – specialist tuition, discussion of compensatory strategies, and, above all, explanations which make clear to the child that he is not just 'stupid' and that his difficulties over reading and spelling and in other areas are not his fault.

Sometimes the failure to acknowledge that the child is dyslexic is accompanied by not only an unsympathetic attitude but by teaching methods which are now known to be unsuitable. The following are extracts from a letter addressed to S 12 from a senior remedial teacher (though it may have been intended primarily for his mother):

'H., you must get quite clearly in your mind that there is no good reason or excuse why your spelling should not be far better than it is. You are capable of becoming at least average in spelling ability, in my opinion, almost certainly above average.

Whether you achieve this depends on three things.

1. The first thing is to get clear in your mind that success depends entirely on your own efforts . . .

2. Having fallen behind on reading, spelling and speed of completing your written work, the only way you can hope to catch up is by doing some work regularly every day . . . The hardest part is to make yourself do at least ten minutes work every day out of school time for the next year or two.

3. The first thing you must set yourself are (sic) a series of clear targets which you will aim to achieve each week, or each day . . . In addition to setting targets, you must work out the most effective method for teaching yourself. I believe that you have been using inefficient methods, otherwise you would be having no difficulty . . .

Your target should be to collect a minimum of ten words every week from your school written work, which you have had difficulty with in spelling correctly . . . By writing words repeatedly, you can, in time, transfer all the words you need to your automatic muscle memory. All that is needed is time, determination, and revision . . . Finally, H., do not expect to read through these notes once and understand everything in them. We spent an hour together a little while ago and I made all these suggestions then. I bet a pound to a penny you have forgotten most of what I said then. Read these notes every week for the next month or two . . . I will call into your school occasionally to ask how you are getting on. I hope you will be able to report that this method is working well'.

It is perhaps worth spending a few moments indicating how the use of the concept of dyslexia would have led to a different view of the situation. (i) One would not use the expression 'no reason or excuse' but would make clear that there is a very obvious reason why the boy was having difficulty, viz. because he is dyslexic, that is, because he has a constitutionally caused handicap which is not his fault. (ii) One would agree that he could be as good or better at spelling than other boys of his age, but one would not expect him to achieve this by his 'own efforts'; such an expression merely adds to the pressure in an unconstructive way. (iii) One would not say that he had 'fallen behind', but rather that such progress as he had in fact made was something to be commended. (iv) It is not 'the hardest part' for a dyslexic person to make an effort. In many cases what has gone wrong is that their efforts have resulted in such a small amount of success. (v) To expect a dyslexic boy of this age to 'work out the most effective method' for teaching himself seems ludicrous if we reflect that dyslexia-centred methods have evolved into their present form only after many decades of work by experienced adults[1]. (vi) If what is advocated is 'writing words repeatedly' without any explanation of the links between sounds, muscular movements, and the letters on the page, it is hard to see why 'muscular memory' should be more effective than memory for auditory or visual representation of letters. (vii) Time, determination and revision are certainly needed, but the thought of an 8-year-old dyslexic boy reading through the proffered notes is an appalling one. Given his memory limitation, he would indeed forget any parts which he had managed to understand. (viii) An 'occasional' visit to the school by a remedial teacher is totally inadequate. (ix) The whole tone of the letter is critical rather than reassuring; and had the measures in fact been adopted their failure would have intensified the boy's feelings of guilt and humiliation.

One can usefully describe acceptance of the concept of dyslexia as 'getting the message'. Without the concept certain things about a child's behaviour may be puzzling (for example his anomalous failure in learning to spell or his lack of self-confidence) and some indeed may be exasperating (for example his mistaking the time of his music lesson or misremembering the telephone number that he was given), but there would be no suggestion that these things are related. Once the concept of a constitutionally caused limitation (dyslexia) is brought in, however, the different parts of the picture fall into place. It is not that for some inexplicable reason the child lacks confidence and therefore has not learned to spell; on the contrary he is lacking in confidence because a constitutionally caused limitation has made learning to spell difficult. Similarly it is not some unexplained cussidness which caused him to mistake the time of the music lesson or misremember the telephone number; these mishaps are the result of the same constitutional limitation which also caused the weak spelling. The evidence reported in this chapter indicates the additional pressures which are put on a dyslexic child and his family if these links are unrecognised.

CHAPTER TWENTY THREE

Effects of Diagnosis

As was indicated in Chapter 2, the final stage of the assessment usually consisted of a discussion between myself, the child and his parents.

In most cases I started by giving the results of the reading and spelling tests, the intelligence test, and the dyslexia test. Although this information was intended primarily for the parents, it also gave the child a chance to understand why I had asked particular questions. The majority of my subjects listened attentively during the discussion, and even those younger ones who appeared to have 'switched off' would sometimes become alert again when some aspect of their case was being discussed which appeared to interest them.

In the case of older children I would refer to their 'strengths and weaknesses' with an indication of what exactly their handicap involved. To the seven and eight year-olds I would say much the same thing in rather simpler words, for example, 'We'll be talking about the things that you are good at and the things that you are less good at'. I did not hesitate to use the word 'dyslexia' even with younger children if it seemed likely to help them, though it was important to explain what it meant; for example I might say, 'It doesn't mean you are stupid or lazy but there are some few things, like reading and spelling, which you will find more difficult than some of the other boys (or girls) in the class'.

At no point was it my intention to impose a diagnosis which the child or his parents could not accept or understand. Frequently I might say, 'Does this make sense to you?' or 'Does this seem to you to be a correct reading of the situation?'[1].

It was also an important point of principle never to give misleading information or false reassurance. Even during testing I would never tell a subject that he had 'done well' if this was not the case. It was possible to be constructive and encouraging without having to pretend that there were no difficulties ahead. Where there had been some striking success – for example on a difficult item from the intelligence test – I would call the parent's attention to this; and indeed during the testing I would sometimes say to the subject, 'Would you like to try this very difficult one? It is really for older people'. This kind of procedure makes it possible to *show* him that he is not stupid, as opposed to just *telling* him[2].

Secret fears that they were stupid, or even mad, were regularly found among my subjects, and it was sometimes possible to bring these fears into the open. For example, it transpired that S 127 had earlier been worried that he was, in his words, a 'nut-case'; and when his mother described how he and some slower children had been 'loaded' together (i.e. put in the same 'band' at school) he commented 'Some *were* nut-cases'.

Sometimes I was able to make clear that I understood the subject's feelings of frustration. For example, in the case of S 167 his mother had reported that he used to fly into a rage and 'resented being told to pull his socks up'. I therefore started the discussion by saying, 'I am sure he must have had a miserable time earlier on', and later indicated that he might have underestimated his own ability. Another procedure which I sometimes found useful was what I call the 'prophylactic warning'. This involves making clear to the subject that there are still, unfortunately, people who are unsympathetic to the notion of dyslexia and that he must not mind too much if they start saying to him that he is stupid, lazy, or 'playing up'. Since this was always said in the presence of the parents my hope was that the whole family would co-operate in trying to offset any damage which might otherwise be caused by unimaginative and unsympathetic handling. I was also implicitly conveying to the child that at least his parents understood the problem or, if there had previously been misunderstandings within the family, that these misunderstandings could now be regarded as a thing of the past. Finally, this kind of warning was an indication that I myself understood the position; and it was perhaps an additional reassurance that such a warning should come from someone who was outside the family and was in a position to speak authoritatively. It was once reported to me, after I had appeared in a television programme on dyslexia, that a young dyslexic boy had said to his parents, 'Thank goodness there are some grown-ups who know how you feel'. If the child realises that there are people who understand his problems, this may well help him not to take too seriously the strictures of the unsympathetic.

Sometimes, too, it was possible for me to show how the dyslexia had contributed to family tensions. For example, S 183 came to see me with his stepfather, and they made clear when I spoke to them after the assessment that they had quarrelled in the past. I was able to interpret the dyslexic difficulties as a source of the misunderstanding between them, and it was plain that, with these difficulties explained, there was the chance of a fresh start and new understanding between the two of them.

In all cases I followed up the discussion by sending a written report in which I summarised the main points of the assessment. Many of the letters which I received after the assessment were something more than conventional expressions of gratitude; and there seems little doubt that suitable discussions with dyslexic children and their families can result in significant changes in behaviour. The extracts which follow illustrate the kind of thing which I have in mind[(3)].

The mother of S 47 wrote: 'Since his visit to Bangor S is much happier; his difficulty has at last been recognised, and he is co-operating readily in our efforts to help him overcome it'.

A month after the assessment the mother of S 61 telephoned me and I noted down the following remarks: 'I used to cry myself to sleep, as I could see there was something wrong, but they would only say he was lazy. When I asked him he said, "I needn't worry any more about being called lazy". I really am very grateful'. Soon afterwards she said in a letter, 'As I mentioned on the 'phone there is a remarkable change in G's attitude and he's happier than we have seen him for a long time'.

The mother of S 62 wrote: 'He is, and has been since (date of assessment), a much more relaxed and happy boy, with lots of self confidence which has taken away his need to be aggressive with his little brother and sisters. This has made the whole family more relaxed'.

The mother of S 67 wrote: 'We all came away feeling as though a load had been lifted from us; most especially M. I know he has worried for so long about what was wrong with him and to be told he is an able intelligent boy who has a problem called dyslexia which with a lot of effort and the right sort of help he can overcome is to him a tremendous relief. You must have received many similar letters! . . . My big regret is that I didn't take things into my own hands earlier and thus saved M. such a struggle and so much worry'.

S 75 was reported by his mother to have been singing in the car on the way home, and to have said: 'I'm so glad I've been to see Professor Miles. Now I know I'm not stupid'.

The mother of S 107 wrote: 'As you can imagine, we all feel happier in our minds knowing what the problem is'.

The mother of S 125 wrote: 'I can't tell you how much more relaxed he is now, and how much your advice has helped both my husband and I, and also J's teachers'.

The father of S 137 wrote: 'Your discussion with my wife and the formal report are a great comfort to us and to G.'.

The father of S 139 wrote: 'We have been much enlightened and greatly encouraged by the interview and your report'.

The mother of S 146 wrote: 'M. seems to be tackling his problems in a much more relaxed manner since his visit to you . . . I can never thank you enough for your help with M. and explaining to us his problems thus enabling us to have a very happy relationship with him'.

After S 147 had been accepted at a sympathetic school his father wrote: 'T. is now well upon his way and such success he will undoubtedly now make of life will certainly in large part be due to you'.

The mother of S 155 wrote: 'Your report on W. has been tremendously helpful . . . All in all we have been most fortunate in that your report has sparked off interest and help from the other departments whose teachers have W. in their classes . . . We have a lot to thank you for'.

The mother of S 192 wrote that her son 'appears to be a very much happier boy, more settled and relaxed'.

The mother of S 193 wrote: 'I cannot say how relieved we were to hear your diagnosis – for though we had felt T. to be bright, the last few years at school, and our early attempts to find him work, had been very discouraging. Now we feel we have a new lease of life. T. has gone off to . . . College of Education in good heart and with a very different attitude to work from what we have been seeing up to now'.

The tutor of S 200, who was at a College of Education, wrote: 'It was very clear from the way he spoke in the car on our journey home last Friday that C's morale had been considerably boosted by his visit to Bangor'.

The mother of S 189 and S 204 wrote: 'Both boys came away feeling less despair than for a long time and more assured that they were not idiots doomed to failure'.

The father of S 212 wrote: 'We are very grateful to you for the time and trouble you gave to J's case. The psychological encouragement has been a real reward for his own personal efforts to overcome his difficulty and has vindicated our feeling that he was not as backward as we had been led to believe'.

The mother of S 218 wrote: 'D. is in such elated form – it is quite obvious that his session with you lifted a long endured burden: he now feels exonerated and his personal dignity has been restored. I cannot thank you enough'.

The mother of S 241 wrote: 'The school is still making S. do French – his report comes "could do better with more consistent effort". However S. has now accepted that he must at least show willing to please his French teacher and, thanks to you, we understand and pay no attention to his poor results. We have noticed a remarkable change in S. during his 4 years at school. During the first year he was miserable because the boys made fun of his dreadful spelling – he became white and introverted. Then you came along, assessed his problem and he knew what was wrong. He still had an uphill fight and since children are cruel and attack the weakest member was still made miserable at times, but at least the family understood, supported and encouraged while making it clear he himself had to fight his battles'.

CHAPTER TWENTY FOUR

Towards a Theoretical Understanding

In Chapter 1 a brief account was given of a theory which I believed would make sense of much of the evidence presented in this book. In this final chapter I shall try to show in more detail how the data relate to the theory.

The starting point for the theory was that each of us builds up entries in a kind of internal lexicon or dictionary. Any new stimulus, for example the heard sound 'dog' or the written letters d - o - g, can be compared with existing entries in the lexicon, and as a result some of the energy-changes in our environment are identified as words. It is also necessary to postulate further mechanisms by means of which we can draw on these lexical entries in making appropriate movements of speech and writing. The processes involved are undoubtedly of a complexity which is truly staggering, but it is not unreasonable to try to describe the essentials in simple terms.

Let us now suppose that in a dyslexic person there are a variety of faults in this lexical system. In particular there may be a slowness in building up lexical entries, a slowness in gaining access to entries which are already present, and a slowness in producing the right word for 'output'.

If we take the sense of sight in particular, there is evidence that it is not visual patterns as such which create difficulty for a dyslexic person but visual patterns which need to be treated as symbols[1].

Basically, then, we need a word – whether 'dyslexia' or some synonymous term – which refers to a group of faults in the lexical system when these occur in the absence of any more gross deficiency.

On this showing the poor reading and spelling of the dyslexic person are manifestations of a more general weakness which can show itself in different ways. There is an underlying homogeneity despite the existence of considerable individual variation.

A dyslexic person who, like S 95, tries out the 'look' of a word in order to check the spelling is in effect making use of one of his strengths – memory for non-symbolic visual patterns – as a way of compensating for his weakness at memorising symbols. The trouble is that written words considered simply as visual patterns are of a high degree of complexity and exact memory for detail is therefore virtually impossible. It is scarcely surprising, therefore, that this compensatory strategy was not used more often.

It is plain from Chapter 8 that even those who were reading adequately at the time of the assessment had had considerable struggles earlier on. One can perhaps tentatively reconstruct the situation as follows. The non-dyslexic child aged 4 or 5 (or sometimes a little earlier), when confronted with marks on paper, is able to learn without much difficulty that, for example 'That is an A' or 'That is a B'. The situation is somewhat like that in which older children are asked to learn arbitrary names for nonsense shapes; and it is known that in the latter situation dyslexic subjects require more joint presentations of name and shape than do controls before they can respond with the correct names for all the shapes[2].

There is, of course, no suggestion of complete failure, and it is preferable, I believe, to think in terms of stunted growth. This makes sense of the fact that a dyslexic person, as a result of suitable practice and training, can sometimes be more successful in certain language tasks (for instance reading) than a non-dyslexic person whose system is undamaged but who has not received the appropriate stimulation. Of course if the growth of a system is stunted one cannot expect that system to be fully normal in the future; and, to take up again the example given in Chapter 19, the situation for a dyslexic person is unlike that of a child with an undamaged motor system who is late at learning to walk but afterwards walks normally. He does not 'grow out of' his difficulties but may success-fully learn to compensate for them.

With regard to spelling, it makes sense that those with a stunted lexical system should not find it easy to hold in mind complex conjunctions of symbols. Indeed this limitation explains not only their weak spelling but their difficulties in recall of digits (Chapter 17) and in saying the months of the year (Chapter 14). The bizarre nature of their spelling arises from the fact that they cannot easily build up representations in their 'lexicon' of words to which they are not often exposed, and indeed even the spelling of short, familiar words sometimes generates uncertainty. The normal speller picks up without any special difficulty the fact that particular letters often represent particular sounds, and this enables him, when in difficulties, to work out spellings 'orthographically', that is, by splitting the word into its components and then writing down the appropriate letters. Dyslexic subjects can be taught this skill, but it seems that they do not normally pick it up without explicit training. The great advantage of learning to spell orthographically, whether one is dyslexic or not, is that one then has an alternative strategy which can be used whenever 'immediate memory' for the word is not forthcoming. For a dyslexic person in particular this is very necessary, since in his case the number of 'immediate memory' words is likely to be limited because of impairment to the system which builds up lexical entries. Any young child, even if he is not dyslexic, may produce bizarre spelling if he is 'out of his depth' and trying to spell words that are too difficult for him; but as he learns about sound-letter correspondences the more bizarre errors are likely to disappear. In contrast, a dyslexic child, though he may gradually learn to spell phonetically, may produce the so-called 'PAM' error ('phonetic attempt misfired', see Chapter 9), and may largely fail to master the more subtle forms of sound-letter correspondences.

This is not a book about how to teach dyslexic pupils. It is worth noting, however, that the teaching programmes which have been successful are 'structured, sequential, cumulative, thorough, and multisensory'[3]. What is in fact involved is the progressive and systematic building up of lexical entries, not indeed for each whole word – a formidable and indeed virtually impossible task for someone with a weak lexical system – but for single letters and afterwards digraphs, blends, and the more familiar prefixes and suffixes. A relatively small number of these entries gives the person the means of working out the spelling of a very much larger number of words. In contrast, learning lists of spellings or writing a word out many times over is unlikely to be effective with a dyslexic pupil unless at the same time he is being made to think about the ways in which particular sounds are represented. The multisensory approach is likely to contribute to the building up of lexical entries since, for instance, the entry corresponding to the letter 't' can be activated by the sound of this letter, by its visual appearance, by the hand movements made in writing it and by the vocal movements made in saying it. As I have argued elsewhere[4], I believe that dyslexia-centred methods have been successful precisely because they take account of the dyslexic person's weakness at processing symbolic information.

As was indicated briefly in Chapter 1, the theory also makes sense of the difficulties over left/right, east/west, and b/d (see Chapters 10, 11, and 12). I am not sure to what extent it is direction as such which creates difficulty for the dyslexic person; but I suspect that some – and possibly all – of his difficulties originate with the fact that *labels* for direction are not easy to master. This may affect his thinking about direction in all kinds of subtle ways.

With regard to left and right, as I have argued elsewhere[5], it is possibly the lack of permanence which makes these two words particularly confusable, since if one turns and faces a different way what had been the left becomes the right. There is a similar lack of permanence about east and west, though of a more subtle kind; and indeed uncertainty over left and right may well contribute to a dyslexic person's uncertainty over east and west, since when he comes to read maps the implicit instruction 'west is on the left' may itself generate confusion. Dyslexic persons are of course not alone in being vulnerable in this respect; even an undamaged lexical system can be prone to occasional errors, particularly over 'left' and 'right'.

With regard to mistakes over 'b' and 'd', it is possible that these arise because 'b' and 'd' are the only pairs of letters which are confusable both auditorily and visually. If it is asked why a dyslexic subject does not confuse P and R since they look alike, the answer seems to be that he has learned to associate these two letters with totally different sounds. Similarly, it it is asked why he does not confuse S and F, since they sound alike, it could again be answered that the 'look' of these two letters is sufficiently different to make possible the formation of two easily distinguishable lexical entries. Now the main difference between 'b' and 'd' lies neither in their visual appearance nor in their sound but in the movements which are necessary for writing them, and it is in fact common educational practice to make the pupil start his d's with the loop and start his b's at the top[6]. According to the present theory one could say that, in the absence of a distinctive visual appearance or a distinctive sound, the distinctive writing movements can facilitate the formation of a lexical entry which is not subject to confusion. This is yet another example of the way in which a 'multisensory' method of training can be successful.

Mention was made in Chapter 13 of of the difficulty experienced by many dyslexic persons in repeating polysyllabic words, such as 'preliminary' and 'statistical', and of their tendency to put the syllables in the wrong order, for example 'an enemy' for 'anemone'. This difficulty appears to be most common when the word consists of letters or sounds which are auditorily confusable, for example if one syllable contains an 'm' and the next one an 'n'; and one can perhaps describe it as a sequencing or 'loss of place' phenomenon. One possibility is that where letters are confusable, such as 'm' and 'n', those with a weak lexical system are particularly at risk in mistaking the one for the other.

The uncertainty over times and dates, also mentioned in Chapter 13, may similarly be the consequence of a weak lexical system. For example, when S 114 was unaware that it was evening and that the shops would therefore be shut, it is reasonable to assume that he had not picked up the full significance of the word 'evening' as most other children do. Similarly when S 233 said that he was born in 1862, this seems to reflect some uncertainty as to how 'date' words function.

Numerals, of course, no less than letters, have to be interpreted as symbols, and the present theory would predict – what is known to be the case – that dyslexic persons often tend to have difficulty with basic arithmetic. Many of their problems can, of course, be put right with teaching; and in particular the use of solid objects such as blocks or beads may help to generate the appropriate lexical entries. Thus just as a multisensory approach helps in the building up of entries for letters, combinations of letters, and words, so the visible and tangible presence of say, seven objects, the mark on paper, '7', the written letters 's-e-v-e-n-', and the sound 'seven' can jointly contribute to the formation of the same lexical entry. The extent to which number-sense is impaired can be expected to vary considerably between one dyslexic individual and another, since the amounts of compensatory early training are likely to be different. Learning to read or write numerals, however, is not relevantly different from learning to read or write letters, and once this skill is acquired there is every reason to expect that the intelligent dyslexic person will be able to understand difficult mathematical concepts just as he is able to carry out abstract reasoning with words. It is not surprising, however, that because of early difficulties with numerical symbols some dyslexic subjects fail to pick up characteristics of the number system which the rest of us take for granted and that even those who understand the number system find 'concrete aids' helpful (see Chapter 15).

Just as it is possible to build up lexical entries for words and word-parts as well as for single letters, so, too, it seems reasonable to suppose that there are lexical entries which represent not only numbers but combinations of numbers. Thus the typical non-dyslexic adult knows that $52 - 9 = 43$ without having to work it out, whereas he does not know, unless he is very exceptional, that $323 \times 17 = 5491$; and in general we are all aware intuitively of the difference between situations when we can instantly give the answer to a calculation sum and situations where we need to work this out. According to the theory, therefore, one would expect a lesser range of 'immediate knowledge' on the part of the dyslexic person. Thus, to cite the example already quoted in Chapters 2 and 15, it is coherent with the theory that some dyslexic subjects should not immediately know that $9 + 4 = 13$, and observations of their performance on the relevant Terman Merrill 'ingenuity' item (concerned with cans of water) confirms that this was indeed the case.

These considerations also enable us to make sense of the distinctive, and almost universal, dyslexic weakness in the memorising of arithmetical tables (see Chapter 16). Most of us 'just know', for instance, that $8 \times 8 = 64$, whereas if a dyslexic subject has learned this it is only after considerable effort. Sufficient exposure to the smaller numbers (up to, say, 6) may result in the acquisition of appropriate lexical entries; for example, most of my subjects when asked, 'Six, take away three', were able to say 'three' without the need to calculate. Many fewer, however, could give an instant answer to 'nineteen take away seven'. Similarly, when they were asked to say their 6, 7, and 8 × tables, few could 'rattle' them off correctly, and the great majority needed recourse to calculation with all its consequent hazards. Reliance on such calculation is comparable to reliance on orthographic strategies in the area of reading and spelling: the presence of fewer lexical entries, whether for number-combinations or for whole words, forces the dyslexic subject into alternative strategies even though these may be relatively less efficient[7]. There is the further point that if one is to recite tables in the traditional way ('One six is six, two sixes are twelve', etc.) two different sets of lexical entries need to be activated, those corresponding to the multiplier and those corresponding to the multiplicand. A breakdown in one of the two is therefore not surprising; and it makes sense not only of the fact that many dyslexic subjects lose their places when saying tables ('Was it six sevens I was up to?') but also of the fact that many of them are happier if they are allowed to leave the multiplier out ('Can I just say "Six, twelve, eighteen"?').

The relative weakness of dyslexic subjects at recall of series of digits (see Chater 17) can also be seen as a consequence of their weak lexical system. In this case it would appear that lexical entries have been appropriately built up, since there is clearly no problem over identification if sufficient time is allowed; but as a result of slowness in activating the correct lexical entry it is inevitable, in the absence of compensatory procedures, that fewer digits should be recalled in a given time, and this is precisely what the evidence shows to be the case. Whether there are significant differences if the presentation is visual as opposed to auditory, or vice versa, should perhaps be left an open question for the present; but there was no support in Chapter 17 for the view that those who were weak in the visual condition were strong in the auditory condition or vice versa, and it is likely that the processing limitations in dyslexia are not limited to a single sense-modality.

With regard to the miscellaneous items reported in Chapter 18, there is much which seems to cohere with the general theory. In particular, if lexical access is difficult for the dyslexic person but the ability to 'process for meaning' is undamaged, it is not surprising that verbatim recall of sentences should be difficult. As for the uncertainty over rhymes, I am doubtful if this is a widespread phenomenon in dyslexic subjects, though it clearly occurs from time to time. Perhaps one should simply say that, where there is a weak lexical system, this particular form of relationship between words, viz. that they 'sound the same', is not always grasped easily.

There is, of course, no reason, as far as the theory is concerned, to predict any particular difficulty for a dyslexic person in art or creative writing except in so far as the training requires mastery of symbols. Nor need there be any special difficulties for a dyslexic person in doing music unless he is also poorly co-ordinated or has particularly severe problems with sight-reading. In contrast, the theory predicts that dyslexic persons, unless they receive highly specialised training, are likely to be unsuccessful as shorthand typists, telephonists, bank clerks or morse operators, since in all these cases a large amount of verbal information has to be processed in a very short time.

That the lexical system is stunted rather than totally deficient is strongly supported by the data given in Chapter 19. In particular the socially useful tasks, reading and spelling, can be considerably improved with practice. Even when this happens, however, the evidence suggests that other language-processing tasks, for example the ability to recall series of digits, still present difficulty.

The theory makes no distinctive predictions about the familial incidence of dyslexia (Chapter 20), but it is quite compatible with the view that the lexical weaknesses characteristic of dyslexia are sometimes genetically determined. They may also occur alongside damage of a more diffuse kind which results in speech difficulties or some degree of clumsiness or poor co-ordination[8].

With regard to the presence of unusual patterns of handedness and eyedness in dyslexic persons (Chapter 21), there is no reason in the theory to expect these and – as far as the evidence in this book is concerned – no good grounds for believing that they occur.

Chapter 22 presents evidence of what can happen when the dyslexic handicap goes unrecognised and Chapter 23 shows what can happen when the difficulties are explained. For these purposes a detailed theory of what mechanisms are involved is unnecessary. The important point is that the dynamics of the family situation can sometimes undergo radical change once it is realised that the source of the learning difficulties is constitutional in origin. As has been shown, the child's feelings of inadequacy can be relieved, while the parents realise that they need no longer feel guilty for having mishandled the situation.

The theory outlined in this chapter is of course an over-simplification. What is important is not so much its correctness as its role in directing attention to the characteristic ways in which a dyslexic person behaves. The central claim of this book is that his responses are not just isolated curiosities but that they form a coherent pattern; and I have tried to present the evidence in such a way that this pattern can be recognised.

Notes

Notes to Chapter 1

1 Throughout this book I shall refer to the persons whom I assessed as 'subjects'. Other possibilities were considered but rejected. Thus 'children' would have been misleading, since many of them were adolescents and some were adults; 'patients' would have implied a medical rather than an educational assessment, while 'assessee' or 'person-being-tested' would have been unbearable. (Nor would it have been practicable to follow the lead of that delicately nurtured Dickensian, Mr Podsnap, who invariably referred to his daughter as 'the young person'). 'Subject', however, is the standard word used by psychologists when they report on their research and it has the merit of being both brief and accurate.

2 The Bullock Report, *A Language for Life* (H.M.S.O., 1975) states on p.587 that the term dyslexia 'is not susceptible to precise operational definition'. No reasons are given for this curious and dogmatic statement.

3 This term has been advocated by Dr Rutter and Dr Yule (see, for instance, M. Rutter and W. Yule, 'The concept of specific reading retardation', *J. Child Psychiat.*, **16**, 1975, 181-197). I cannot but feel, however, that Dr Rutter's views on dyslexia are somewhat unnecessarily over-cautious. In contrast, there seems little objection to the expression 'specific learning difficulty' which has recently found favour with the Department of Education and Science (see P. Tansley and J. Panckhurst, *Children with Specific Learning Difficulties*; Windsor: Nelson-NFER Publishing Co., 1981).

4 This book is, of course, concerned with *developmental* dyslexia rather than with any form of acquired dyslexia, and when the words 'dyslexia' and 'dyslexic' are used the qualifying adjective 'developmental' should be understood throughout. For an account of recent developments in acquired dyslexia see, for example, M. Coltheart, K. E. Patterson, and J. C. Marshall, *Deep Dyslexia*. London: Routledge and Kegan Paul, 1979.

5 See W. Pringle Morgan, 'A case of congenital word-blindness'. *British Medical Journal*, **2**, 1896, p.1378.

6 See J. Hinshelwood, *Congenital Word-Blindness* (London: H. K. Lewis, 1917), especially Chapter 2, pp.40-63.

7 Ibid., Chapter 2, p.63, and Chapter 3, pp.64-74.

8 See S. T. Orton, *Reading, Writing and Speech Problems in Children*. London:

Chapman and Hall, 1937. I have the greatest admiration for Orton's writings and for the astuteness of his observations in particular. This does not of course mean that I agree with his basic *theory* of dyslexia. In particular I remain unconvinced by his explanation of b-d confusion in terms of the failure of the two halves of the brain to fuse the two 'engrams' (or traces) of letters which are mirror-images of each other. This idea has generated some decidedly dubious speculations about the role of left-handedness and mirror-images in dyslexia. (For further discussion see Chapters 9 and 21).

9 See M. MacMeeken, *Ocular Dominance in Relation to Developmental Aphasia*. London: University of London Press, 1939.

10 Ibid. p.27.

11 See P. Blanchard, *Psychoanalytic Study of the Child*, 2, 1946, 163-187.

12 See T. R. Miles, 'Two cases of developmental aphasia'. *J. Child Psychol. Psychiat.*, 1961, 48-70.

13 It is interesting that the word 'dyslexia' by derivation means a failure of language function (*dys* and *lexis*). Derivations are not always reliable but this one is remarkably apposite. It is perhaps unfortunate, however, that associations with the Latin word *lego*, as opposed to the Greek word *lexis*, have led people to suppose the 'dyslexia' means 'reading disability'. In particular, many of those working in the field of acquired dyslexia appear to have made this assumption. There is nothing contradictory, however, in asserting, as I frequently do, that some of my dyslexic subjects can read quite well; it is in certain areas involving *language* that their disability shows itself.

14 See in particular M. Critchley, *The Dyslexic Child* (London: Heinemann Medical Books, 1970) and M. and E. A. Critchley, *Dyslexia Defined* (London: Heinemann Medical Books, 1978).

15 See S. Naidoo, *Specific Dyslexia*. London: Pitman, 1972. I should also like to call attention to some very useful material in A. W. Franklin and S. Naidoo (eds.), *Assessment and Teaching of Dyslexic Children*. London: Invalid Children's Aid Association, 1970.

16 See *Children with Specific Reading Difficulties*. (Report of the advisory committee on handicapped children). London: H.M.S.O., 1972.

17 See note 2, above.

18 See *Special Educational Needs* (Report of the Committee of Enquiry into the Education of Children and Handicapped Young People). London: H.M.S.O., 1978.

19 See, in particular, S. Hampshire, *Susan's Story*. (London: Sidgwick and Jackson, 1981), and E. Simpson, *Reversals* (London: Gollancz, 1980).

20 See T. R. Miles. *On Helping the Dyslexic Child*. London: Methuen Educational, 1970.

21 See T. R. and E. Miles, *More Help for Dyslexic Children*. London: Methuen Educational, 1975.

22 I have sometimes been asked if any of my own family are dyslexic. To the best of my knowledge the answer is 'no'.

23 See T. R. Miles and T. J. Wheeler, 'Towards a new theory of dyslexia'. *Dyslexia Review*, 11, 1974, 9-11.

24 A similar technique had already been used with presentation of groups of letters. See G. D. Stanley and R. Hall, 'A comparison of dyslexics and normals in recalling letter arrays after brief presentation'. *Brit. J. Educ. Psychol.*, **43**, 1973, 301-4.

25 For further details of a more technical kind see J. B. Anderson, *Cognitive Psychology and Its Implications*. San Francisco: W. H. Freeman & Co., 1980.

26 See N. C. Ellis and T. R. Miles, 'A lexical encoding deficiency I'. In G. Th. Pavlidis and T. R. Miles (eds.), *Dyslexia Research and Its Applications to Education*, Chichester: John Wiley & Co., 1981.

27 In the paper in question (see note 26) Ellis and I make considerable use of the concept of a 'logogen' which we took from earlier work in the area of cognitive psychology. Basically a logogen can be regarded as a pattern-recogniser for words, and we therefore argued that there are faults in the dyslexic person's logogen system, even though his 'semantic system' (i.e. the mechanism by which he is able to process for meaning) remains unaffected. To save complication I have avoided any further reference to the concept of a logogen in the present book.

28 See C. Spring and C. Capps, 'Encoding speed, rehearsal, and probed recall of dyslexic boys'. *J. Educ. Psychol.*, **65**, 5, 1974, 780-786.

Notes to Chapter 2

1 I myself received no money for carrying out the assessment as this formed part of my research work for the university, but those families who could afford it paid small sums to the Dyslexia Unit funds. This point requires mention, since arrangements for payment could in principle have influenced what happened during the assessments, though I have no reason for thinking that it did so in any relevant way.

2 See F. J. Schonell and F. E. Schonell, *Diagnostic and Attainment Testing*. Edinburgh: Oliver and Boyd, 1952, p.42.

3 For convenience I have used the old norms, since they were the only ones available when the research started. The differences between old and new norms are in fact not large enough to have any significant effect on my arguments.

4 Ibid. p.71.

5 In a sense, no doubt, a child who writes 'bancing' for *dancing* knows how to spell the word. One could argue, for instance, that if he had not been asked to write but had been told to spell 'dancing' by choosing from a pool of letters placed in front of him he might have answered correctly. In this case, as in some others, a dyslexic person may perform some components of a task but not others, and how to score his performance will then depend on which components one chooses to regard as important. In this particular case the difference in score would have been minimal whichever ruling had been given.

6 Nor, of course, is it sensible to coach a child on the particular words which occur in a spelling test. Each word is, in a sense, representative of a population of words of similar difficulty, and if a word is specially taught one is therefore misleading oneself by sampling that population in a biased way.

7 See L. M. Terman and M. A. Merrill, *Measuring Intelligence*. London: H. K. Lewis & Co., 1961.

8 The instructions for this item are quite explicit: 'The subject is not allowed to use pencil and paper' (ibid. p.134). Although departure from these instructions resulted in a wealth of interesting material it was important not to present the scores as though they had been obtained under the conditions laid down in the manual.

9 See *The Wechsler Intelligence Scale for Children*, by D. Wechsler. The original version was published by the Psychological Corporation, New York, in 1949. A revised version, the WISC(R), to which I changed over towards the end of the research, was published by the National Foundation for Educational Research, Slough, in 1976.

10 See T. R. Miles and N. C. Ellis, 'A lexical encoding deficiency II'. In G. Th. Pavlidis and T. R. Miles (eds.), *Dyslexia Research and Its Applications to Education*. Chichester: John Wiley & Co., 1981 (especially pp.230 seq.).

11 I cannot resist referring to the situation where a very bright 9-year-old (S 34), after testing, said to his mother 'What's my I.Q.?' and received the admirable answer, 'Thanks very much, but we're not entering the I.Q. stakes today'.

12 I have sometimes heard it said that because of their 'language' difficulty dyslexic children are likely to score lower on the Verbal than on the Performance half of the WISC. This has not been my experience. Dyslexic children of school age are not necessarily weak at tasks involving oral language, and in any case the division of the WISC into 'verbal' and 'performance' does not seem to me to be of any major theoretical significance.

13 See J. C. Raven, *Advanced Progressive Matrices*. London: H. K. Lewis & Co., 1965.

14 I originally used A, B, C, D, E, and F. By convention, however, these letters represent grades, and imply that a person with an A is more meritorious than a person with a B, and so on. In contrast Z does not at present imply anything more meritorious than U. Admittedly it is hard to escape the widely held view that high reasoning ability is to be admired, but at least one can avoid a notation in which such an assumption is 'written in' without examination.

15 I have managed to collect data in respect of 11 dyslexic children, aged between 7 and 9, to whom a full-scale WISC was given, exclusive of the Digit Span and Mazes items. The mean difference between each subject's 'composite' I.Q. (based on the results of these 10 items) and the 'selected' I.Q. (based on extrapolation from the results on Similarities, Vocabulary, Comprehension, Picture Completion, Block Design, and Object Assembly) was found to be 9 points. This figure may, of course, vary at different ages and at different I.Q. levels and may be greater in the case of the Terman Merrill test. Where a full-scale WISC had already been given to one of my subjects, with a resultant 'composite' I.Q., I assigned a grade-label one higher than that corresponding to the same level of 'selected' I.Q.

16 Raven gives a norm of 21 for university students, s.d. 4. Since it seemed reasonable to suppose that subjects obtaining grades X, Y, and Z would have the necessary intellectual skills for taking a university degree, I decided to equate the range of scores 17-21 with grade X. If 26 or higher is then treated as very exceptional (grade Z), this leaves the range 22-25 for grade Y. These are of course approximations but not, I think, wholly meaningless ones.

17 The norms for the Wechsler scale are so arranged that 'average for age' is set at

10, with a standard deviation of 3 units. Thus a score of 13 is one standard deviation above the average and therefore equivalent to an I.Q. of 115, while a score of 16 is two standard deviations above the average and therefore equivalent to an I.Q. of 130. Any child scoring above 7 or 8 is therefore within the average range or above it. The Terman Merrill is scored somewhat differently. Each test item is assigned to an age-level, with a range between 2 and 14 years; above this level there are four groups of items, labelled respectively Average Adult, Superior Adult I, Superior Adult II, and Superior Adult III. In the Summary Chart I have used Roman figures to indicate the age-level of the subject's highest passes if these were at the 14-year level or below and at higher levels I have used the abbreviations AA, SA I, SA II, and SA III.

Notes to Chapter 3

1 With hindsight I believe the position to be somewhat more complicated than this. There is reason to believe that any slow or inexperienced language user is likely to be slow at a variety of 'information processing' tasks such as those included in the dyslexia test. (Compare N. C. Ellis and T. R. Miles, 'Visual information processing as a determinant of reading speed', *Journal of Research in Reading*, 1, 2, 1978, 108-120). The dyslexic person is different not because of the slowness of his performance as such but because he remains slow despite constant practice. A person whose first language is not English would also be expected to have difficulty with some of the items in the dyslexia test, just as anyone except a native speaker would be expected to display some degree of 'dyslexic'-type behaviour if the items were presented in French.

2 See Chapter 1, note 23.

3 I have been particularly influenced on this matter by the writings of E. Tulving who has systematically investigated the presence of 'cueing' in recall tasks. See, for instance, E. Tulving and S. Osler, 'Effectiveness of retrieval cues in memory for words', *J. Exp. Psychol.*, 77, 1968, 593-601.

4 The data collected by Pollard were later used in a more systematic way. See Chapter 7 and Appendix III.

5 I am grateful to Miss Gillian Morgan for this information.

6 In saying this, I am of course not disputing that, in the context of his research, a research worker needs to specify with full precision how his dyslexic and control subjects were selected; indeed without such a specification the research could not be replicated. Such an operational definition should not be regarded as immutable, however, since methods of classification may change in the light of advancing knowledge.

7 What are legitimate ways of treating the 'dyslexia index' figure statistically seems to me a difficult question. One can presumably say that a subject with an index-figure of 6 'did more dyslexic things' than a subject with an index-figure of 3, and indeed that he did *twice* as many such things. As a consequence it therefore seems legitimate to calculate the mean number of 'pluses' for dyslexic (or allegedly dyslexic) subjects and controls in order to make comparisons between them, as is done in Chapter 7. Any implication, however, that a subject with an index-figure of 6 is 'twice as dyslexic' as a subject with an index-figure of 3 should of course be resisted, and even the validity of using the index-figures to give a rank-order of probability of dyslexia seems to me questionable, since the exact value of a particular index-figure may depend in part on extraneous factors such as the amount of compensatory teaching which the subject has received. Indeed from the clinical point of view it is perhaps safest to regard the index-figure simply as an aid to diagnosis. For a positive diagnosis stronger additional evidence is needed if the figure is low than if it is high, while for a negative diagnosis stronger additional evidence is needed if it is high than if it is low.

Notes to Chapter 4

1 Somewhat over 300 files were taken from the Department and heaved into a caravan where, during a period of study leave, I was able to work without interruption. I decided not to make use of material obtained before 1972, and a few further files were discarded because there had been only brief consultation and not a full assessment. Two cases, one boy and one girl, were also omitted because they came from a predominantly Welsh-speaking background and spoke English only as a second language.

2 See M. and E. A. Critchley, *Dyslexia Defined*, London: Heinemann Medical Books, 1978, Chapter 9.

3 In one of these cases a young man aged 20 had recently discharged himself from a mental hospital and was either unwilling or unable to attempt the items in the dyslexia test.

4 The fact that only 24 out of my 291 subjects (8%) were classified as belonging to Group III is in part, of course, a function of the referral system. It was known that I and my colleagues carried out educational rather than medical assessments, and those needing chiefly medical help would therefore mostly have gone elsewhere. The smallness of the percentage figure also suggests that the typical or pure cases of dyslexia are not difficult to identify, since there would be no point in seeking an assessment at Bangor unless there was some suspicion of a dyslexic problem. In addition, there is no support in my experience for the suggestion that there are parents who have taken refuge in the erroneous belief that their child is dyslexic as a way of avoiding having to face other problems. For what it is worth, not one of my 291 cases came in this category.

5 See, for instance, M. Critchley, *The Dyslexic Child*. Heinemann Medical Books, 1970, p.91.

6 It is perhaps worth recording (see Chapter 12) that S 126, who scored only 2 'pluses' at the time of testing, produced some written work at the age of 18 in which 'd' had been written for 'b'. This seems to me a striking confirmation of the original diagnosis. In contrast, a recent re-examination of the file of S 21, who scored 2½ pluses at age 8, has made me think that she should have been placed in Group II.

7 The 34 subjects for whom there were incomplete records are, of course, also part of the same 'pool'.

Notes to Chapter 5

1 George Pavlidis, personal communication. For further details of the work of Dr

Pavlidis in investigating the eye movements of dyslexic subjects see G. Th. Pavlidis, 'Sequencing, eye movements and the early objective diagnosis of dyslexia'. In G. Th. Pavlidis and T. R. Miles (eds.), *Dyslexia Research and its Applications to Education*. Chichester: John Wiley & Co., 1981.

Notes to Chapter 6

1 I have assumed throughout the book that the reader is familiar with the concepts of 'standard deviation' and 'statistical significance'. In Chapter 19 I also assume familiarity with the concepts of correlation and regression. Otherwise statistical technicalities are mentioned only in end-of-chapter notes.

Notes to Chapter 7

1 It is, of course, widely accepted that if a scientific theory is not to be mere 'wind of words' (William James' phrase: see *Varieties of Religious Experience*, London: Longman's Green & Co., 1902, p.443) it must be capable in principle of being falsified. 'Confirmations', says Sir Karl Popper, 'should count only if they are the result of *risky predictions*' (his italics). See K. Popper, *Conjectures and Refutations*, London: Routledge and Kegan Paul, 1963, p.36.

2 I am grateful to Ian Pollard for collecting control data for subjects aged 9 to 12 and to Barbara Large and Celia Hopkinson for their help in administering the dyslexia test to subjects aged 7 to 8 and aged 13 to 18.

3 J. C. Raven, *Standard Progressive Matrices*. London: H. K. Lewis & Co., 1938.

4 Although the matching was only approximate it was not wholly arbitrary, since use was made of the percentile rankings given in the manual for the Raven Progressive Matrices (see note 2) and also of the fact that the WISC is standardised so as to give a mean of 10 and a standard deviation of 3. It should be noted that the control subjects, like the dyslexic subjects, were appreciably above average in general intelligence level and that their results on the dyslexia test are not therefore an accurate indication of the norm for their particular age.

5. See Chapter 2, page 9.

6 As with the dyslexic subjects (see Chapter 8, note 1), no attempt was made to take into account the months of the subject's age since the gain in precision by so doing would have been minimal.

7 The appropriate 'pairs' among the dyslexic subjects were found to be : 2, 4, 6, 7, 8, 9, 10, 11, 12, 13, 14, 15, 16, 17, 18, 19, 21, 22, 23, 24, 25, 28, 31, 32, 33, 35, 36, 38, 39, 40, 42, 43, 45, 49, 50, 51, 52, 54, 55, 56, 57, 58, 59, 60, 62, 63, 64, 65, 66, 67, 68, 69, 70, 71, 72, 73, 75, 76, 77, 78, 79, 80, 81, 82, 83, 85, 86, 87, 88, 90, 91, 92, 93, 94, 96, 97, 98, 99, 101, 102, 103, 104, 105, 106, 107, 108, 110, 111, 116, 117, 120, 121, 122, 124, 125, 126, 127, 128, 129, 130, 131, 140, 142, 145, 146, 147, 149, 150, 151, 155, 156, 157, 159, 160, 162, 166, 171, 175, 176, 180, 182, 183, 184, 191, 193, 194, 207, 208, 209, 210, 211 and 218. These are the subjects marked (m) in the Summary Chart.

8 It should be noted that in the scoring of the 'digits reversed' and 'polysyllables' items the subject's age is taken into account and that a *history* of early difficulty contributes to a 'plus' in the case of the 'left-right' and the 'tables' tests. In these items, therefore, comparison of the number of 'pluses' at different age-levels is illegitimate (compare also Chapter 19, note 1).

9 Ages 7- 8: $t = 3.23$, $p < 0.005$.
  Ages 9-12: $t = 15.26$, $p < 0.001$.
  Ages 13-18: $t = 11.28$, $p < 0.001$.

Notes to Chapter 8

1 To save complications the earlier Schonell norms were used (see Chapter 2, note 3) and subjects were assigned to an age-level in years, with months discounted. It follows that the range for any 8-year-old is a score of between 30 and 40, and 80% of the bottom point of the range therefore comes to 24. In what follows I shall speak of the 'top' and 'bottom' points of the range, and I shall also have occasion to refer to those who were below the bottom point of the range but above 80% of the bottom point. In the case of the 8-year-olds this would comprise those with scores between 24 and 29; in the case of the 9-year-olds it would comprise those with scores between 32 and 39, and so on.

2 Where the criterion was not satisfied the reading score in the Summary Chart has been underlined.

3 These were subjects 2, 3, 6, 7, 15, 19, 21, 22, 23, 30, 31, 32, 33, 40, 41, 43, 45, 48, 53, 54, 62, 63, 67, 73, 75, 76, 77, 80, 97, 99, 100, 101, 106, 109, 110, 112, 113, 114, 115, 118, 121, 123, 125, 127, 135, 137, 139, 145, 147, 154, 159, 168, 186, 187, 196, 204, 206, 220, 221 and 222.

4 Since a score of 100 gives a 'reading age' of 15 it is impossible for the notion of 'above-the-range' to be applicable in the case of any one aged 15 or over. This means that the 8 subjects who were classified as 'above' were drawn from a pool of 164, not 223.

5 For further discussion of this point see in particular W. Yule, M. Rutter, M. Berger, and J. Thompson, 'Over- and under-achievement in reading: distribution in the general population'. *Brit. J. Educ. Psychol.*, **44**, 1974, 1-12.

6 Although I believe this argument could be valid in the present case it is one which should be used sparingly, since in some contexts it may be difficult to specify the difference between a 'potential' problem which has been overcome and no problem at all. To take an extreme case, if a left-hander, for constitutional reasons, has a weak backhand at lawn tennis which improves as a result of constant practice, does one say that he has 'compensated for a disability' or simply that his backhand has improved? I owe this example to my colleague, Dr. N. M. Cheshire.

7 See C. Spring and C. Capps, 'Encoding speed, rehearsal, and probed recall of dyslexic boys', *J. Educ. Psychol.*, **65**, 5, 1974, 780-786. Compare Chapter 1 of this book, note 28.

8 See N. C. Ellis and T. R. Miles, 'Visual information processing in dyslexic children'. In M. M. Gruneberg, P. E. Morris, and R. N. Sykes (eds.) *Practical Aspects of Memory*. London: Academic Press, 1978.

Notes to Chapter 9

1 See T. R. Miles, *Understanding Dyslexia*. London: Hodder & Stoughton, 1978, pp.49-50.

2 See, for instance, B. Hornsby and T. R. Miles, 'The effects of a dyslexia-centred teaching programme'. *Brit. J. Educ. Psychol.*, **50**, 1980, 236-242.

3 Even in the absence of specialist teaching some degree of success appears to be possible, since my older subjects spelled more words correctly on the S_1 test than did my younger subjects (see Chapter 19). At all ages, however, the great majority were severely retarded.

4 See in particular M. Peters, *Spelling: Caught or Taught?* (London: Routledge and Kegan Paul, 1967). An excellent classification has also been proposed recently by Sylvia Farnham Diggory in a paper given at Southampton University in 1981, which I hope will be made more widely available.

5 See Elaine Miles, 'A study of dyslexic weaknesses and the consequences for teaching'. In G. Th. Pavlidis and T. R. Miles (eds.), *Dyslexia Research and Its Applications to Education*. Chichester: John Wiley & Co, 1981.

6 In this connection I should like to report an incident of which I was told during my schooldays. A boy who had been asked to write down the French for 'they are' wrote 'ils ont' (when the answer should, of course, have been 'ils sont'). When asked what he had written he said, 'Please, sir, I left out the "s" on "sont"'. This was literally true; but his chosen form of words has the effect (as he no doubt intended) of making the mistake seem more trivial than it was, viz. the careless omission of a single letter. A better account of the error would have been to say that he had muddled up 'avoir' with 'être'. I owe this story to that most stimulating of pedagogues, the late Geoffrey Bolton.

7 The only two misspellings I have met which would have been unsuitable for the Victorian drawing room are this one and S 136's spelling of *would* as 'whored'. I cannot at this point forebear to mention a story told to me by a headmaster's wife who had been using the Kathleen Hickey cards with a young teenage boy. When he reached the card with the digraph 'ff' he duly said 'ff' and turned the card over so as to see the full word, accompanied by the appropriate picture, of which 'ff' was a component. The word is in fact 'cuff', but dyslexic children are sometimes known to read from right to left instead of from left to right, and, slightly abashed, he said to the headmaster's wife, 'That's a naughty word!' (For further details of the Kathleen Hickey cards see S. Naidoo, 'Teaching methods and their rationale', in G. Th. Pavilidis and T. R. Miles (eds.) *Dyslexia Research and Its Applications to Education*. Chichester: John Wiley & Co., 1981, pp. 275-6.)

8 See, in particular, R. Conrad, 'Acoustic confusion in immediate memory'. *Brit. J. Psychol.*, **55**, 1964, 75-84.

9 See Chapter 1, note 12.

10 Elaine Miles, 'A study of dyslexic weaknesses and the consequences for teaching', in G. Th. Pavlidis and T. R. Miles (eds.) *Dyslexia Research and Its Applications to Education*. Chichester: John Wiley & Co., 1981, p.253.

11 For a summary of the evidence see N. C. Ellis and T. R. Miles, 'A lexical encoding deficiency I'. In G. Th. Pavilidis and T. R. Miles (eds.) *Dyslexia Research and Its Applications to Education*. Chichester: John Wiley & Co., 1981. Further evidence appears in Chapter 17 of the present book.

12 The question of consistency in spelling has been studied in detail by Dobson, who in fact suggests that it could be a more advantageous topic for spelling research than is correctness. See C. J. Dobson, *The use of instability as the dependent variable in the study of young children's spellings*. Ph.D. thesis, University of Wales, 1978.

13 See, for instance, D. J. Done and T. R. Miles, 'Learning, memory and dyslexia'. In M. M. Gruneberg, P. E. Morris and R. N. Sykes, *Practical Aspects of Memory*. London: Academic Press, 1978.

14 For example I might all too easily have written 'from time to time to time' in the above sentence. It is also of interest that on some of the occasions when I have cited dyslexic misspellings for illustration purposes typists have inadvertently 'corrected' what I wrote to something more like the normal spelling. For example I once wrote that a dyslexic student had written 'corelatated' for *correlated*, and in the typed version it said that he had written 'corelated' for *correlated* – a much less spectacular mistake.

15 See Chapter 1, note 12.

16 The following 'translation' was given by this subject's mother: 'And all the time that he worked, the little butterfly sat on the brim of his hat, just above the left eye. At nightfall when the miller went tired to bed the butterfly folded its wings and slept by the leg of the miller's chair.'

Notes to Chapter 10

1 Similar phenomena have been noted by my colleague, Alun Waddon (personal communication).

2 This is an example of the situation, familiar to many research workers who use statistical methods, where results which are significantly *worse* than chance demand explanation no less than results which are significantly *better* than chance.

3 Since on the present method of scoring RR and EQ responses contribute to a 'plus' it might be objected that such a procedure is circular. It would, however, be an easy safeguard to exclude RR and EQ responses from the criteria for dyslexia, since there is no shortage of other criteria.

4 See T. R. Miles and N. C. Ellis, 'A lexical encoding deficiency II'. In G. Th. Pavlidis and T. R. Miles (eds.) *Dyslexia Research and Its Applications to Education*. Chichester: John Wiley & Co., 1981.

5 C. Spring and C. Capps, 'Encoding speed, rehearsal, and probed recall in dyslexic boys', *J. Educ. Psychol.*, **66**, 5, 1974, p.782.

6 T. R. Miles and N. C. Ellis, op. cit. See note 4.

7 Chi-squared = 23.05, p <0.001. In all calculations of chi-squared Yates' correction has been applied.

Notes to Chapter 12

1 In a few cases parents brought school exercise books which contained b-d confusions. When this happened it was scored as 'plus', even though the mistakes could have been made a year or two before the assessment.

2 I received at the same time a letter from this subject's mother saying that he had just been accepted to read Physics at Oxford University. This seems to me a remarkable triumph in view of his earlier struggles.

3 See T. Bottomley, (1980), *An Analysis of Spelling Errors in Dyslexic and Non-Dyslexic boys* (unpublished). Bottomley was in fact analysing data which had been collected at the Word Blind Centre in London and used in Naidoo's book, *Specific Dyslexia* (London: Pitman, 1972). Naidoo reports that her controls were 'unselected for reading and spelling ability', and the possibility that a few of these were in fact dyslexic is not totally ruled out. I am grateful to the Invalid Children's Aid Association for making these spellings available.

4 Ian Pollard, personal communication.

5 She was also known to have had a quite remarkable pattern of eye-movements in reading. See Chapter 5, note 1.

6 For further discussion of this point see T. R. Miles and N. C. Ellis, 'A lexical encoding deficiency II', in G. Th. Pavlidis and T. R. Miles (eds.), *Dyslexia Research and Its Applications to Education*. Chichester: John Wiley & Co., 1981.

7 It is a matter of familiar experience that any of us can have had a 'bad day' or be 'off form' in respect of a variety of skills. A possible way of talking about this situation is in the language of signal detection theory. (For a readable account see Chapter 2 of *Sensation and Perception,* by S. Coren, C. Porac, and L. M. Ward. New York: Academic Press, 1978). One could say that on a 'bad day' there is extra 'noise' in the nervous system and hence less reduction of uncertainty.

Notes to Chapter 13

1 This is true, for example, when we represent time by the angular distance travelled by the hands of a clock. As Kant points out, we 'represent the course of time by a line progressing to infinity' (*Critique of Pure Reason*, Transcendental Aesthetic, ii, 7).

2 I have heard it suggested that the famous Spooner, who was Warden of New College, Oxford, was in fact dyslexic. The evidence from a recent study, however, seems to me to make this suggestion unlikely, and there is reason to believe that many reports of 'Spoonerisms' are in fact apocryphal. See J. M. Potter, 'What was the matter with Dr. Spooner?' In V. A. Fromkin (ed.), *Errors in Linguistic Performance*. New York: Academic Press, 1980.

Notes to Chapter 14

1 For the pool of 132 dyslexic subjects and 132 controls chi-squared $= 36.95$, $p <$ 0.001.

2 Tulving and Pearlstone have suggested that a word can be 'available' without necessarily being accessible. See E. Tulving and Z. Pearlstone, 'Availability versus accessibility of information in memory for words'. *J. Verbal Learning and Verbal Behaviour*, **5**, 1966, 381-391.

3 I noted that both S 69 and S 90 ended 'months reversed' with 'March, February, July' (though S 90 immediately corrected to 'January'); and one can perhaps leigitimately ask why, if a wrong month is to be given, it should be the same month on both occasions. It seems to me possible that there is sufficient acoustic similarity between 'January' and 'July' to account for the error: both months begin with 'J' and end in 'y' (though the y-sound is admittedly slightly different in each) and I suspect that auditory confusability may have played a part here. (Compare the reference to Conrad's work; see Chapter 9, note 8).

4 This point should of course be considered in conjunction with the evidence cited in Chapter 19. 'Months forwards' and 'months reversed' were more susceptible to 'learning overlay' than 'digits forwards' and 'digits reversed', but there were plenty of older subjects who still displayed difficulty.

5 Some of my subjects also reported uncertainty over the alphabet. Thus S 257, a successful business man who came to me at the age of 38, reported that he had never been able to learn the alphabet, and this was also reported of S 214. S 95 said, 'No, I don't know my alphabet – A B C . . . D E . . . G H I J K L M N O P Q R S T . . . W X Y Z'; and in reply to 'Do you use a dictionary?' he said, 'Yes, it's horrible, I can hardly do it at all'. S 244 recited the alphabet correctly as far as R, after which he said, S W X Y Z. S 193 used the well-known mnemonic of chanting: 'It took me a long time to learn the alphabet until I discovered a song'. I did not investigate knowledge of the alphabet systematically, but one would certainly expect dyslexic subjects to have difficulty with it since it involves arranging a long series of symbols in the correct order. The problems experienced by dyslexic subjects in looking words up in a dictionary are, of course, widely known.

Notes to Chapter 15

1 According to Mrs Jill Playford, of the Helen Arkell Dyslexia Centre in London, this kind of mistake is regularly found in dyslexic children (personal communication).

2 There would, of course, be advantages for the dyslexic person if instead of the 'teens' (thirteen, fourteen, etc.) we spoke of 'one-ty three', 'one-ty four', etc. I am grateful to my colleague, John Griffiths, for calling my attention to this point. For further discussion of the dyslexic subject's arithmetical difficulties see J. M. Griffiths, *Basic Arithmetic Processess in the Dyslexic Child.* M.Ed. Dissertation, University of Wales, 1980.

3 Ibid.

4 In a widely read paper G. A. Miller has cited evidence which suggests that for a typical adult in a variety of tasks there is an upper limit of about 7 items which can be handled instantly without resort to 'working out' or counting (see G. A. Miller, 'The magic number seven, plus or minus two. Some limits on our capacity for processing information', *Psychol. Review*, **63**, 1956, 81-97). It is possible, therefore, that in certain tasks this limit is somewhat lower in dyslexic persons.

5 The subject is required to bring back 13 pints of water using a 5-pint-can and a 9-pint-can and is told that he must begin by filling the 9-pint-can.

6 In this item the subject is given 4 items of increasing complexity in which he has to give the total number of boxes when specified numbers of boxes are placed inside each other.

7 In this item the subject is told the heights of a tree at the time of planting and at yearly intervals for the next three years. He is then required to work out its height at the end of the fourth year.

Notes to Chapter 16

1 This mistake appears to be similar to that reported in connection with 'months reversed' (see Chapter 14, note 3). Just as in that case the j-sound appears to have suggested the wrong month, so in the present case the similar sounding 'sixty' is substituted for 'six'. All such confusions presumably arise because the difficulty of the task puts the subject under pressure.

2 See note 1, above.

3 For the two matched groups chi-squared $= 43.26$, $p < 0.001$.

Notes to Chapter 17

1 For a discussion of the evidence see T. R. Miles and N. C. Ellis, 'A lexical encoding deficiency II'. In G. Th. Pavlidis and T. R. Miles (eds.), *Dyslexia Research and Its Applications to Education* (Chichester: John Wiley & Sons, 1981). The main sources for this discusson were G. D. Spache, *Investigating the Issues of Reading Disabilities* (Boston: Allyn & Bacon, 1976) and R. P. Rugel 'WISC sub-test scores of disabled readers', *J. Learning Disabilities*, **7**, 1974, 48-55.

2 Many of the records were only marginally incomplete, and since all the subjects in this group were dyslexic it seemed justifiable to increase the size of this particular sample from 40 to 42.

3 Two different tachistoscopes were used, one 3-field, one 2-field, both having been made by Electronic Developments Ltd. Digits were printed on cards by means of Letraset, about 1 cm. high. Each exposure followed the preceding one without a break except for the time required for me to write the subject's answer down and insert the next card. Choice of digits was determined on the basis of a random number table but with the additional stipulation that no digit should appear more than once in any array. Zero was included.

4 According to this method of scoring, which I owe to Ian Pollard, each correctly named digit scores a point if and only if it is in the correct directional relationship to another correctly named digit. Thus if the stimulus was 4 3 2 8 5 1 and the subject responded 4 3 2 8 1 5 this would score 5 out of 6, since the 1 and the 5 are not both in the correct directional relationship and only one of them (it does not matter which) satisfies the criterion. If the subject responded 4 8 7 6 0 5, this would score 3 out of 6 since the 4, 8, and 5 all satisfy the criterion, whereas if he replied 4 5 8 7 6 0 this would score only 2 out of 6 since only one of the 8 and the 5 is in the correct directional relationship to the 4. In practice this procedure is easier to operate than it sounds!

5 I am not, of course, suggesting that this represents a prediction as to what the subject would in fact do at an exposure-time of 1000 ms., since the relationship between exposure-time and number of digits correctly identified is not necessarily linear or at any rate cannot be assumed to be so. The figure is simply a mathematical device to aid comparisons.

6 In the auditory condition a score of 7 or more for 'digits forwards' was counted as 'high', a score of 6 as 'medium', a score of 5 as 'low' and a score of 4 or less as 'very low'. In the visual condition a comparison ratio of 5 or more was counted as 'high', one between 4.00 and 4.99 as 'medium', one between 2.00 and 3.99 as 'low', one under 2.00 as 'very low'.

7 These relate to 133 children in the Manchester area who were within 80% of their age-level on the Schonell S_1 test. 7 digits were exposed for 800 ms., and the mean number of digits correct, with scoring as described in note 4 above, was 4.99. The comparison ratio is obtained by multiplying this figure by 10/8.

8 See N. C. Ellis and T. R. Miles, 'Dyslexia as a limitation in the ability to process information', *Bulletin of the Orton Society*, **27**, 1977, 72-81. The conditions of this experiment were different from those described here, since only 5 digits were presented and a measure was taken of the minimum time needed for correct responding. For 41 control subjects aged 10-14 the figure was 289 ms., s.d. 156; for 41 dyslexic subjects the figure was 1331 ms., s.d. 585. There is also evidence that dyslexic subjects are slower than controls in identifying visual arrays of letters (see G. Stanley and R. Hall, 'A comparison of dyslexics and normals in recalling letter arrays after brief presentation', *Brit. J. Educ. Psychol.*, **43**, 1973, 301-304).

9 I re-examined this subject's file but saw no grounds for revising my view that he was dyslexic.

10 For further discussion of this point see Elaine Miles, 'A study of dyslexic weaknesses and the consequences for teaching'. In G. Th. Pavlidis and T. R. Miles (eds.) *Dyslexia Research and its Applications to Education*. Chichester: John Wiley & Co., 1981.

11. If Table 17.2 is 'telescoped' into a 4-cell table with pooling of 'high' and 'medium' and pooling of 'low' and 'very low', the value of chi-squared comes to 0.80, which is non-significant.

12 It seems to me possible, though this is admittedly speculative, that the occasional successes, for example S 49 in the visual condition and S 34 and S 174 in the auditory condition, are task specific and do not imply that their speed of processing is higher in general than for most dyslexic subjects. Certainly S 49 was not a fast processer in general since he could repeat no more than four digits in the auditory condition. What I have in mind is, for instance, strong eidetic imagery in the visual condition and a clever strategy of grouping in the auditory condition; there is no reason why a dyslexic subject should not use these or other personal idiosyncrasies to help him with one or other task.

Notes to Chapter 18

1 It seems to me unlikely that this was simply a case of 'not hearing what I said' in the popular sense, but was probably a memorising error similar to those described by Conrad (see Chapter 9, note 8).

2 T. R. Miles, *Understanding Dyslexia*. London: Hodder & Stoughton, 1978, p.104.

3 See L. Bradley and P. Bryant, 'Difficulties in auditory organisation as a possible cause of reading backwardness', *Nature*, **270**, 1978.

4 S. Naidoo, *Specific Dyslexia*. London: Pitman Press, 1972.

5 Perhaps even more compelling is the fact that two recent postgraduate students whom I know very well personally are both extremely talented musicians despite their dyslexia.

Notes to Chapter 19

1 Some of the other items were unsuitable because of the method of scoring: in the case of the left-right task, tables, and b-d confusion a *history* of earlier difficulty contributed to a 'plus' score; familial incidence is clearly unrelated to age, and in the case of polysyllables the method of scoring took age into account. In scoring the two digits tests the figure used was the highest series-length at which the subject responded correctly.

2 Because their ages were appreciably beyond those of all other subjects the scores for Ss 221, 222, and 223 have been omitted from all calculations in this chapter.

3 I am grateful to Dr. J. Y. Kassab for considerable help with the statistical aspects of this chapter.

4 The proportion of the total variability in each test predictable from age is given by the value of r^2. Expressed as percentages these values were: Reading, 61; Spelling, 53; Months Forwards, 14; Months Reversed, 12; Digits Reversed, 9; Digits Forwards, 7.

5 The existence of a linear relationship was checked in each case. Analysis of residuals showed no serious departure from the underlying assumption, viz. that true errors are independent and normally distributed and have constant variance.

6 Compare the larger number of trials needed by dyslexic subjects in order to match arbitrarily chosen names with particular shapes. See D. J. Done and T. R. Miles, 'Learning, memory, and dyslexia'. In M. M. Gruneberg, and P. E. Morris, and R. N. Sykes (eds.) *Practical Aspects of Memory*. London: Academic Press.

7 As an example of what a dyslexic child can achieve by hard practice the following experience is perhaps worth recording. Some years ago (too early for the results to be included in the present book) I assessed a boy who scored a solitary 'minus' on months of the year despite a whole series of 'pluses' on other parts of the dyslexia test. When I said to his mother that I was surprised that he could do the months of the year so well, she replied: 'We have spent *hours and hours* working on them!'

8 A minor adjustment was necessary to take account of the fact that in the two Schonell tests an increased score of 10 words represents an increase in reading or spelling age of 12 months. The difference between the 'numbers of words correct' on the two occasions had therefore to be modified so as to represent differences in reading and spelling age. The figures in both the final two columns are, of course, ratios, and therefore, decimals, since they were obtained by dividing the reading and spelling gains in years and months by the time-interval between the two assessments also in years and months. The loss of accuracy arising from the use of the earlier Schonell R_1 norms (see Chapter 8, note 1) was considered to be minimal.

9 The figures for rate of gain on Table 19.7 are in many ways unsatisfactory. In particular they take no account of the fact that if there were relatively high scores on the first testing then even a fully adequate performance on the re-test necessarily gives a relatively small rate of gain; and the figure becomes even more misleading if there is a long time-interval between assessments. The figure of 0.2 for reading gain in the case of S 118 is an example where both these factors were at work and certainly does not reflect slow progress. Similarly S 143 has a 'rate of gain' at spelling of only 0.4, yet an advance from 61 words correct at age 13 to 75 words correct at 17 is by no means a failure. In spite of these artificially low figures, however, there is still evidence for considerable improvement. The rates of gain are not, of course, as large as those reported by Hornsby and Miles (see 'The effects of a dyslexia-centred teaching programme', *Brit. J. Educ. Psychol.*, **50**, 1980, 236-242); but the children in that study were known to have received tuition from dyslexia specialists, whereas in the case of the subjects mentioned in this chapter the possibilities of skilled help may have been more variable. Part of the difference, of course, must be accounted for by the fact that the children in the Hornsby and Miles study would certainly have been discharged when their progress was adequate, and hence the time-interval between assessments would have been less. It should also be noted that, of the 21 subjects who were re-assessed, 1 had an intelligence rating of V, 3 a rating of W, and the remaining 17 a rating of X or above. Although improvement is possible if the child is only of average ability, as the Hornsby and Miles study shows, the high intelligence of the present group of subjects may well have been an important factor in their successes. Certainly 'high I.Q.' is cited by Dr. Critchley as one of the 'pentagon' of factors which contribute to a good prognosis. See M. Critchley, 'Dyslexia: an overview', in G. Th. Pavlidis and T. R. Miles (eds.) *Dyslexia Research and Its Applications to Education*, Chichester: John Wiley & Co., 1981, p.9.

10 It should again be borne in mind that events in the subject's past history can contribute to the number of 'pluses'. This information would still have been available, however, to someone who was assessing the subject for this first time.

11 She was therefore assigned to Group II (see Chapter 4). I had wondered at one stage whether to assign S 190 to Group II also, but the re-testing showed enough residual difficulties to justify a placement in Group I.

12 These are the 'formes frustes' of dyslexia described by Dr. Critchley and his wife. See M. and E. A. Critchley, *Dyslexia Defined*. London: Heinemann Medical Books, 1978, Chapter 9. Compare Chapter 4 of this book, note 2.

13 It is not always easy, of course, to convince unsympathetic listeners of this point of view. For example, I was told by the mother of S 34 that she had failed to convince a particular official that there was anything wrong with her son and had therefore had to arrange teaching help without any assistance from him. Fortunately the boy made striking progress. However, when the official came to hear of this he asked her disparagingly what she had been worrying about! Her good-humoured comment was, 'Sometimes you can't win!'

Notes to Chapter 20

1 It is worth recording that S 259 was the sister of S 6 and S 110 and S 260 the brother of S 234. These two cases have not been included in the statistics in this chapter since the degree of handicap seemed insufficiently severe.

2 The earlier assessments took place before 1972, the later ones after 1978, and therefore fell outside the period of time chosen for the case-studies reported in this book.

3 She in fact achieved a university degree late in life after her dyslexia was recognised. The mother of S 97 was also dyslexic, but had nevertheless achieved a degree in mathematics.

4 Throughout the chapter I have used my 'full' number of 257 cases, not the 223 of Group I. The records all contained the necessary information on sex and on familial incidence, and since a larger sample of cases was available it seemed advantageous to make use of it.

5 In one case (S 86) a report of an earlier assessment mentioned that there was 'a suspicious family history' of dyslexia; but this evidence seemed to me insufficient to justify a 'zero'.

6 T. R. Miles, *Understanding Dyslexia*. London: Hodder & Stoughton, 1978, pp.70-71.

7 The evidence has been carefully summarised by Dr. Critchley. See M. Critchley, *The Dyslexic Child*. London: Heinemann Medical Books, 1970. See also F. Owen, 'Dyslexia: Genetic Aspects'. In A. L. Benton and D. Pearl (eds), *Dyslexia. An Appraisal of Current Knowledge*. New York: Oxford University Press, 1978.

8 For further discussion see N. C. Ellis and T. R. Miles, 'A Lexical Encoding Deficiency I'. In G. Th. Pavlidis and T. R. Miles (eds.) *Dyslexia Research and Its Applications to Education*. Chichester: John Wiley & Co., 1981. There is evidence that when digits are presented to deaf children their span is relatively low.

9 Again see M. Critchley, *The Dyslexic Child*, op. cit., p.91.

10 For some figures relating to such anomalies see D. B. Hier, 'Sex differences in hemispheric specialisation', *Bulletin of the Orton Society*, **29**, 1979, p.75. Autism, stuttering, and cerebral palsy are among the conditions which are reported to be more common in boys.

11 Chi-squared = 0.09, which is well below the 5% significance level.

Notes to Chapter 21

1 I am grateful to Miss Joanna Watts for supplying me with the data in respect of these 62 subjects.

2 Chi-squared = 0.09. This result is not significant at the 5% level.

3 Chi-squared = 1.95. This result is not significant at the 5% level.

4 For example Rutter reports 'no association between left handedness or mixed handedness and specific reading retardation' (See M. Rutter 'The concept of dyslexia', *Developmental Medicine*, **33**, 1969). For further references and discussion see also M. D. Vernon, *Reading and Its Difficulties*, pp.141 seq. Cambridge: Cambridge University Press, 1971.

5 For a recent summary of the evidence in this area see R. L. Masland, 'Neurological aspects of dyslexia'. In G. Th. Pavlidis and T. R. Miles (eds.) *Dyslexia Research and Its Applications to Education*. Chichester: John Wiley & Co., 1981.

6 Chi-squared = 3.70. A value of 3.84 is needed for significance at the 5% level.

7 The two values of chi-squared are 0.08 and 0.79. Neither reaches the 5% significance level.

8 The two values of chi-squared are 1.24 and 0.58. Neither reaches the 5% significance level.

Notes to Chapter 22

1 See, for instance, the discussions on teaching methods in chapters 2, 10, and 11 of G. Th. Pavlidis and T. R. Miles (eds.), *Dyslexia Research and Its Applications to Education*. Chichester: John Wiley & Co.

Notes to Chapter 23

1 Those with a psychodynamic orientation might say that I was doing 'family therapy'. I accept this description, provided two important qualifications are made. In the first place my 'interpretations' were far more restricted in their range than those commonly offered by psychotherapists, since they were usually limited to remarks such as, 'You must have found it extremely frustrating' or 'No wonder you felt discouraged'. Secondly, most therapists tend to avoid giving direct advice or making practical suggestions, whereas I regularly made clear by word and gesture that I was on the parents' side in their struggles to obtain help. Indeed, I often made a point of encouraging parents to back their own judgement, particularly if others had implied that they were being neurotic or over-fussy.

2 I am sometimes asked, 'This is all very well with bright children, but how can you be similarly encouraging with slower children?' Even here, however, it is perfectly possible to be constructive, for example in making suggestions as to how the child might be taught or given other kinds of help; and over the years I have met very few parents indeed who have had unrealistic expectations about their child's future.

3 I hope that in this part of the chapter I do not give the impression of parading all the bouquets which I have received! The point is quite an impersonal one, viz., that suitable explanations of what dyslexia is are likely to be quite striking in their effects.

Notes to Chapter 24

1 For a detailed survey of the evidence in this area see N. C. Ellis and T. R. Miles, 'A lexical encoding deficiency I'. In G. Th. Pavlidis and T. R. Miles (eds.) *Dyslexia Research and Its Applications to Education*. Chichester: John Wiley & Co., 1981. In 'Towards a new theory of dyslexia' *(Dyslexia Review*, 11, 1974, 9-11) Dr. Wheeler and I suggested that *any* stimulus material of sufficient complexity might present problems to a dyslexic person. I now believe that this is a mistake and have returned to my earlier view (for reference, see Chapter 1, note 12) that it is symbols which are the main source of difficulty.

2 See D. J. Done and T. R. Miles, 'Learning, Memory. and Dyslexia'. In M. M. Gruneberg, P. E. Morris, and R. N. Sykes (eds.), *Practical Aspects of Memory*. London: Academic Press, 1978

3 Various versions of this formula are current. See, for example, M. B. Rawson, 'The structure of English: the language to be learned', *Bulletin of the Orton Society*, 20, 1970, 103-123.

4 See T. R. Miles and N. C. Ellis, 'A lexical encoding deficiency II'. In G. Th Pavlidis and T. R. Miles (eds.) *Dyslexia Research and Its Applications to Education*. Chichester: John Wiley & Co., 1981.

5 Ibid.

6 I am grateful to my wife, Elaine Miles, for calling my attention to this point.

7 An interesting report was written some years ago on a Professor of Mathematics who had quite striking powers of calculation (see I. M. L. Hunter, 'An exceptional talent for calculative thinking', *Brit. J. Psychol.*, **53**, 1962, 243-258). It appears, however, that Professor Aitken's success was due not to an excessively wide knowledge of 'instant' calculations (that is, an extra large number of entries in the lexicon) but rather to the wide range of strategies which he was able to deploy.

8 It has not been possible to collect systematic evidence on the extent to which clumsiness occurs in dyslexic subjects, but 'anecdotal' evidence suggests that it is common without being by any means universal.

The Dyslexia Test*

(During the period of the research minor amendments were made to the lay-out of the test-sheet. The wording remained the same, however, except for minimal changes. Where the instructions to the tester are not obvious they are given in brackets).

Test Items

IMPORTANT

It is very important that someone who later reads this form should have a record of exactly what happened. Use of a tick is in order if the subject gives the correct response instantaneously, but please record all delays and hesitations and always indicate if the subject asks for the question to be repeated, echoes the question, or tries to reorientate himself by repeating what went before. (Use the abbreviations RR = requests for repetition, EQ = echoed the question, and EP = epanalepsis, taking up what he has already said). Please do *not* put a cross if the answer is wrong, but record as accurately as possible *what the subject said*. Where appropriate, record any supplementary questions which you yourself ask.

Name _____   Date _____

*Copies of the Dyslexia Test are available as a pack of 30 test sheets, and a users' manual from:
LDA, Duke Street, Wisbech, Cambs PE13 2AE, England.

1.   Left-right (body parts)

              Instruction   Subject's response

(a)   Show me your right hand
      (Did you have difficulty when you
      were younger?)   _____

(b)   Show me your left ear   _____

(c)   Touch your right ear with your left
      hand   _____

(d)   (Putting hands on table)
      Which is *my* right hand?   _____

(e)   Touch my left hand with your right
      hand   _____

(f)   Point to my right ear with your left
      hand   _____

(g)   Touch my right hand with your
      right hand   _____

(h)   Point to my left eye with your right
      hand   _____

(i)   Point to my left ear with your left
      hand   _____

(j)   Touch my right hand with your left
      hand   _____

Special strategies: _____

      _____

      _____

2.   Repeating polysyllabic words

I am going to say some words and I want you to say them after me

                                              Subject's response

      preliminary   _____

      philosophical   _____

      contemporaneous   _____

      anemone   _____

      statistical   _____

3. Subtraction

What is: 9 take away 2   _____

6 take away 3   _____

19 take away 7   _____

24 take away 2   _____

52 take away 9   _____

44 take away 7   _____

4. Tables

Did they teach you tables at school   _____

Did you have difficulty with them   _____

Say your — times table   _____

(Give at least three tables. These should normally be the $6\times$, $7\times$, and $8\times$, but failures at the $2\times$, $3\times$, and $4\times$ can of course be informative. In the case of children aged 7 or 8, give the $4\times$ only).

5. Months forward

Say the months of the year   _____

6. Months reversed

Now say them backwards   _____

7. Hand

Show me the hand you write (draw) with   _____

Show me how you clean your teeth   _____

Show me how you throw a ball   _____

(Record which hand is used)

8. Eye

(Cut a small hole in a sheet of paper and, holding up a pencil in three different positions, ask the subject if he can see the pencil through the hole. Record which eye is used.)

9.   Repeating digits

(Give the digit span test as descibed in the Wechsler Intelligence Scale for Children)

10.   Memory for sentences

(Use 3 of the sentences from the Terman Merrill test, one from age iv, one from age xi, and one from age xiii. In the event of a near-miss give 6 to 8 trials. Responses should be recorded verbatim).

11.   Rhymes

(Give the Rhymes item from the Terman Merrill test. If the subject has difficulty ask):

(a)   Give me any two words which rhyme

(b)   I shall give you two words and ask you if they rhyme. You must say 'Yes' or 'no'.

Cat	Dog	_____
Cat	Sat	_____
Mouse	Elephant	_____
Mouse	House	_____
Fish	Dish	_____
Butter	Gutter	_____
Butter	Jam	_____
Egg	Bacon	_____

12.   Familial incidence

	(a) Definitely	(b) Possibly	(c) No difficulties	(d) No evidence
Father				
Mother				
Brothers Sisters				
Other relatives				

(In the case of (a) and (b) please give as much detail as possible.)

SUMMARY

Name _____

Date _____

Age _____

Reading Age _____

Spelling Age_____

Intelligence rating	Z	Y	X	W	V	U

Indicators
(Score as +, 0, or −)
 Digits forward
 Digits reversed
 Left-right (body-parts)
 Polysyllables
 Subtraction
 Tables
 Months forwards
 Months reversed
 b-d confusion
 Familial incidence

Samples of spelling

_____
_____
_____
_____

Scoring the Dyslexia Test

Notes

1. The following symbols should be used:

    + = subject fails the test or satisfies the other specified criteria. This indicates a 'dyslexia-positive' response.

    − = subject succeeds in the test without showing any of the specified criteria for 'dyslexia-positive'; his performance is therefore 'dyslexia-negative'.

    0 = subject satisfies some of the less stringent criteria but his response cannot be scored unambiguously as dyslexia-positive or dyslexia-negative.

    (In the digits test the 'zero' category is not used. In other tests two or more responses scored as 'zero' count as 'plus').

2. In some cases a score of 'zero' is obtained by any *two* of a particular kind of response, e.g. two corrections or two pauses. In these cases a single correction and a single pause can in conjunction be scored as 'zero'.

3. For purposes of summing the total performance a 'zero' may be scored as half a 'plus'. From the index-figure (the total number of 'pluses') no conclusions about dyslexia can be drawn if the subject is too young (under about 8) or of limited ability (under I.Q. about 90). In the case of other subjects with a history of reading or spelling problems discrepant with their intelligence the index-figure is a rough guide as to the strength of the presumption that other dyslexic signs will manifest themselves.

    The scores in this column should not be assumed to be on an equal-interval scale, nor is the number of 'pluses' necessarily an indication of the degree of severity of the dyslexia. Its precise significance must be determined according to context.

3. The following abbreviations may be used on the test form:
   hes. = the subject hesitated
   RR = the subject asked for the question to be repeated
   EQ = the subject echoed the question
   EP = the subject 'cued' himself in by repeating what he had said before ('epanalepsis')

DIGIT SPAN

(The first number represents the series-length of the highest success, the second number the series length of the lowest failure. Any 'double inversion', i.e. a score in which the first figure is *two* more than the second, is scored as 'plus' – for example 53 – unless a weaker performance involving only a single inversion, in this case 43, would count as 'minus'.

(a) DIGITS FORWARDS

Age	Any failure to reach	Any failure at	Score as plus	Score as minus
7	5	4	43, 44	55
8	5	4	45, 54	56
9	5	4	64	
10	6	5	54, 55	66
11	6	5	56, 65	67
12	6	5	75	
13	6	5		
14	6	5		
15	7	6	65, 66	77
16	7	6	67, 76	78
17	7	6	86	
18 and over	7	6		

(b) DIGITS REVERSED

Age	Any failure to reach	Any failure at	Examples of +	Examples of −
7	3	2	32	33
8	3	2	23	34
9	4	3	33	44
10	4	3	34	45
11	4	3	43	55
12	4	3	53	54
13	4	3		

Age	Any failure to reach	Any failure at	Examples of +	Examples of −
14	5	4	44, 45 ⎫	55 ⎫
15	5	4	54, 64 ⎪	56, 65 ⎪
16	6	5	⎬	65 ⎬
17	6	5	55 ⎭	⎭
18 and over	6	5		

In the case of those aged 14 and over a failure at 'five digits reversed' should be scored as 'plus' only in the case of those in intelligence categories Z, Y, and X.

LEFT-RIGHT

Score as +   1.   Two errors or more
             2.   Consistent mirror image of correct answer
             3.   Subject turns in his seat (real or imagined)

Score as 0   1.   Report of earlier difficulty over left and right and/or report of special strategy (watch, scar, 'the hand I write with' etc.)
             2.   Hesitations in working out the answer in at least two items ('hes.')
             3.   Any two examples of echoing the question or asking for it to be repeated (e.g. 'my left with your right, was it?') (RR or EQ)
             4.   One error
             5.   Two corrections

POLYSYLLABLES

All ages: 4 or 5 errors, score as +
In other cases score as follows:

No. of errors	Age	7	8	9	10	11	12	13	14	15	16	17	18 and over
3			0	0	0	+	+	+	+	+	+	+	+	+
2			−	−	−	0	0	0	0	0	+	+	+	+
1			−	−	−	−	−	−	−	−	0	0	0	0

SUBTRACTION

Score as +   1.   3 or more errors or failures
              2.   Any use of concrete aids such as fingers or marks on paper

Score as 0   1.   2 errors or failures
              2.   Special strategy
              3.   Any two examples of echoing the question or asking for it to be repeated (EQ or RR)
              4.   2 hesitations (hes.)
              5.   2 corrections

(A single error, hesitation, or correction is scored as − .)

TABLES

(Age 9 and over)

Score as +   1.   Any 4 or more errors over the three tables
              2.   Any loss of place (or uncertainty, as exemplified by questions such as 'Was it six sevens I was up to?')
              3.   Any request to leave out the preamble (i.e. to leave out 'one six is. . . ' 'two sixes are. . . ', etc.)
              4.   Any consistent error (e.g. $6 \times 3 = 20$, $7 \times 3 = 23$)
              5.   Any change into the 'wrong' table (e.g. in the case of the $6\times$, 6×7 are 42, 6×8 are 48, 8×8 are 64)

Score as 0   1.   Any 2 or 3 errors in 3 tables
              2.   Any attempt to reorientate by repeating the previous product (EP) (e.g. 'four sixes are twenty four, five sixes are . . . mm . . . let me see, four sixes are twenty four, five sixes are thirty')
              4.   Any 2 slips or corrections (e.g. 'Eight eighties, I mean eight eights')
              5.   Any one 'skip', e.g. from 6×8 to 8×8
              6.   Any report of earlier difficulty

(Age 7 or 8)

($4\times$ table only)

Score as +   1.   Any 2 errors or more

Score as 0   1.   1 error
              2.   2 pauses
              3.   Any two attempts to reorientate by repeating an earlier product (e.g. 'Four fours are sixteen, five fours are . . . let me see . . . four fours are sixteen, five fours are twenty')

MONTHS FORWARDS

Score as +
1. Any 2 or more omissions
2. Any 2 or more inversions (e.g. 'October, September' for 'September, October')
3. Any uncertainty where to start
4. Any query about the importance of order (e.g. 'Do I have to say them in order?')

Score as 0
1. Any 2 corrections
2. Any 1 omission (e.g. leaving out September)
3. Any 1 inversion
4. Any report of earlier difficulty or special tuition

MONTHS REVERSED

Score as +
1. Any 2 or more omissions
2. Any 2 or more inversions

Score as 0
1. Any 2 corrections
2. Any 1 omission
3. Any 1 inversion

Note that in both months forward and months reversed a single corrected error is scored as minus.

b-d CONFUSION

First-hand evidence is scored as plus; second-hand evidence is scored as zero, and absence of evidence is scored as minus. (Note that the placing of letters in the wrong order, e.g. 'on' for 'no' or 'was' for 'saw' may be a different phenomenon and should not be uncritically assimilated to b-d confusion.)

If a 'plus' is to be given the tester must himself have evidence of b-d confusion, whether by examining the child's written work or in listening to him read. If a parent or teacher *reports* that the child has or had difficulty, this is scored as zero.

FAMILIAL INCIDENCE

First-hand evidence is scored as plus; second-hand evidence is scored as zero, and absence of evidence is scored as minus. Note that absence of evidence does not *exclude* familial incidence: in case of adopted children, for instance, relevant evidence may not be available, and in place of 'minus' it is preferable to write 'nk' (= 'not known').

If a 'plus' is to be given the tester must have unambiguous evidence that at least one other member of the family is affected. For example, if he or a colleague has actually tested a brother, sister, cousin, etc. and found him to be dyslexic, this would count as 'plus'. In contrast a report e.g. by a parent that he (the parent) has similar difficulties is scored as zero. (As a rough guide, 'I was very late at learning to spell and I still can't remember telephone numbers' scores zero, but a single 'oddity' in isolation, e.g. 'I am bad at remembering names' is scored as minus.)

Performance of Control Subjects

The notation is the same as that used in the Summary Chart. Data are not available, however, in respect of digits forwards, b-d confusion, or familial incidence, and the maximum possible number of 'pluses' is therefore 7. For details of the selection of dyslexic subjects for comparison purposes see Chapter 7.

Performance of Control Subjects

Case no.	Sex	Age	Int.	S_1	DR	L-R	Pol.	Sub.	Tab	MF	MR	Index
1	F	7.5	X	34	−	+	−	+	+	−	+	4
2	M	7.5	Z	47	−	+	−	+	+	−	−	3
3	M	7.10	X	33	−	−	−	+	+	+	+	4
4	F	7.11	Z	23	−	+	0	+	+	+	+	5½
5	M	8.0	Z	59	−	−	−	−	−	−	−	0
6	M	8.1	U	25	−	+	−	+	+	+	+	5
7	M	8.2	W	54	−	+	−	−	−	−	−	1
8	M	8.2	W	38	−	0	−	0	−	+	0	3
9	F	8.4	X	39	−	0	−	−	−	−	+	2
10	M	8.4	X	22	−	+	−	+	+	+	+	5
11	F	8.4	X	40	−	0	−	+	+	−	−	2½
12	M	8.5	Y	45	−	+	0	+	0	−	+	4
13	M	8.5	X	29	−	0	+	−	+	−	+	4
14	F	8.6	X	46	−	0	−	0	+	0	−	2
15	M	8.6	W	30	−	+	−	0	+	−	+	4
16	F	8.6	W	50	−	+	−	0	+	−	+	3½
17	M	8.7	X	29	−	+	+	0	+	−	+	5
18	M	8.8	Y	22	−	0	0	0	+	+	+	4½
19	M	8.10	X	45	−	+	0	0	−	−	+	2½
20	M	8.11	U	50	−	+	−	−	−	0	0	2
21	M	8.11	X	42	−	+	0	+	−	+	+	5
22	M	9.1	V	51	+	+	−	+	+	+	+	5
23	F	9.1	V	41	+	+	−	0	+	−	−	3½

Performance of Control Subjects

Case no.	Sex	Age	Int.	S_1	DR	L-R	Pol.	Sub.	Tab	MF	MR	Index
24	F	9.2	W	55	+	+	0	–	–	–	–	2½
25	M	9.2	V	53	+	0	–	–	+	+	+	4½
26	F	9.4	W	42	+	+	–	–	+	–	–	3
27	M	9.6	X	46	–	+	–	–	0	0	+	3½
28	M	9.6	W	44	–	–	–	–	+	0	+	2½
29	M	9.7	W	53	–	–	–	–	+	–	0	1½
30	M	9.7	X	59	–	0	–	–	+	–	–	1½
31	F	9.8	U	34	+	0	–	0	+	+	+	5
32	M	9.8	V	46	+	+	–	0	+	–	–	3½
33	F	9.8	X	50	–	–	–	–	–	–	0	½
34	M	9.9	Y	73	–	–	0	–	+	0	+	2½
35	F	9.10	W	48	+	+	–	+	+	0	–	5
36	M	9.11	W	56	–	–	–	–	+	0	–	1½
37	M	9.11	X	47	–	+	–	–	–	–	0	1½
38	F	9.11	Y	43	+	0	–	–	–	0	0	2
39	M	9.11	W	55	+	–	–	0	+	–	–	3
40	M	10.1	U	48	+	0	–	0	+	0	–	2½
41	F	10.1	V	43	+	0	0	0	+	–	+	4½
42	M	10.1	Y	46	–	0	+	–	–	0	0	2½
43	F	10.2	U	59	+	+	–	+	+	–	+	5
44	M	10.2	W	63	+	–	0	–	–	–	–	1½
45	M	10.4	Y	54	–	–	0	–	–	–	–	0
46	F	10.5	X	85	–	0	–	–	–	–	+	1½

Performance of Control Subjects

Case no.	Sex	Age	Int.	S₁	DR	L-R	Pol.	Sub.	Tab	MF	MR	Index
47	F	10.6	Z	81	–	0	–	–	–	–	–	½
48	F	10.6	W	49	+	–	–	–	–	–	–	1
49	F	10.7	X	66	–	–	0	–	–	–	–	0
50	M	10.7	W	42	+	–	0	0	–	–	–	2
51	M	10.8	X	55	–	0	–	–	+	–	+	2½
52	F	10.8	X	67	+	+	0	0	+	+	+	5
53	M	10.8	W	40	–	0	+	–	–	–	+	3½
54	F	10.8	X	65	+	+	–	–	+	–	0	3
55	F	10.8	W	53	–	–	+	–	+	–	0	2½
56	M	10.9	X	85	–	+	–	–	+	0	–	2
57	M	10.9	X	67	+	–	+	–	+	–	0	2½
58	M	10.9	X	41	+	0	–	+	–	–	–	3
59	F	10.9	V	62	+	+	–	–	–	–	–	2
60	F	10.9	W	53	–	–	–	–	0	–	–	½
61	M	10.9	Y	66	–	0	–	–	–	0	–	½
62	F	10.10	Y	81	–	0	–	–	–	–	–	½
63	F	10.11	X	69	+	–	–	+	–	–	–	2½
64	F	10.11	W	70	–	+	–	–	–	–	–	0
65	F	10.11	X	57	+	–	–	0	–	0	–	2½
66	F	11.0	V	80	–	–	–	–	–	–	–	0
67	M	11.0	W	63	+	–	0	–	–	–	+	3
68	M	11.1	X	72	+	+	–	+	+	0	–	4
69	F	11.1	U	71	+	–	+	–	+	–	0	3½

Performance of Control Subjects

Case no.	Sex	Age	Int.	S_1	DR	L-R	Pol.	Sub.	Tab	MF	MR	Index
70	F	11.2	Y	69	−	−	−	−	0	−	−	½
71	F	11.2	W	65	−	+	−	0	+	−	−	2½
72	M	11.3	W	64	+	−	0	−	+	−	0	3
73	M	11.3	X	87	−	−	−	−	−	−	−	0
74	F	11.3	V	69	+	−	0	−	+	−	−	1
75	F	11.3	U	49	+	0	−	−	−	−	−	2½
76	F	11.4	V	82	−	+	+	+	+	−	−	½
77	M	11.4	W	51	−	+	+	−	0	−	0	3
78	M	11.4	U	50	−	+	−	0	−	−	−	4
79	M	11.5	Y	70	−	−	0	−	+	−	0	1
80	F	11.5	V	50	+	+	+	−	+	−	−	3½
81	M	11.6	X	54	+	−	−	−	−	0	0	4
82	M	11.6	X	74	−	−	−	−	−	0	−	1
83	F	11.6	W	61	−	0	−	−	−	−	−	½
84	M	11.6	Y	77	−	+	+	0	−	−	−	1
85	F	11.6	X	70	−	−	−	−	−	−	−	1½
86	M	11.7	X	74	+	0	−	−	+	−	−	1½
87	M	11.8	X	76	+	0	−	−	−	−	−	2½
88	F	11.8	W	50	+	+	0	0	−	−	−	2½
89	M	11.8	V	51	−	0	−	−	−	−	−	2
90	F	11.11	V	65	−	−	+	−	−	−	−	1
91	F	12.0	W	62	−	0	+	−	+	−	−	2½
92	F	12.0	X	62	−	−	+	−	+	−	0	2½

Performance of Control Subjects

Case no.	Sex	Age	Int.	S₁	DR	L-R	Pol.	Sub.	Tab	MF	MR	Index
93	M	12.0	W	66	+	-	+	0	+	-	0	4
94	F	12.1	X	87	-	0	-	-	+	-	-	1½
95	F	12.5	V	75	-	+	-	0	+	-	+	3½
96	F	12.5	X	65	+	+	0	0	+	-	0	3½
97	M	12.5	X	78	-	-	-	-	-	-	-	1
98	M	12.7	X	82	-	-	0	-	0	-	-	½
99	F	12.8	Z	63	+	-	-	-	-	-	-	1½
100	M	12.9	Z	93	+	-	-	-	-	-	0	1
101	F	12.9	U	64	-	0	-	0	+	-	-	2½
102	F	13.5	V	80	-	+	-	-	0	-	-	1½
103	F	13.6	W	89	-	+	0	-	-	-	0	1½
104	F	13.7	W	86	-	-	-	-	0	-	-	1
105	M	13.8	V	83	-	+	-	-	-	-	-	1
106	F	13.11	U	82	-	0	0	-	+	-	-	1½
107	M	13.11	V	77	-	-	0	-	+	-	-	1½
108	F	14.0	U	76	+	+	-	-	+	-	0	3½
109	F	14.0	U	94	-	-	-	-	-	-	-	0
110	F	14.3	Z	97	-	0	-	-	-	-	-	½
111	M	14.3	W	79	+	0	-	-	+	-	0	3
112	M	14.5	V	79	+	0	-	-	0	0	-	4
113	F	14.7	X	87	+	0	-	+	+	-	-	4
114	F	14.8	W	96	-	+	-	-	-	-	-	1
115	F	14.9	X	83	+	+	-	-	+	-	0	3½

Performance of Control Subjects

Case no.	Sex	Age	Int.	S_1	DR	L-R	Pol.	Sub.	Tab	MF	MR	Index
116	M	15.0	V	81	+	0	+	−	+	−	−	3½
117	F	15.1	X	83	+	−	0	0	+	−	−	3
118	F	15.1	W	86	+	+	−	−	−	−	−	2
119	M	15.4	Y	96	+	0	−	−	−	0	−	1½
120	M	15.4	W	95	+	+	+	−	−	−	0	4
121	F	15.5	X	97	−	−	−	−	+	−	+	1
122	M	15.6	X	90	+	0	0	−	+	−	−	4
123	F	15.9	W	95	+	0	−	−	+	−	0	2½
124	F	15.11	X	92	−	+	−	−	+	−	−	2½
125	M	16.0	W	91	−	−	0	0	−	−	−	½
126	F	16.4	Y	94	+	0	0	0	+	−	−	3½
127	F	17.3	X	89	+	0	0	−	+	−	−	3
128	F	17.4	Z	90	+	0	−	−	−	−	−	1½
129	M	17.6	Y	80	+	0	0	−	+	−	−	3
130	F	17.8	Z	97	−	−	0	−	−	−	−	½
131	M	17.11	Z	97	−	−	−	+	−	−	−	1
132	F	18.0	X	92	−	+	−	−	−	−	−	1

Index of Names

Index of Subjects

Note. Where a page number is given in bold type, this indicates that this and the following pages are devoted mainly to the topic in question.